A MAP DEPICTING THE

MILITARY POSTS OF THE OLD WEST

1850 · 1890

NORTH OF THE FORTIETH PARALLEL

SHOWING APPROXIMATE LOCATIONS OF THE POSTS OF THE ARMY (AND SOME STATE MILITIAS), THE MILITARY DEPARTMENTS AS OF 1874, THE RAILROADS AS OF 1883, AND SOME OF THE MAJOR TRAILS.

ILLUSTRATED BY PAUL J. HARTLE
RESEARCHED BY HERBERT M. HART

FT BROWNING, 1868-72

CP POPLAR RIVER 1880-93
FT UNION, 1864-65
CP REEVE, 1868
MAGINNIS, 1880-90
FT BUFORD 1866-85
CP PORTER, 1880-81
FT BERTHOLD, 1864-67
CP ATCHESON, 1863
FORT TOTTEN, 1867-90
FT STEVENSON-FORT TOTTEN TRAIL
FORT STEVENSON, 1867-83

A

N P
FT KEOGH, 1876-1908
CP HOUSTON-1880
CP MERRITT EI TOUNGUE R. CANT., 1876
CP HANCOCK, 1872-77
FT MCKEEN, 1872-81
FT ABRAHAM LINCOLN, 1872-91
FT RICE, 1864-78
FT SEWARD, 1872-77
FT SANBORN, 1862
CP J.M. BACON, 1856-1900

CANT. BADLANDS 1879-83
FT RANSOM, 1867-72
FT ABERCROMBE, 1857-71
FT RIPLEY 1849-PRES.

FT CUSTER, 1877-98
FT C.G SMITH, 1866-68
FT YATES 1874-1903

GRAND RIVER AGENCY, 1870-75
FT SISSETON, 1864-90

FT PHIL KEARNEY, 1866-68
FT MCKINNEY, 1877-94
OLD CP DEVIN 1874
CP STURGIS, 1878
FT CONNOR RENO, 1866-68
CANT. RENO, 1876-77
FT MEADE, 1878-1940
CP RELEASE, 1860
CP BELLE PLAIN, 1857
CP YELLOW MEDICINE, 1860
CP LIVINGSTONE, 1860
FT SNELLING 1819-1946
FT RIDGELY, 1853-67
CAMP LAKE VIEW

FT BENNETT, 1870-91
NEW FT SULLY, 1866-94
FT CEDAR, 1856
OLD FT SULLY, 1863-66
OAKWOOD CANT. 1857, 64-65
FT PIERRE 1855-57
FT LOWER BRULE
FT THOMPSON, 1863-71

1870-1909
1857-58
FT CASPAR 1865-67
CP DAVIS 1855-56
FT FETTERMAN 1867-82
CP MARSHALL 1863
CP COLLIER, 1876
FT HALE, 1870-84
FT LOOKOUT-1856-57
FT JAMES, 1865-73
FT DAKOTA, 1865-70
CP EDWARDS, 1859

GH 1878-78
CP RAINS, 1874, 1877-78 (SPOTTED TAIL AGENCY)
CP KEYA PAHA, 1879
WHETSTONE AGENCY, 1870-72
FT RANDALL, 1856-84
FT HUTCHINSON
FT ROBINSON, 1874-1948
CP SHERIDAN, 1874, 81
FT NIOBRARA 1880-1906
FT PONCA, 1865-66 (CP PONCAS 1856)
CP CANFIELD, 1855

ITE

CP PAYNE, 1858
FT LARAMIE, 1849-90
CP BITTER COTTONWOOD, 1856
FT FRED STEELE, 1868-86
FT HALLECK, 1862-66
FT MITCHELL, 1864-67
CP RUGGLES, 1874
FT HARTSUFF, 1874-81
POST COLUMBUS 1864-67
FT ATKINSON, 1819-27

FT SANDERS, 1866-82
CP WALBACH, 1858-59
FT D.A. RUSSELL, 1867-1948
CP CARLIN, 1867-88
CP O.O. HOWARD, 1895
FT SIDNEY, 1867-74
FT GRATTAN, 1855
POST AT BEAUVAIS STATION, 1864-66
POST ALKALI, 1864-66
POST FALLONS BLUFF, 1864-66
CP VINCENT
FT OMAHA, 1863-1947

SOUTH
UP
FT CROOK, 1891-1948

FT SEDGWICK, 1864-71
NORTH PLATTE STA POST 1867-81
FT MCPHERSON 1863-80
POST AT GILMAN'S STATION, 1864-66
POST PLUM CREEK, 1864-66
CP ALVIN SAUNDERS
FT COLLINS, 1862-67
FT LATHAM
FT VASQUEZ, 1837-70
FT MORGAN, 1864-68
NEW FT KEARNY, 1848-71
POST AT PAWNEE RANCHE, 1864-67
OLD FT KEARNY, 1846-48
FT LUPTON, 1864
CP RED WILLOW, 1872
POST LITTLE BLUE RIVER, 1864-66
CP AT PAWNEE AGENCY

OLD FORTS
of The Northwest

OLD FORTS
Of the Northwest

by Herbert M. Hart

Illustrations by Paul J. Hartle

SUPERIOR PUBLISHING COMPANY-SEATTLE

FIRST EDITION

This is a Triple Dedication:

TO THE WESTERN ARMY OF 1850–1890
who, with their families, called these forts "home;"

TO THE HISTORIANS,
especially those of the National Park Service, who are striving to preserve the story of these forts;

TO THE OTHER HARTS,
Teresa, Bridget (2½), Erin (1½), and Bret (½) who journeyed 11,000 miles to see these forts even if they didn't know what they were seeing at the time.

Foreword

"A military necessity for the soldier's presence at a certain
point arose, and orders were issued for a post to be built.
A command was marched out, say on to the wide plain far
from every one else, and halted beside a stream. It had been
told to 'build a post,' and a post was built."

—Bvt. Brig. Gen. George A. Forsyth writing in 1900 of frontier forts.

AND SO a chapter in American history was written. It was a chapter of
exploration and exploitation, courage and cowards, progress and pathos.

The chapter has been closed and its true nature all but forgotten, the
facts lost behind the romanticized clouds of modern novels, motion pictures,
and television. Its memorials remain, scattered throughout the west as the
names of cities, hamlets, ghost towns, and mere sites.

These are the places visited in this book via pictures taken during 1962
photography, historical sketches or photographs, and simplified plats. It may
be a surprise to see that so little remains of most forts, and this was a factor
involved in selecting what forts to visit, and to include here.

In the absence of complete data at the federal and state government level,
we had to resort to more than 1,000 inquiries to local, state and federal sources
to find out what forts existed, and their present condition.

A combination of remaining evidence, and of historical significance, decided the 70-some forts for this book, and the 120-some to be included in its
later companions in the series. The geographical division along the 40th parallel
was arbitrary, as was the north-south line along Nebraska and Minnesota.

New Yorkers might consider anything beyond the Hudson as the "west,"
but we felt the true Northwest began at Fort Snelling, and here placed our
boundary. We also felt that the true period of western movement under the
Army's guardianship was 1850 to 1890, and those years became our time
boundaries.

Every fort covered in this book actually was visited, except for one.
That was Fort Washakie, Wyoming, left out by a schedule that was too tightly
packed. We did get to the others in 11,000 miles of driving, one tornado, one
hail storm, one Dakota rainy season, 16 thunderstorms, a car breakdown,
and a toothache (repaired with minimum time lost by our local contact,
coincidentally a dentist).

Photographs have not be limited to those of the trip. When prying hands of a 2- or 3-year old exposed forty negatives, state and federal historians had to be called upon for help. Our tight schedule did not provide for all photography to be under optimum conditions, and these same sources came to the rescue when early- or late-day exposures did not prove satisfactory.

We do not pretend that we are providing a definitive history of these forts. Rather, we have tried to tell something of each fort which sets it aside from its contemporaries. A complete history of each post would require far more time and space than possible in this general treatment.

In our research, as described in the "Acknowledgements" section and hinted at in the "Bibliography," we found many contradictions from apparently equally reliable sources. Agreement could not even be found on spellings. Was it Caspar or Casper, McDermit or McDermitt, Lyon or Lyons, Keogh or Keough, Lapwei or Lapwai? In all of these matters, we tried to settle upon the most logical or what appeared to be the most accepted version.

We have tried to give understandable directions to each fort site, though we might not recommend trying to visit some of them. These are routes that worked in 1962, after many unsuccessful shortcuts and blind alleys. Road maps sometimes only generalize the locations of fort sites, placing them on the wrong sides of rivers, mountains, or towns. These routes are the ones we would take if we were going to return to any sites and it is in this spirit that these directions are given.

It should be noted that many sites are privately owned. Visitors should respect the rights of the owners. Souvenir and artifact hunters are urged to remember that what they find and take away from abandoned sites only accelerates the deterioration, depriving others of an historical excursion into the past, and minimizing the success of any possible scientific investigations of the site.

By the time we finished this book, we had encountered close to 300 military fort sites in the Northwest. This book visits more than seventy. These sites remain today as memorials to the Army of the West, but an even greater memorial commemorates this tiny force of soldiers: the thriving home for almost 20 million Americans, the great Northwest.

H. M. H.

Quantico, Virginia
Saint Patrick's Day, 1963

Contents

	Page
Foreword	6
The Sometimes War	10
About the plats	12
The Headquarters Forts	13
Fort Snelling, Minnesota	14
Fort Vancouver, Washington	17
Fort Omaha, Nebraska	19
Fort Humboldt, California	21
Fort Douglas, Utah	23
Fort Shaw, Montana	26
The Queen (Fort Laramie, Wyoming)	28
Hog Ranch	32
Post-graduate school for future generals	33
Fort Lane, Oregon	34
Fort Yamhill, Oregon	36
Fort Steilacoom, Washington	37
Fort Gaston, California	39
The Bloody Bozeman	41
Forts Connor and Reno, Wyoming	42
Fort Phil Kearney, Wyoming	45
Fort C. F. Smith, Montana	47
Guardians of the River	49
Fort Randall, South Dakota	50
Fort Lookout, South Dakota	53
Fort Sully, South Dakota	55
Fort Rice, North Dakota	58
Fort Buford, North Dakota	61
Fort Union, North Dakota	64
Camp Cooke, Montana	65
Fort Benton, Montana	67
Guardians of the Trails	69
Fort Mitchell, Nebraska	70
Fort Kearny, Nebraska	72
Fort McPherson, Nebraska	74
Camp Collier, North Dakota	76
Fort Sedgwick, Colorado	77
Fort Lupton, Colorado	79
Fort Fetterman, Wyoming	80
Fort Caspar, Wyoming	83
Fort Abercrombie, North Dakota	86
Fort Totten, North Dakota	88
Fort Bridger, Wyoming	91
Camp Ruby, Nevada	94
Fort Halleck, Nevada	96

Page

    Fort Boise, Idaho 98
    Fort Walla Walla, Washington 100
    Fort Dalles, Oregon 102

Guardians of the Rails 104
    Fort Ransom, North Dakota 105
    Fort Sidney, Nebraska 107
    Fort D. A. Russell, Wyoming 110
    Fort Sanders, Wyoming 113
    Fort Fred Steele, Wyoming 116

The Peacekeepers 118
    Fort Ridgely, Minnesota 119
    Fort Sisseton, South Dakota 121
    Fort Hartsuff, Nebraska 124
    Camp Lyon, Idaho 126
    Fort Bidwell, California 128
    Fort Harney, Oregon 130
    Fort McDermit, Nevada 132
    Camp Winfield Scott, Nevada 134
    Fort Logan, Montana 137

The Protectors 140
    Fort Simcoe, Washington 141
    Camp Lincoln, California 144
    Fort Robinson, Nebraska 146
    Fort Yates, North Dakota 148
    Fort Lapwai, Idaho 150
    Fort Washakie, Wyoming 152

A Home for General Custer 154
    Fort McKeen, North Dakota 155
    Camp Hancock, North Dakota 157
    Fort Abraham Lincoln, North Dakota 158

Twilight 161
    Camp Sturgis and Fort Meade, South Dakota 162
    Fort McKinney, Wyoming 165
    Fort Custer, Montana 167
    Fort Missoula, Montana 169
    Fort Sherman, Idaho 171
    Fort Spokane, Washington 173
    Fort Maginnis, Montana 175
    Fort Assinniboine, Montana 177
    Fort Keogh, Montana 179

A Directory of Military Forts of the Northwest 1850 to 1890 182

Bibliography 186

Acknowledgements 189

Index 190

The Sometimes War

AN ARMY of old men and new lieutenants led the Sometimes War that began in 1850. At first, its senior officers had been around since the War of 1812, the rest were fresh from West Point.

Its time span placed the War with Mexico on one end, the Spanish-American War on the other. The Civil War paralleled it for a while in the middle.

It was a fracas fought on a shoe string, sometimes in spite of Congress and public apathy. But it earned twelve campaign streamers for the colors of the United States Army, and settled the Western Frontier.

From 1866 to 1875, it involved more than 200 battles, mostly with the Sioux Indians. Totally, from 1790 to 1898, the subjugation of the American Indian involved 69 campaigns and 19 reasonably definite wars.

The discovery of gold in California brought the Forty-niners. This was the final breaking point for the Indians who had watched trappers, traders, and farmers slowly encroach on their hunting grounds.

In the Pacific Northwest, the Indians refused to settle on reservations. General Harney then opened the area to settlers. In the Plains of the Northwest, a raw lieutenant named Grattan and a drunken interpreter tried to convince the Sioux they should not kill a stray cow. The Grattan force of 30 was killed, and the Sioux took the warpath.

Depending upon semantics involved, wars or expeditions were fielded against the hostile red men, and a semblence of peace returned. Relatively junior officers with names like Grant, Sherman, Sheridan, Crook, Pickett, McClellan, Ord, Stuart, Auger, obtained experience that led to generals' stars in the Civil War.

A tiny, 12,000 man Army fought the first stage of conflict, 1850–62. When rebellion drained the Army of its southern officers and men, and pulled many regular troops to the Eastern fronts, militia volunteers tried to keep the peace.

A massacre in Minnesota, uprisings in Oregon and California, an expedition in Wyoming, the constant threat of secession, and ambushes of the stage lines kept the volunteers busy, though unrecognized.

Even the Confederacy tried to help settle the Indian problem. Its treaty council on the Washita drew 20,000 red men, but the Lee's surrender left the commissioners without authority and the deliberations were less than academic.

With peace in the East, the vast Army of the Civil War was reduced to almost nothing. It was authorized sixty regiments, but each to consist of ten rather than 24 companies, and each company of 64 men. The private's pay was cut to $15 a month, less than 1840. Of the 54,000 men authorized, this low pay had attracted only 38,000 by October 1, 1866. And of this number, only 5,000 could be spared for the western frontier.

The area of operations was as large as Europe and numbered more than 300,000 Indians

GENERALS IN THE NORTHWEST included the eight pictured here and on the opposite page. Left, George Crook (1829–90) fought in the Pacific Northwest and against the Sioux. Alfred Sully (1821–79) led expeditions throughout Dakotas during Civil War. George Armstrong Custer (1839–76) was most flamboyant cavalry leader, died at Battle of Little Big Horn. William S. Harney (1800–89) commanded Pacific Northwest and in Dakotas before Civil War, was on treaty commissions after.

FIREBRAND OF UTAH, P. Edward Connor (1820–91) was California militiaman who led Army in Utah in Civil War and expedition against Sioux after the war. Nelson A. Miles (1839–1925) led largest single force ever assembled against the Indians. Ranald S. Mackenzie (1840–89) was fearless officer, wounded seven times, but died in mental institution at age of 49. Oliver O. Howard (1830–1909) lost right arm at Civil War Battle of Fair Oaks, fought Indians on western plains and Pacific Northwest. (All photographs courtesy National Archives. All from Brady Collection except Generals Sully and Connor.)

who felt they had first call upon that area. Treaties were tried, only to go up in the smoke of the Bozeman Trail forts. In 1869, President Grant refused to recognize that the Indian tribes had a treaty-making capability, and their status as independent nations ended.

The Indian fighters launched winter campaigns and spring campaigns and summer campaigns. The peace makers trying to end the Modoc War of Northern California were massacred in 1872. Custer's 1873 Black Hills Expedition discovered gold in the Sioux hunting grounds. The pot was bubbling and in 1876 it spilled over. Campaigns along the Powder River and the Rosebud lead to the high water mark of the Indian Nations: the Battle of the Little Big Horn on July 25, 1876.

This disaster jolted Congress and the public out of its apathy. Everything after this was anti-climactic. The Indians straggled into forts throughout the northwest, and within a year almost all had surrendered. The Nez Perce and Bannocks of Idaho took to the war path, the former to lead the Army on a masterful 2,000 mile chase before they, too, surrendered. In 1890, the last faint hope of the hostile red man died at the Battle, or Massacre, of Wounded Knee. The surrender of the Brule Sioux on January 30, 1891, closed this chapter in the advancing of the frontier.

This was a saga in which the principal role was played by an undermanned and underpaid Army. It was down to 25,000 men in 1874. Three years later Congress forgot to pay its officers and the War Department had to float loans at banking houses.

But it was an Army that brought peace, and more than peace, to the West. Soldiers at Fort Atkinson, Nebraska, in 1819, spent so much time farming that the Army Inspector suggested they didn't know how to fight. They proved agriculture could succeed, though, and doubting settlers doubted no longer.

Sawmills were brought by the Army to build its forts, and the lumber industry of the northwest was born. Cattle were driven west to feed the Army, and the great cattle industry was born. Chaplains and schoolteachers were stationed at the forts and ministered to the needs of both military and townspeople, and religion and education helped settle the rawness of the new territory.

Army families were shifted from East to West and back again, and their news of fashion, society, and the happenings along the seaboard retained bonds between the pioneers and the land they had left behind. Amateur theatricals at the forts provided a degree of culture. Mining, mapping, road building, path finding opened a Pandora's box for which the Army deserves primary credit.

There were hundreds of forts at various places and various times, keeping the peace and advancing the frontier. The presence of the Army's sheltering arm was the beacon to which settlers came, to plant their crops and plat their towns within the shadows of the military.

Seldom did a town grow without a fort in its vicinity. The Army brought not only peace, but progress, and from such a climate the seeds of the New West took root.

By 1890, the Sometimes War was over. The frontier Army had put itself out of business. The frontier was no more.

About the Plats

CONTEMPORARY novels spawned an idea carefully nurtured by Hollywood that Western forts were affairs of logs, surrounded by palisades, blockhouses at each corner, and with a heavy, creaking gate surmounted by the name of the fort burned into a marquee-type sign.

It wasn't quite like that, to be brutally frank.

The real forts usually were clusters of rude log or mud huts, sometimes hugging a hillside, sometimes out in the middle of a plain. Some were forts in the Hollywood tradition, but most were merely semi-permanent bases from which troops could move to wherever the peace was threatened.

Before the Civil War, some forts had stockades. The psychology changed after the war, and the need for an offensive spirit dictated an open, ready-to-move-out post. Those are the type that predominated, and the type most common in this book.

The plats shown here have been simplified and redrawn from various sources. Little attempt was made to retain an exact scale and small or unimportant buildings were left out. The "artifact hunter" will have to supplement these plats with an active imagination as his most lucrative sources are not shown: the trash pits, sinks, and dumps usually behind each barracks and officers' quarters, and the sizable dump usually near the hospital.

Each plat shows the fort as of a specific date.

Repairs and re-building were so frequent that a plat of one year may bear no resemblence to a plat of another. This explains why some plats and old photographs do not appear to agree.

Every effort has been taken to insure accuracy. Many of the plats were redrawn from the original sketches in the National Archives. These are indicated by the abbreviation *NA*. The source of other plats is spelled out, though *SHS* indicates the state historical society of the area concerned.

The following abbreviations are used to identify those buildings appearing most frequently:

HQ or ADJ—Headquarters or Adjutant's Office
S or ST—Stables
B—Barracks
BK—Bakery
SH—Storehouse or warehouse
H—Hospital
GH—Guardhouse
C—Chapel
EM or NCO—Married Soldier's Quarters
T—Tower or blockhouse
MESS or MH—Mess Hall
P.O.—Post Office

LAUN—Laundry or laundresses' quarters
OQ—Officers' Quarters
CO or COQ—Commander's Quarters
BLK—Blacksmith
TR, SUT or TRAD—Sutler or Post Trader
K or KIT—Kitchen
MAG—Magazine
CEM—Cemetery
COM or COMM—Commissary
CARP—Carpenter
CAV—Cavalry
INF—Infantry
REST—Restaurant

The Headquarters Forts

"Omaha is as safe as St. Louis. I don't believe in conducting
hostilities from the Rear."

—Sherman to General Cooke, 1866.

A FORT might have seemed alone in the vast emptiness of the Northwest, but a proverbial "big brother" was watching it from a headqarters fort somewhere. Most likely, several headquarters forts were watching, in fact.

These posts were similar to any other, except for more barracks and stables, and an office building for the general's staff. On occasion, depending upon the rank of the senior officer present, they might even be plusher—if such a term could be applied to western forts.

The status of these forts changed as headquarters were shifted about. Sometimes this depended upon the extent to which Sherman's comments were taken seriously.

In general, the Pacific Division from the Presidio, San Francisco, commanded California and the Pacific Northwest. The Division of the Missouri controlled the plains states, with headquarters at St. Louis and, toward the end, Chicago.

The Pacific had several subdivisions at various times, including the Columbia (Washington, Oregon, Idaho), Humboldt (Northern California), and California. The Missouri retained its organization in the northern plains almost without change. Fort Snelling, Minnesota, commanded the Dakota Department, from Minnesota to and including Montana. From Omaha, the Platte Department included all states along the Platte river to Utah.

One headquarters had a peculiar function. In 1874, the chief of the Army, Sherman, became disgusted with the politicing in Washington. He packed up Department of the Army headquarters lock, stock, and campstool, and moved it to Saint Louis.

Here at 10th and Locust, the entire Army was run until a new Secretary of War took office in 1876 and Sherman decided the air was clear enough to return to the capital city.

Fort Snelling, Minnesota

It cost $200 and $60 in whiskey to buy the site of Fort Snelling in 1805, but from that purchase the United States got a military post that operated for 126 years.

It was the Lord of the Northwest for part of this time. Its commander was the king, its officers the nobles, its towers and stone walls atop a 100 feet bluff, the castle. Not only did it command the junction of the Mississippi and Minnesota immediately below, but it was the supreme law of the Federal government in the wilderness.

Construction of the fort started in 1819 near Mendota where the Army spent a miserable winter at Cantonment New Hope. In 1820, new hope must have urged them to move to a camp with an even less promising name, Camp Coldwater. This was near the site ultimately selected for a post named Fort Saint Anthony, then renamed in honor of its first commander, Colonel Josiah Snelling in 1825.

More than any fort in the Northwest, Snelling was the ultimate in medieval fortifications. It was atop a bluff so that its stone walls seemed to be continuations of nature's work. Four towers commanded the corners of its diamond shape, and most of its buildings were inside, behind the parapets.

Prior to the Civil War, Snelling's main business was keeping the peace between the Indians and the new settlers.

Holding down the liquor trade was the key to this and Colonel Snelling blamed "ardent spirits" for most of its troubles. As he reported, whiskey could be obtained by the Indians from traders "who are little better than the savages themselves."

The fort was left behind as the frontier progressed. In 1857 it was sold to the former post sutler in a questionable arrangement, but this was cancelled when the Civil War needed it as a training camp.

In 1871 it was a military post again, and in 1872 a travel guide described it as "a supply post whence are sent men and supplies to the frontier forts now hundreds of miles further in."

Fort Snelling was a Headquarters Fort in the twilight period when it commanded the Department of Dakota. New buildings were added and much of the wall torn down.

Many leading Army officers served here and Snelling could claim one president: Zachary Taylor, who was here as a lieutenant colonel.

The fort had its periods of near-abandonment, and on October 14, 1946 the final abandonment came. At that time the present occupants, the Veterans Administration, acquired it . . . but by this time all that was left were two towers and some officers' quarters.

TO GET THERE: *From downtown Minneapolis, take Hiawatha avenue south to the intersection with highways 5 and 100. Follow signs to Fort Snelling above this underpass.*

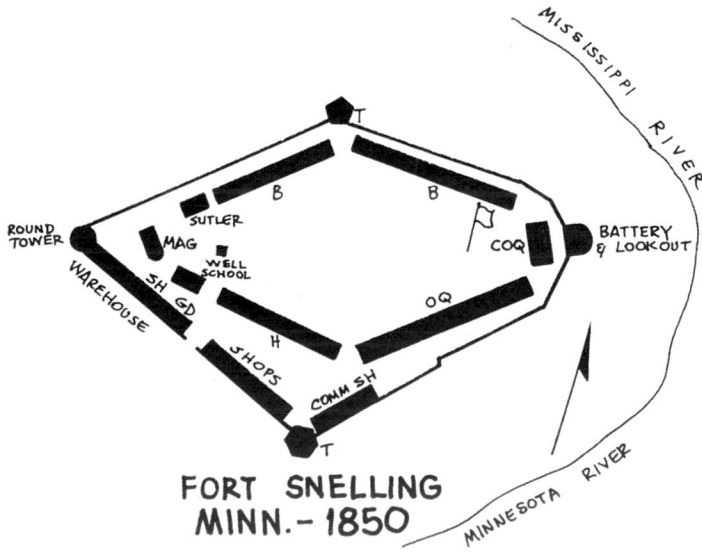

FORT SNELLING
MINN.- 1850

ONLY TWO OF the four towers shown remain today. Round Tower is considered oldest building in Minnesota, Hexagonal Tower (at lower corner) is least altered. (Redrawn from SHS data.)

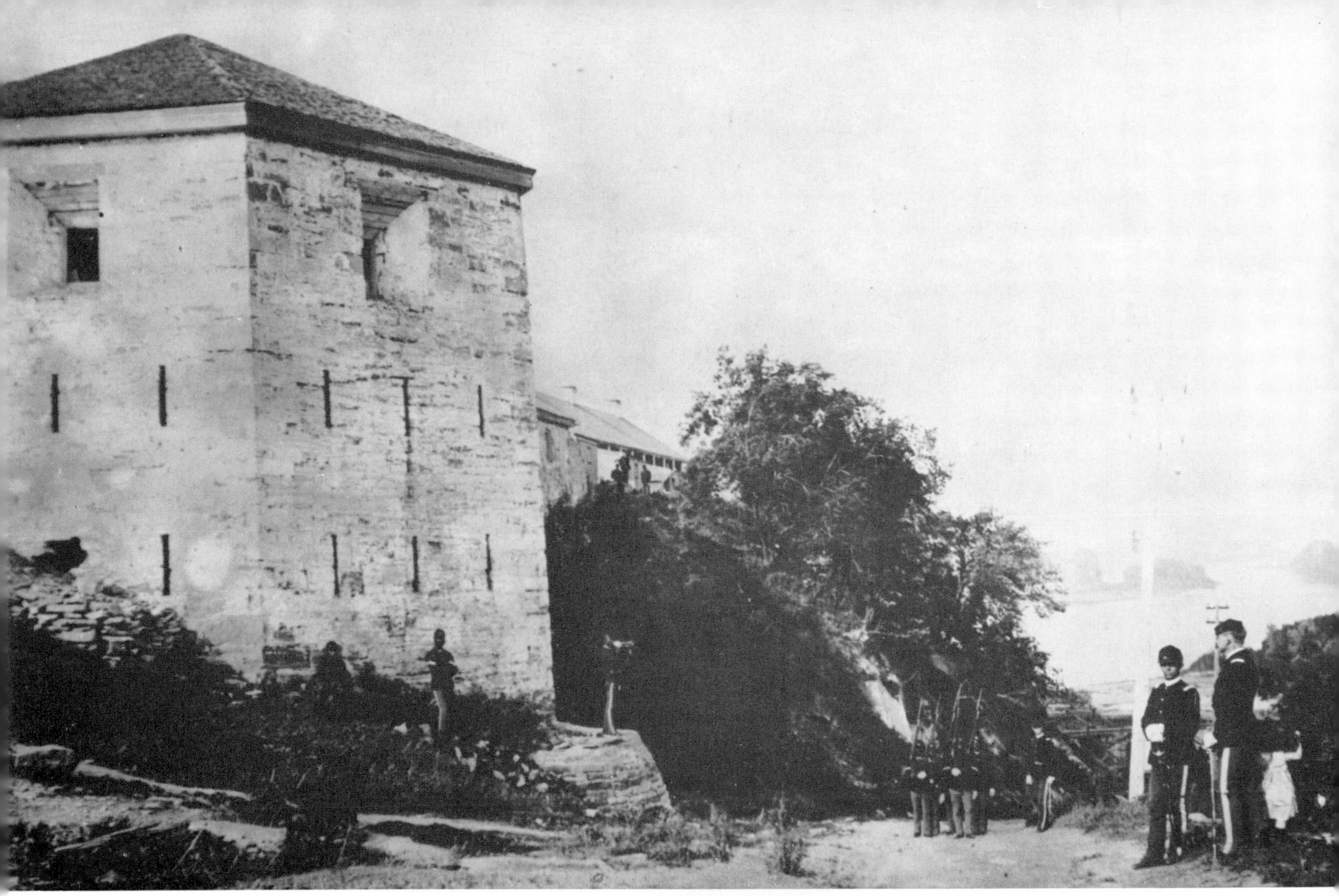

(Courtesy National Archives.)

HEXAGONAL TOWER in 1887 looked almost the same as its present appearance. Junction of rivers is in background.

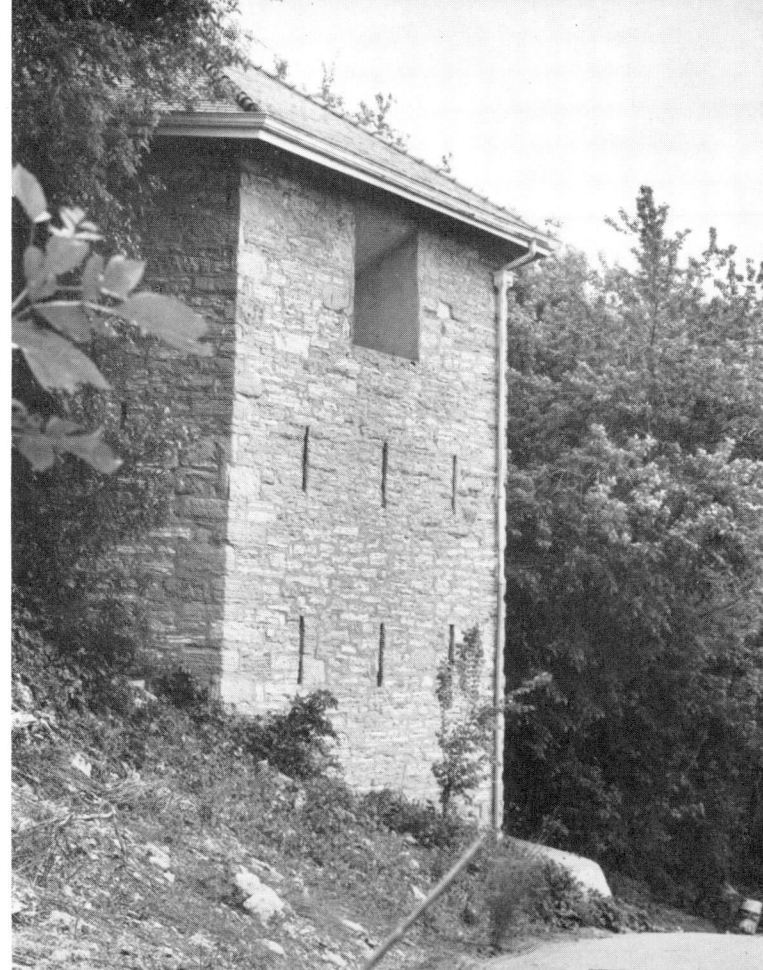

HEXAGONAL TOWER today has more foliage around it. Only the soldiers are needed to restore it to early appearance.

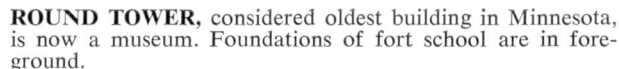

SHARP DROP from Snelling's site shows intersection of Mississippi and Minnesota rivers.

OFFICERS' QUARTERS are original, but bear little resemblance to early days. California-style exterior was added in 1904.

ROUND TOWER, considered oldest building in Minnesota, is now a museum. Foundations of fort school are in foreground.

Fort Vancouver, Washington

The Hudson Bay Company helped the Army establish a fort in 1849 and within eleven years found that its guest had taken over the household.

The place was Fort Vancouver, Washington, a major post for the trade company from 1824 to 1860, and a strategic headquarters for the Army from 1849 until 1946.

Vancouver started as a stockaded affair 732 by 325 feet with eight 3-pounders in a bastion at the northwest corner. It had 22 buildings plus a factor, or superintendent, who stood six foot four inches: John McLoughlin, considered by many to be the "Father of Oregon."

McLoughlin was a friend to all and kept peace with all so that settlers were attracted to his Columbia river location. His hospitality was broadcast back along the trails. One Englishman brought him some appleseeds and, legend claims, McLoughlin planted these as a forerunner of the Washington apple industry.

When the Army came, the fur company was happy to receive them. The 1846 treaty between Great Britain and the United States placed them outside of Canada, and they felt the Army's presence would reduce the pressure from the settlers to take over.

The Army built on a rise 20 feet above the trading post, fronting 1,200 yards on the river with buildings on a line 2,000 yards from the water. The Hudson Bay Company helped the Army to get established, but new officers transfered in soon forgot that any debt was owed. Pressure against the fur post mounted and on June 14, 1860, the last boat left for Vancouver Island with the company's remaining goods. Keys to the fort were turned over to the Army. In 1869, the United States paid Great Britain $650,000 for the claims of the Hudson Bay Company at Fort Vancouver.

The Army first called its post Columbia Barracks, changing the name to Fort Vancouver in 1853. It had its fluctuations in strength, hitting bottom in 1861 when only 50 men were on the rolls. It saw many soldiers, including Sherman, McClellan, Sheridan, and Crook, and, in later years, George C. Marshall, later to be a General of the Army and "Father of the Marshall Plan."

In 1875, two double story barracks were on both sides of the parade ground, each with a kitchen and mess room to the rear. Seven log and four frame buildings served as Officers' Quarters. Because of a design with two rooms on either side of a corridor, they were known as "four pens and a passage."

TO GET THERE: *From downtown Vancouver, Washington, take East 5th street into the fort at the overpass with U.S. 99.*

MILITARY POST was all that remained in 1870, but site of Hudson Bay Company's fort was the clear area below barns in this plat. (Redrawn from Surgeon-General Circular, 1870.)

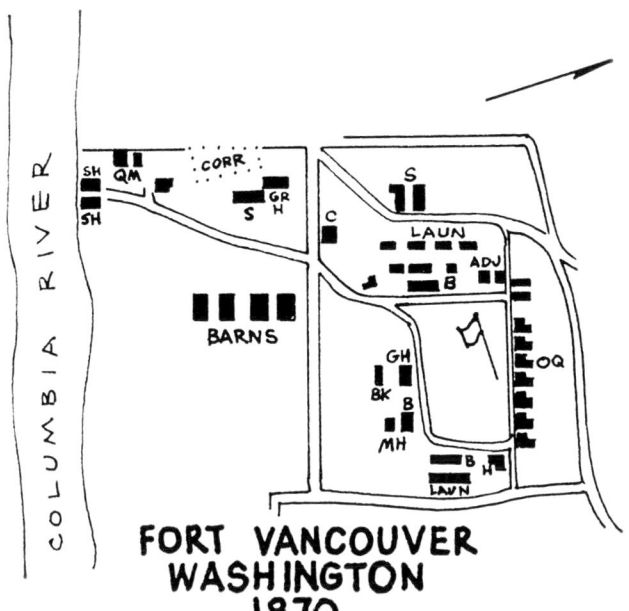

SKETCH by unknown artist shows military Fort Vancouver in the 1850's. Grant House is double story building in center of Officers' row, left. First site was to the right edge of sketch.

(Courtesy Mrs. G. M. Donaugh, Vancouver, and National Park Service.)

COMMANDING OFFICER'S house, built in 1849–50, was office of U. S. Grant when he was quartermaster at Fort Vancouver. It is now a museum.

PARADE GROUND is dwarfed by fir trees while present day Army unit forms in front of barracks. Reserve units use the post.

Fort Omaha, Nebraska

Sherman was thinking of Fort Omaha when he said he was opposed to conducting hostilities "from the Rear." He had another name for it: "hindquarters," for he thought that Omaha was so far from the fighting it could hardly be called headquarters.

The city of Omaha wasn't much when the fort was started on November 20, 1868. "Two or three blocks of warehouses, shops and offices, among them a theatre," is how one officer described it. "It boasted of two or three half-blocks in brick, a number of frame shops, as well as bar-rooms and cheap eating houses, all ending at the Herndon Hotel, at the edge of the steep bluffs which stand well above the highest floods of the Missouri."

Omaha Barracks, the fort's first name, was four miles northwest of the city and almost two miles from the river. Ten wooden barracks, 30 by 80 feet, and 14 officers' quarters were arranged around a rectangular parade ground.

The post was the headquarters for the Department of the Platte, but the offices were in downtown Omaha at first. In the 1870's buildings were added and General Crook moved his headquarters from the city.

Indian and non-Indian affairs occupied the Army. In 1877, six companies were sent to Chicago during a railroad strike. In 1879, a company went to Hastings, Nebraska, to convince a mob that it was unwise to intimidate a Federal court during a murder trial.

Seven buildings of the early era remain, though Navy blue outnumbers any other uniform. The Navy Reserve's national headquarters is here, and its chief occupies the main residence. It's named appropriately for one of its past occupants, "The Sherman House," though that the General must have found it hard to accept staying so far from hostilities at "hindquarters."

TO GET THERE: *Take 30th street (U.S. 73) from downtown Omaha, north to Fort street. Main entrance is on the left.*

LIVING QUARTERS monopolized area at old Fort Omaha. (Redrawn from Division of the Missouri report, 1876)

SCOUTS
Q   H   ST
K
B
OQ   QM SH
                      SUTLER
MAJOR   GH
COL   HQ
MAJOR   COMM
OQ   BAND
                      BK
              B
              K
                      SHOPS
STABLES
        LAUN

OMAHA BARRACKS NEBR. - 1876

SHERMAN SLEPT HERE, 1872, states the plaque on front of building No. 1 at Fort Omaha.

(Photo from Bostwick Collection, Nebraska Historical Society.)

FORMER BARRACKS, mess hall behind, was added to Fort Omaha in 1878. Building still stands, remodeled into apartments. This building can be located on plat, though not shown. It would be in middle of parade ground between sutler and officers' quarters.

HEADQUARTERS for present Fort Omaha was built in 1878. Ladders provide necessary fire escapes.

PARADE GROUND looks much like it did in the 1870's. Former administration building, behind flag pole, is now quarters for a non-commissioned officer.

Fort Humboldt, California

Fort Humboldt was headquarters for the Northern California District of the Humboldt, an area of 20,000 square miles during the Civil War.

With its rugged forests and mountains, the Humboldt District presented its commander with no easy task. "There are so many Indians and they are so hard to find," Colonel Francis J. Lippitt reported, "that to bring them all in by sending small detachments after them would take as long as it would to bring in the squirrels and coyotes."

When the fort was built in 1852—a lieutenant named George Crook was in its first detachment —it was just about the only military establishment in the area. By 1861, the Humboldt had four forts (Humboldt, Crook, Gaston, and Bragg) and as many camps (Baker, Lyon, Anderson, and Lincoln). This had shrunk to only Humboldt, Gaston, and Lincoln by 1865, plus Camp Iaqua, built near Blue Lake in 1863.

Humboldt had its problems. One of its early captains, a U. S. Grant, served there for five months in 1854, but spent more time at Ryan's Tavern in Eureka than at the fort. In 1861 the rains were so bad that the 26 buildings were abandoned temporarily and shelter was sought in Eureka.

Twenty-five men scouted through the brambles and brush in the sixties with such enthusiasm that they were "so entirely destitute as to make it impossible for them to leave the camp, however urgently their services are needed," Lippitt reported. In other words, they had no pants.

At one time, Lippitt had 300 Indians and 35 soldiers under guard at the fort. He built a circular stockade 10 feet high and 80 feet in diameter and put everyone in it.

After the Civil War, the need for Fort Humboldt lessened. It was closed in 1866 and abandoned in the seventies. Only one building, the hospital, remains. It was shifted from its original position, so today nothing at Fort Humboldt remains as it once was.

TO GET THERE: *From Eureka, take Highway 101 south to the city limits. Fort site is on bluff overlooking highway. Follow signs.*

U. S. GRANT'S home in 1854 was said to be the L-shaped one in top row of officers' quarters. (Redrawn from California Beaches and Parks data.)

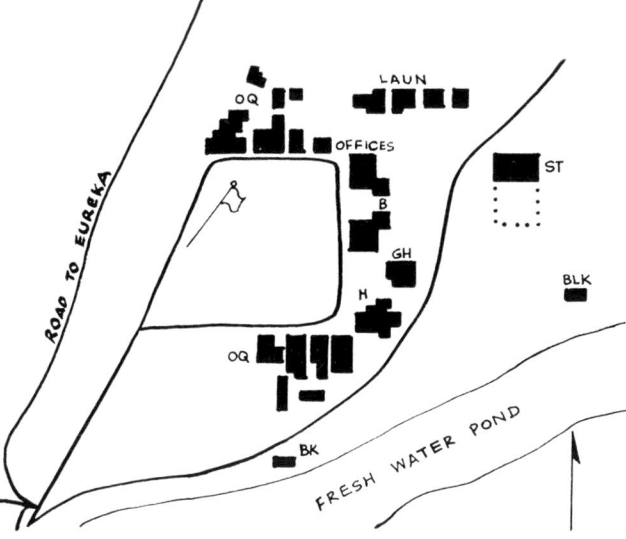

FORT HUMBOLDT
CAL. -1861

MINIATURE fort shows arrangement of buildings, but not necessarily their shape. Model at the site matches the plat.

HOSPITAL is only building left but has been completely remodeled and shifted a few feet and degrees from original site. State offices now use it. Officers' quarters sites are shown by white signs in right foreground.

NORTHERN OFFICERS' ROW is marked by white signs. View is from site of Commanding Officer's Quarters toward Humboldt Bay and Pacific. Perennial mist hugs fort site most of year.

(Photo courtesy Bancroft Library.)

FORT HUMBOLDT stood on 20-foot bluff overlooking Humboldt Bay and Pacific. This view is from the west.

Fort Humboldt, near Eureka.

Where General Grant, then Captain, was stationed in 1853-4.   indicates Grant's quarters.

Fort Douglas, Utah

It's a good question whether Fort Douglas was established to protect against the Indians or the Mormons. General P. Edward Connor considered each equally hostile to the Army and the so-called "Gentile" whites.

The fiery Connor came to Salt Lake City in 1862, first checking the area in civilian clothes. He was sure a musket-shooting Mormon hid behind every bush. Although he was supposed to set up his headquarters at old Fort Crittenden, formerly Camp Floyd, 40 miles away, he thought this was too far from Brigham Young.

From a rise overlooking Salt Lake City, Connor said he planned to "entrench my position and then say to the Saints of Utah, enough of your treason."

The Mormons went to the courts to have the post removed as a public nuisance. And Connor sponsored Utah's first daily newspaper, the "Daily Union Vedette," that was both a post publication and an outspoken critic of the Mormons. Most of the funds came from Connor's pocket, though it faired pretty well from advertisements and subscriptions.

Douglas was first a series of 32 barracks and 15 officers' quarters. These were actually canvas thrown over holes in the ground, politely termed "Connor tents." After the 1862–63 winter, the post was re-built around a 440-foot square parade ground. Wooden barracks flanked the parade and log officers' quarters were at one end. Headquarters for the District of Utah was a building to the northwest. From here Connor ran affairs in Utah, Nevada, and part of Wyoming.

Two of the affairs were the Battle of Bear River in January, 1863, and the Powder River Expedition in 1865. At Bear River Connor hit an Indian camp in a three-pronged maneuver that cut off escape. A counted 224 Indians and 23 soldiers died in the battle.

At the Powder River near the present Wyoming-Montana border, Connor had to attack the Indians on the run when they had learned he was coming. He didn't have enough men for a pursuit so he returned to camp. His report said he had "marched 100 miles, fought the battle and brought our prisoners and captured stock back to camp in 30 hours."

Sporadic activity kept the Army busy at home,

TO GET THERE: *From downtown Salt Lake City, U.S. Alternate 40 goes by the main entrance to Fort Douglas at the eastern edge of the city.*

FORT DOUGLAS in 1864 was an improvement over the "Connor tent" camp of 1862, but bore little resemblance to today's fort. (Redrawn from data courtesy SSgt R. C. Hipes, USA)

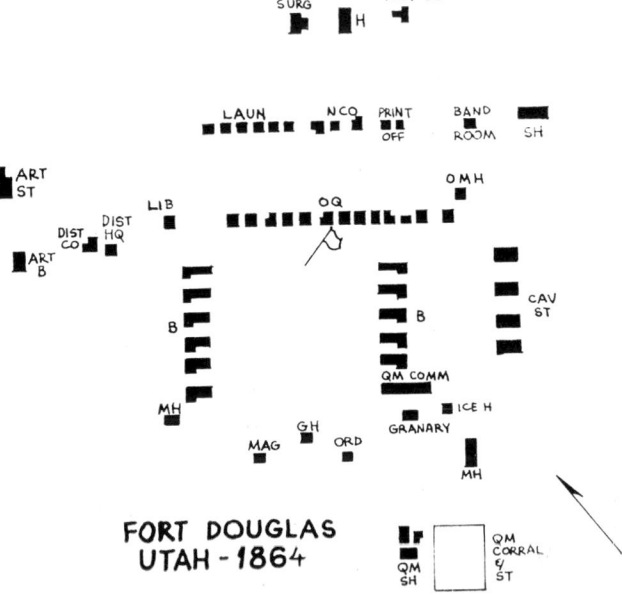

FORT DOUGLAS
UTAH - 1864

MORMONS AND GENTILES no longer fought when, in 1930, drive was conducted to build this memorial for General Connor's grave. Enough money was collected in Salt Lake City for monument and to build an athletic field, Connor field.

ONCE BARRACKS, these buildings remain from those flanking right side of parade ground in 1878 sketch. Red Butte of Wasatch mountains is to the rear. Buildings now used by auditor, reserve administrators, supply officers and veterinarian.

too. The Mormons watched the fort with a telescope mounted atop Brigham Young's headquarters and declared an emergency when cannon started to fire in 1863. They didn't know it was an 11-gun salute in celebration of Connor's promotion to brigadier general.

A cannon was used at Pleasant Valley, Utah, in pursuit of Indian horse thieves. The first blast killed several government mules in a nearby corral. The second split the adobe building that was hiding the howitzer. No more were fired.

Douglas was first a camp, but was designated a fort in 1878. Between 1874 and 1876 it was almost completely rebuilt and the old buildings that remain today are mainly from that and the 1880 era.

FORT DOUGLAS in 1878 looked much like it does today. The circle of officers' quarters at the head of the parade ground and some of the barracks remain. Original camp of 1862 was at far right of sketch.

(Courtesy National Archives.)

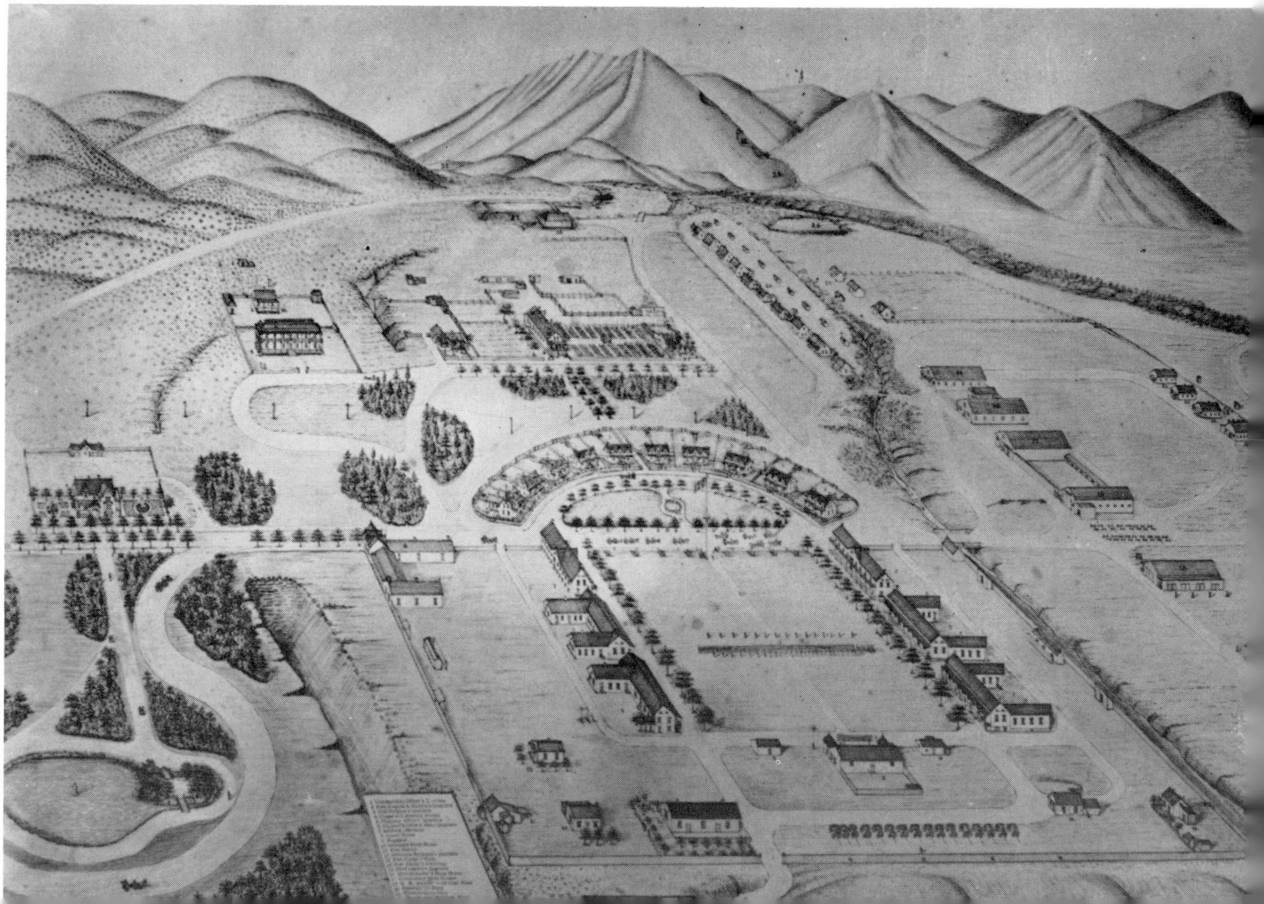

COMMANDING OFFICER'S quarters is located midway in the row of what 1878 sketch shows were barracks on left side of parade.

EMIGRATION CANYON, left rear, is next to post cemetery. From canyon's mouth Brigham Young first saw Great Salt Lake, said "This is the place." Markers in cemetery include those of soldiers killed at Bear Mountain and Powder River.

Fort Shaw, Montana

The District of Montana was commanded by a man more French than American, operating from a new post on the Sun river in mid-Montana. The post was Fort Shaw, the man Colonel and Brevet Major General Philippe Regis Denis de Keredern de Trobriand, son of a French baron and a division commander during the Civil War.

Fort Shaw was established in 1867 as Camp Reynolds, a name that lasted only a month. It was built around a 400-foot square and all of the buildings were adobe and shingled.

From here de Trobriand struck out at the Indians in a winter campaign, 1869. He had spent the summer locating the camps of all Indians, good and bad, biding his time until snow kept them close to their wigwams. Then he attacked the hostile camps in a blinding snowstorm. Not a single good Indian's camp was hit, but the marauding Indians marauded no more.

Another commander of Fort Shaw was Colonel and Brevet Major General John Gibbon. In the seventies he took troops from Shaw to the Little Big Horn country. He was trying an encircling movement when the Sioux attacked General Custer.

Gibbon's troops were in the 1877 Battle of the Big Hole, the dawn attack against the Nez Perce that started their 2,000-mile retreat toward the Canadian border.

Indian troubles aside, Fort Shaw had more than its share of problems with alcohol. A captain, lieutenant, and surgeon all were its victims. Soldiers must have succumbed to the lure of whiskey if an 1869 letter to a Charles A. Bull is any indication.

Bull wanted to know why he was forbidden to visit the post.

"It is a notorious fact," he was told, "that you have been guilty of selling bad whiskey to the soldiers of this garrison at any and all times, also that you have assisted men in getting to the crossing by allowing them to ride in your wagon, this too while they were under the influence of liquor, purchased from you, and without proper authority."

Abandoned in 1890, Shaw was first an Indian school. Some old buildings remain and are now mingled with modern ones of a county grade school.

TO GET THERE: *From Great Falls, Montana, take U.S. 89 west 19 miles to intersection with state 20. Follow state 20 five miles to town of Fort Shaw. Fort site is a school one-half a mile north of the town.*

NOT ALL OF THESE buildings actually existed in 1870, but this was the plan. The district of Montana shared the headquarters building, west side, with the post adjutant. Flagpole probably was in front of guard house. (Redrawn from Surgeon General circular, 1870.)

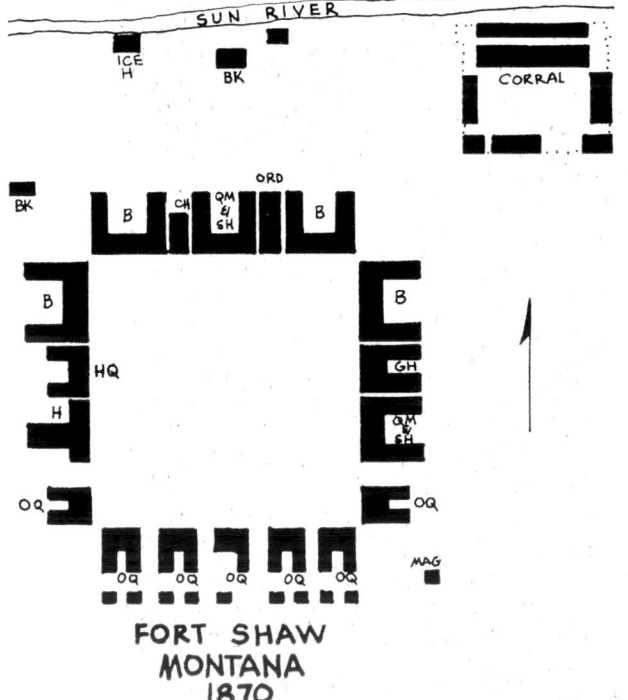

FORT SHAW
MONTANA
1870

OFFICERS' QUARTERS and officers' children stand amidst trees Gibbon planted in the seventies. Probably taken in the eighties, picture looks eastward along row of officers' quarters.

FIREPLACE CHIMNEYS suggest this building might have been occupied as barracks or quarters by soldiers or teamsters assigned to corral. Building is northeast of old parade ground, too close to be a part of corral, too far to be part of barracks shown in plat.

SOUTHERN LINE of Fort Shaw shows remains of officers' row. These buildings appear in the old picture of fort. Gun in foreground dates as World War souvenir, rather than from Indian Wars.

The Queen

HARDLY a diary of western travel, or report of frontier activity, can be found without mention of the leading fort of them all: Fort Laramie, Wyoming.

Laramie was in action longer than most forts. It was larger than several of them put together. And its key location dictated that it play a leading role in the Northwest and its Army.

The Oregon Trail, Pony Express, Mormon Trail, trans-continental telegraph line, all passed Fort Laramie. The routes to the Southwest split from those to the Northwest at this point. When the railroad came to Wyoming, Fort Laramie had a station.

But the story of The Queen of Frontier Posts is more than that of transportation and communications. It had been a fur post, Fort William, in 1834, became an adobe-walled enclosure as "Fort John on the Laramie" in 1841. The government bought it for $4,000 in 1849 and the first half of the second name was dropped.

It was in 1851 that the U. S. government gathered unto itself at Fort Laramie the various and assorted tribes of Sioux, Cheyenne, Arapahoes, Snakes and Crows. The government and the assembled 10,000 redmen agreed to a treaty that boiled down to the Indians surrendering certain lands in return for $50,000 a year for 50 years. (A strange typographical error changed this to 10 years when the treaty was approved in Washington, D. C.).

A three year period of only occasional sniping between whites and Indians followed, and this "too good to be true" treaty existed until August 18, 1854.

That was when a cow strayed from a Mormon caravan camping east of the fort. A visiting Miniconjou brave appropriated the animal, much to the disenchantment of the Mormons.

A brash and cocky Lieutenant John Gratton, 29 soldiers, two cannon and an interpreter went to the Brule Sioux camp to straighten things out. Not only was Grattan a bit too eager, but his interpreter a bit too alcoholic, and untactful words were exchanged with the Sioux.

All 30 soldiers and the interpreter were killed. This unleashed a Pandora's Box of blood letting. It didn't subside until the Civil War, despite the anti-climax when General Harney massacred 86 Brule Sioux after tracking them down 150 miles south of the fort.

After the Civil War, General Sherman met the Indians at Fort Laramie in June, 1866. Another peace conference tried to settle the Indian problems and a goodly number of redmen gathered. It wasn't as impressive or representative an array as before, however.

Of the few real chiefs present, Red Cloud was one of the leaders. He wasn't happy with the conference, and was less happy when it was interrupted by the arrival of the expedition to open the Bozeman Trail. This confirmed Red Cloud's suspicions that the white intentions were less than white. He walked out.

Possibly, had the unfortunate meeting not taken place between Red Cloud and the Bozeman expedition, there might not have been any Indian wars to follow.

Or, were they inevitable?

The Indians had a grievance in a direct proportion to the ambitions of the white man. Maybe these incidents that led to the hostilities were merely the rationalizations rather than the reasons.

Regardless of the later view of the affairs, the key role of Fort Laramie continued into the late nineteenth century. Slowly, but without doubt, its mission was eaten away as relentless progress marched westward, pushing before it the Indian troubles, the bandits, the lawless and the unruly.

Laramie fielded expeditions, patrols and reinforcements to extricate less knowledgeable commanders from hot spots. But the inevitable finally came in August, 1889, when abandonment of the fort was announced.

A year later, token bids of only $1,395 bought 35 lots of buildings at auction. In later years heroic efforts to retain some trace of the fort were made by John Hunton, former fort telegrapher, and friends.

In 1913, they erected an Oregon Trail marker at the site, despairing that this was all that could be done. But in 1927, Wyoming bought the fort and, in 1938 gave it to the federal government.

Today the Queen is maintained as is no other inactive western fort. With painstaking, almost tender loving care, workmen are replacing the buildings of the old fort. The sutler's store, the enlisted and officers' club, a field officer's quarters, old guard house, an officer's duplex, the old headquarters all are slowly and meticulously reappearing on the flatland of the Platte.

The post is being restored to its appearance of no specific era. Rather, each building is going back to its peak use, everything blending into the architecture of the western forts but still maintaining its own personal character when it, and it alone, could mark its place in the movement to the West.

TO GET THERE: *From Cheyenne, Wyoming, take U.S. 87 north 82 miles to U.S. 26. Turn right, go 27 miles to town of Fort Laramie. Follow well-marked gravel road two miles to old Fort Laramie National Historic Site.*

FORT LARAMIE IN 1876. "Old Bedlam" was double-story building left of flagpole, hospital was on hill right of flagpole. Cavalry barracks was long, double-storied, multi-windowed building below hospital.

HOSPITAL IS IN RUINS next to hollow walls of non-commissioned officers' quarters (right). Built in 1873, hospital is believed to stand amidst pre-1866 fort cemetery.

ENLISTED MEN'S BAR was typical of frontier days. Restored by National Park Service, bar is inoperable, bottles and kegs are empty. Original patch of wall paper is above kegs. This room is in sutler's store, operated from 1849 as major trading post on the trails for 40 years. Billiard room was next to bar.

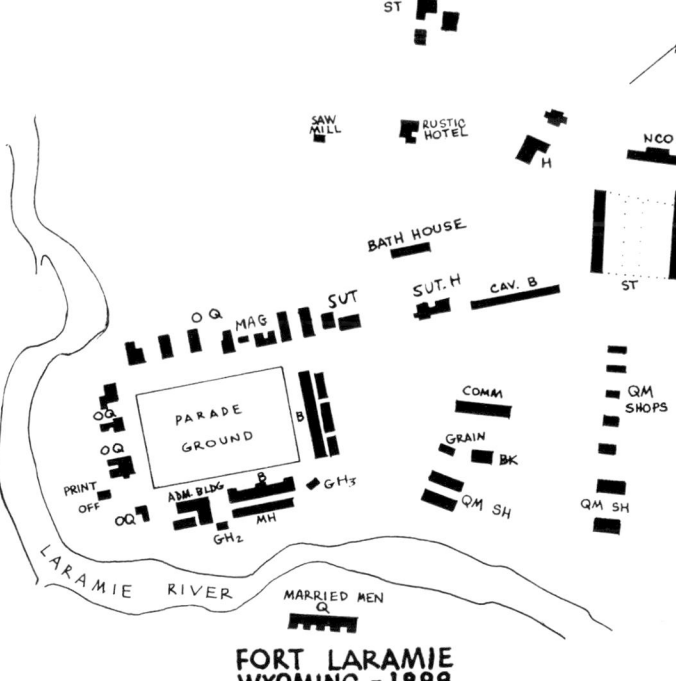

FORT LARAMIE
WYOMING - 1888

TOTAL OF 150 BUILDINGS made up Fort Laramie. Eleven of them are restored today, including sutler's and several of those to left of it, east side of parade ground. Large officers' quarters at southeastern corner, third guard house, cavalry barracks, commissary also were restored. Rustic Hotel and stables above it were used by Cheyenne–Black Hills Stage Line. (Redrawn from Fort Laramie National Historic Society data.)

30

(Courtesy J. McDermott, Fort Laramie National Historic Site.)

FORT LARAMIE TODAY. "Old Bedlam" is still evident. Buildings to its right are magazine, two officers' quarters, sutler's store. Ruins of hospital are on bluff while trees hide all but one wall of cavalry barracks.

NORTHERN EDGE OF PARADE GROUND shows ruins of officers' quarters built in 1881, dismantled for their lumber in 1890. "Old Bedlam," other officers' quarters, sutler's building follow along row.

FIRST AND THIRD GUARD HOUSES face "Old Bedlam," other side of parade ground. While restoring 1876 guard house at western corner of parade, National Park Service found traces of pre-1866 prison underneath. Cells, foreground, suggest guard house stays weren't pleasant. There were five, measuring two-and-a-half by five feet, only six feet high. This was succeeded in 1866 by second jail (see plat), third one was built on this spot later. Across parade ground "Old Bedlam" being restored, was built in 1849 and served variously as headquarters, commanding officer's residence, officers' apartments, and bachelors officers' quarters. Nickname probably came from last use.

BARRACKS AND THIRD GUARD HOUSE mark northeastern corner of parade ground. Barracks was built in 1868 of frame, filled with adobe. It measured 287 by 30 feet, housed three companies, each in dormitories 81 by 30 feet. Mess rooms and kitchens were to rear.

Hog Ranch

Near enough to be convenient, yet far enough away to be free of military control, the "Hog Ranch" was an extra-legal part of almost every frontier fort.

Here the soldier could find those pleasures forbidden or carefully rationed on the post. The trader or sutler may have orders to serve only one drink every half day, or not serve certain soldiers at all. But here at the Hog Ranch, the trooper could drink his fill regardless of regulations (or the need to be ready for duty at reveille).

Another adjunct to the Hog Ranch—some say that was how its uncomplimentary name came about—were the "hostesses." Modern movies and television have whitewashed these ladies of the western evening, but regardless of what they were called, a rose was still a rose.

General George Forsyth said the Hog Ranches came about because whiskey could not be sold at the forts. Originally started to sell liquor, the shanties soon branched into gambling.

Further expansion came, he wrote, with "two or three bedrooms built on to the ranch and two or three of the most wretched and lowest class of abandoned women (for none other could be induced to come out to such surroundings) could be seen standing in the doorway or heard singing and shouting at the bar."

While commanding a New Mexican fort, Forsyth ordered the post trader to sell whiskey in violation of regulations. The results: the hog ranches closed up within five months, incidents of drunkenness decreased, and it turned out the men preferred beer . . . the attraction of whiskey lay in its unavailability!

Fort Laramie's Hog Ranch was one of the most elaborate, befitting its status of serving a post of such importance. It lay at the edge of the western boundary of the post. Started in 1874 as a trading post, saloon and hotel, its slack summer business disappointed the owners, E. Coffee and A. Cuny. They bolstered it by augmenting the staff with a number of ladies from Kansas City and Omaha.

These lovelies occupied small rooms in a building that remains today. Records hint, but do not prove, that Calamity Jane was a resident of the Coffee-Cuny establishment.

Neither Coffee nor Cuny fared very well. Coffee died in 1874, Cuny was killed at their ranch three miles away in July, 1877.

A succession of owners followed, but supply and demand parted ways when Fort Laramie was abandoned in 1889. Business at the Hog Ranch hadn't done well after 1880, and the end of the fort struck the final blow to the less reputable neighbor.

COURTYARD ruins show where rear row of rooms once were. Sunflowers bloom there now.

TO GET THERE: *From Fort Laramie road (south of hospital ruins), take dirt road directly west about three miles. At end of road is Hog Ranch, privately owned and used as a farm building.*

HOG RANCH main building was U-shaped, small rooms bordering all of its sides. This is now a granary and chicken house. Each window-door-window is separate room.

Post-Graduate School
for Future Generals

FROM West Point, the graduate of the 1850's often went around the Isthmus of Panama to California. As a brevet second lieutenant, his schooling continued here, before he achieved true commissioned status and that "brevet" title was removed.

Many of the generals of the Civil War learned practical application of field tactics against the Pit River and Rouge River Indians of the Pacific Northwest. Grant, Sherman, Sheridan, Crook, Pickett, Ord, Auger, Fred Steele, Burnside, Stuart, Pope, all received their Baptism of fire here.

Most of their posts are long gone, only local legend persisting that "the old fort was somewhere around here." But a few, usually the ones used after the Civil War, too, remain to tell the story of how generals got their start in the frontier Army of long ago.

"I must say that my first impressions of the Army were not favorable . . . Most of the Commanding Officers were petty tyrants, styled by some Martinets . . . Most of them had been in command of small posts so long that their habits and minds had narrowed down to their surroundings, and woe be unto the young officer if his ideas should get above their level and wish to expand."

—General Crook's autobiographical comments of his first days as a lieutenant at Fort Humboldt, California, in 1852.

FORT BELLINGHAM (1856–60) is gone except for a few stepping stones on private land, and the memories that in this house Captain George A. Pickett lived with his Indian wife and son. Pickett became a Confederate general, and won immortality during charge at Gettysburg. Home is at 910 Bancroft street, Bellingham, Washington.

(Courtesy Albert P. Salisbury.)

33

Fort Lane, Oregon

Sixty dragoons and a 12-pound howitzer made up the 1853 garrison of Fort Lane, a log and mud post within the shadow of southwest Oregon's Table Rock.

Table Rock rises majestically from the Rogue River Valley and was considered a sacred place by the Indians. Joseph Lane, Oregon's first governor, defeated them here on August 24, 1853, and a treaty was signed atop the rock two weeks later.

Fort Lane had been established in 1852 and protected the peace of this treaty—though Congress didn't ratify it for six years. After the Rogue River War, Lane was the transfer point for the Indians.

Its central location made Fort Lane the rendezvous for most expeditions in the fifties. Lieutenant George Crook came here from Fort Jones, California, while on one such trip.

He wrote in his Autobiography that he was supposed to borrow the fort's cannon. His combination militia-regular Army force needed it to dislodge some Indians from caves.

However, Captain A. J. Smith, commanding at Fort Lane, decided the Indians were merely defending themselves against thieving miners, and called the "battle" off. This was "much to the dissatisfaction of the Volunteers, who were anxious to have the Regulars charge the Indians' stronghold that they might come in for some spoils," Crook commented.

"Captain Smith returned to Fort Lane, and our part of the grand farce returned to our places of abode."

TO GET THERE: *From Medford, Oregon, go north on U.S. 99 to Blackwell road junction three and a half miles past Central Point. Bear right. At Gold Ray Dam Road, 1.7 miles, turn right. In a half a mile, Tolo railroad sign is on right side of road, marker for fort on left side. Table Rock is to right on opposite side of valley.*

SIGNAL GUN TREE supposedly was blown off by firing of howitzer at Fort Lane during military formations. It is only remnant of fort. Marker is 200 yards from actual site.

DURING ITS three years (1853–56) Fort Lane didn't have time to become an elaborate post. (Redrawn from Jack Sutton data courtesy Jacksonville, Oregon, Museum.)

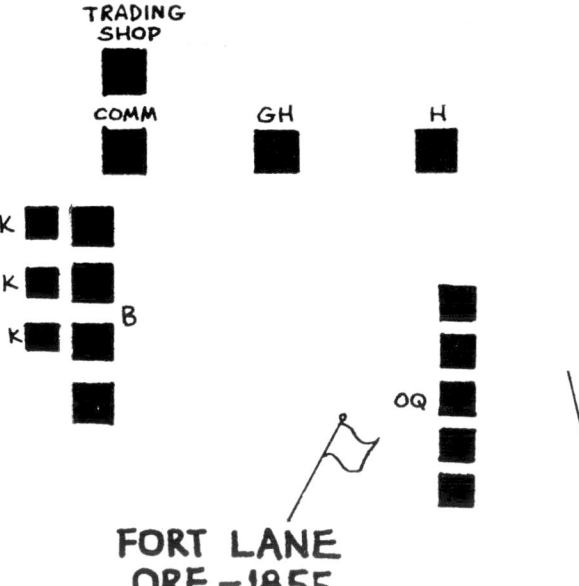

FORT LANE
ORE.-1855

(Courtesy Oregon Historical Society.)

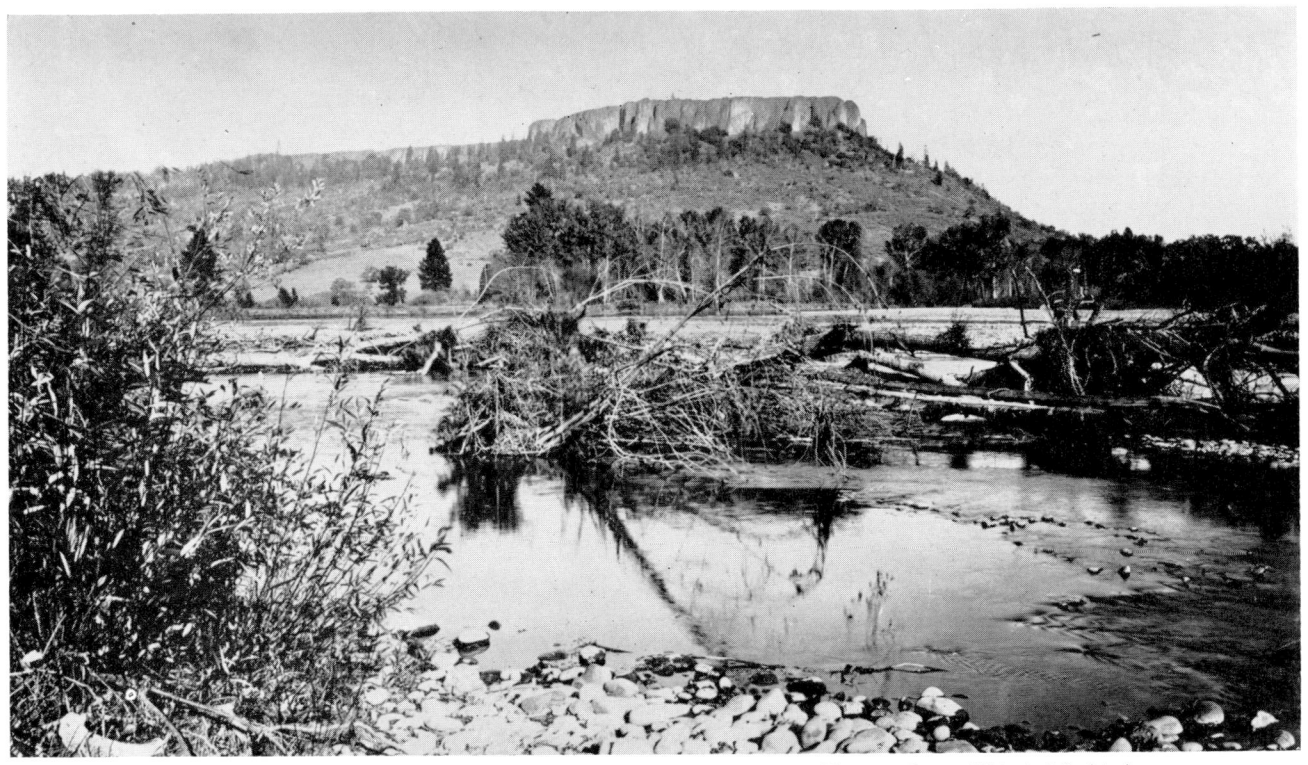

TABLE ROCK as viewed from site of Fort Lane. Rogue River is in foreground.

GENERAL AREA of Fort Lane is now private pasture. No trace of fort can be found.

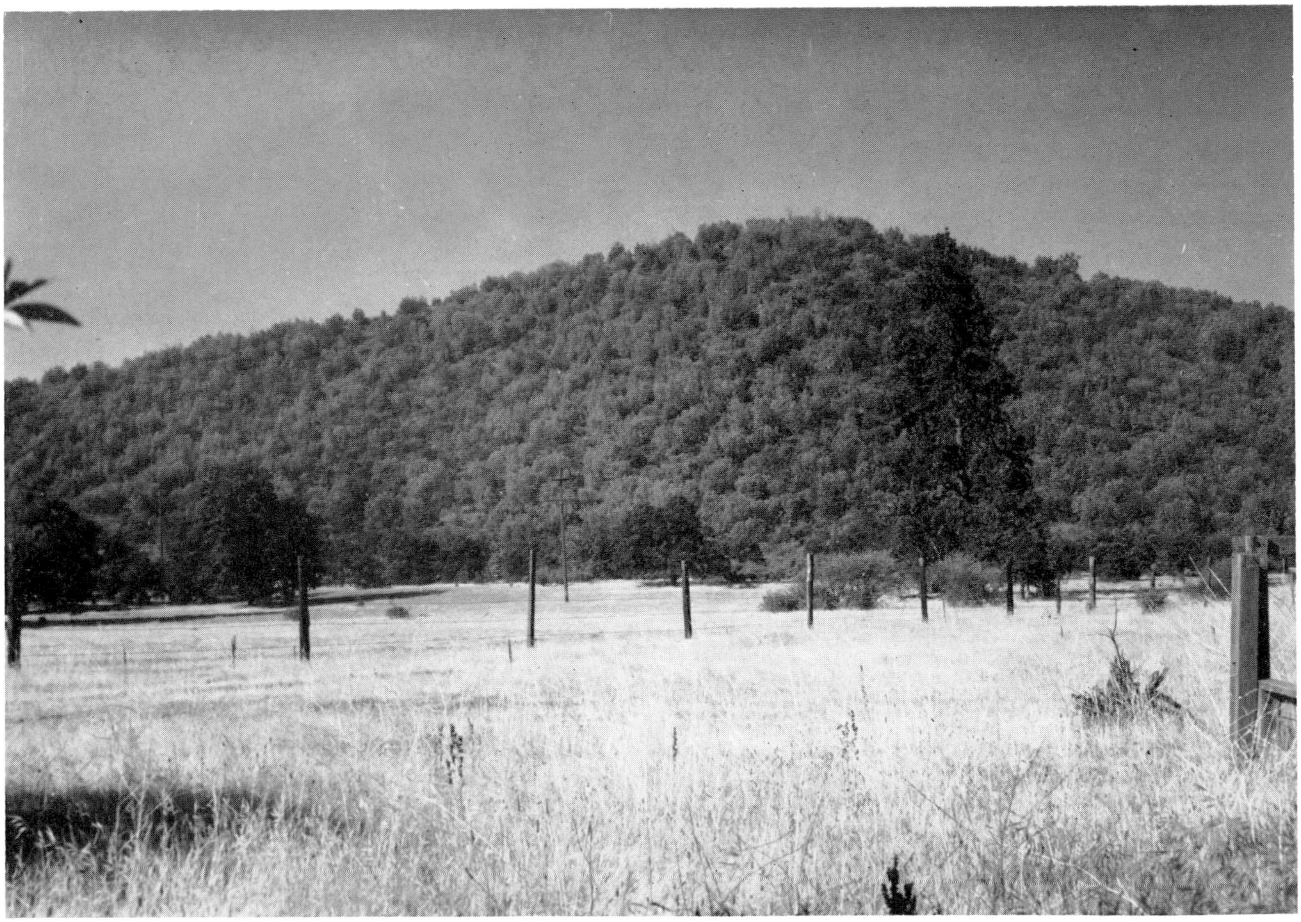

Fort Yamhill, Oregon

Second Lieutenant Phil Sheridan built Fort Yamhill and spent much of his time here before the Civil War. His "Memoirs" speak fondly of the post in northwestern Oregon.

He speaks not too fondly of the incident near Fort Yamhill when a pickpocketing Indian relieved him of his pistol in full view of the Indian's tribe. He said this was an indication of the nerve of the red men, the same nerve that prompted them to kill a female witch doctor in the middle of Yamhill's parade ground a few days earlier.

Sheridan was determined to correct this "flagrant and defiant outrage committed in the teeth of military authority." His troops doubled back to the Indian camp, but by a flanking route. They caught the Indians from the rear preparing an ambush.

The 16 Indians Sheridan captured helped the Army build the new fort that had been started in 1856 by Second Lieutenant William B. Hazen, later a Civil War general. Sheridan followed him in building the post.

Sheridan was here when the Civil War started and he refused to turn the post over to the captain sent to relieve him. Not until an officer of less Confederate leanings arrived was Sheridan willing to relinquish the garrison.

Twice Yamhill was abandoned, but its 1862 abandonment was cancelled. It was finally closed in 1866.

TO GET THERE: *Nothing remains of original fort, but the original blockhouse is in the city park at Dayton City, 25 miles southwest of Portland, Oregon.*

(Courtesy Oregon Historical Society.)

THIS WAS THE BLOCKHOUSE before it was moved to Dayton City in 1912.

TODAY IN DAYTON CITY, Fort Yamhill's blockhouse stands in park. Plaque on side tells of four Civil War generals stationed at Yamhill: Sheridan, Hazen, D. A. Russell, and J. P. Reynolds. Latter two died at Battles of Winchester and Gettysburg, respectively.

BLOCKHOUSE, only remnant of Fort Yamhill, appears on this plat at far edge of parade ground. (Redrawn from data courtesy Sen. C. H. Francis and University of Oregon Library.)

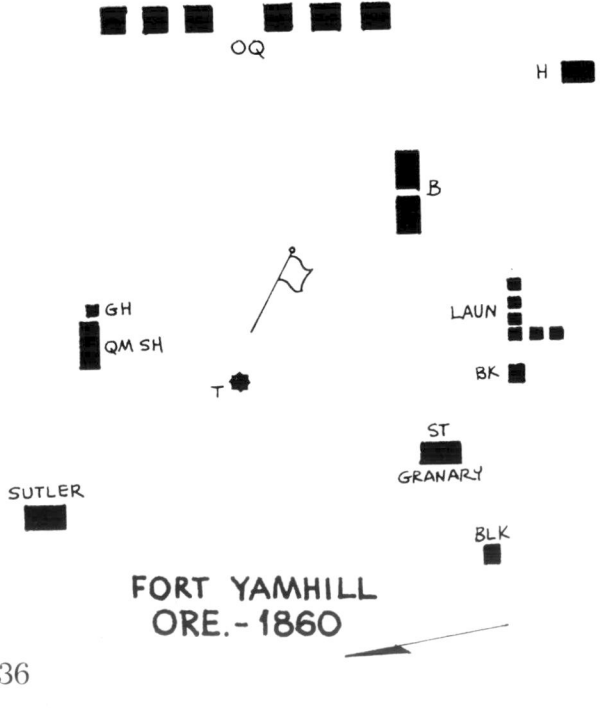

FORT YAMHILL
ORE.- 1860

Fort Steilacoom, Washington

An Englishman who hoped to get rich quick was the first occupant of Fort Steilacoom. He was Joseph T. Heath of Exeter, England, a high-spirited youth whose record of bad bets caused him to write a friend in America, asking whether he could make a fortune there in five years.

He must have got an encouraging reply. He arrived in 1844 and rented 60 acres of Washington land from the Hudson Bay Company. When he died of illness in 1849, he wasn't a millionaire.

About this time, the settlers asked for protection from the Indians and the Army rented the Heath farm. They paid rent to the Hudson Bay Company until 1869.

Fort Steilacoom stood at a strategic point after Congress appropriated $20,000 to build a military road from it to Walla Walla. Captain George McClellan supervised the road work.

Both O. O. Howard and George Pickett were officers at Steilacoom. This was after the post was attacked and almost captured by Indians in 1855.

In 1856 a local Indian chief named Leschi was accused of murder and sold to the Army for 50 blankets by his nephew. Although convicted and sentenced to hang, Lesshi's execution was delayed when Steilacoom's commander refused to believe he was guilty.

The territorial legislature passed a law requiring a second trial, with the same guilty verdict. He was hanged by a detail of 13 law officers in 1858 near Lake Steilacoom, a short distance from the fort.

TO GET THERE: *From Steilacoom, Washington, take Steilacoom Boulevard four miles to the Western State Hospital. This psychiatric hospital is the site of the fort.*

CEMETERY OF FORT STEILACOOM still contains civilian graves. Marker in foreground is for William H. Wallace, volunteer captain in the fifties, who was governor of Washington and Idaho Territories and delegate to Congress from each territory during his lifetime.

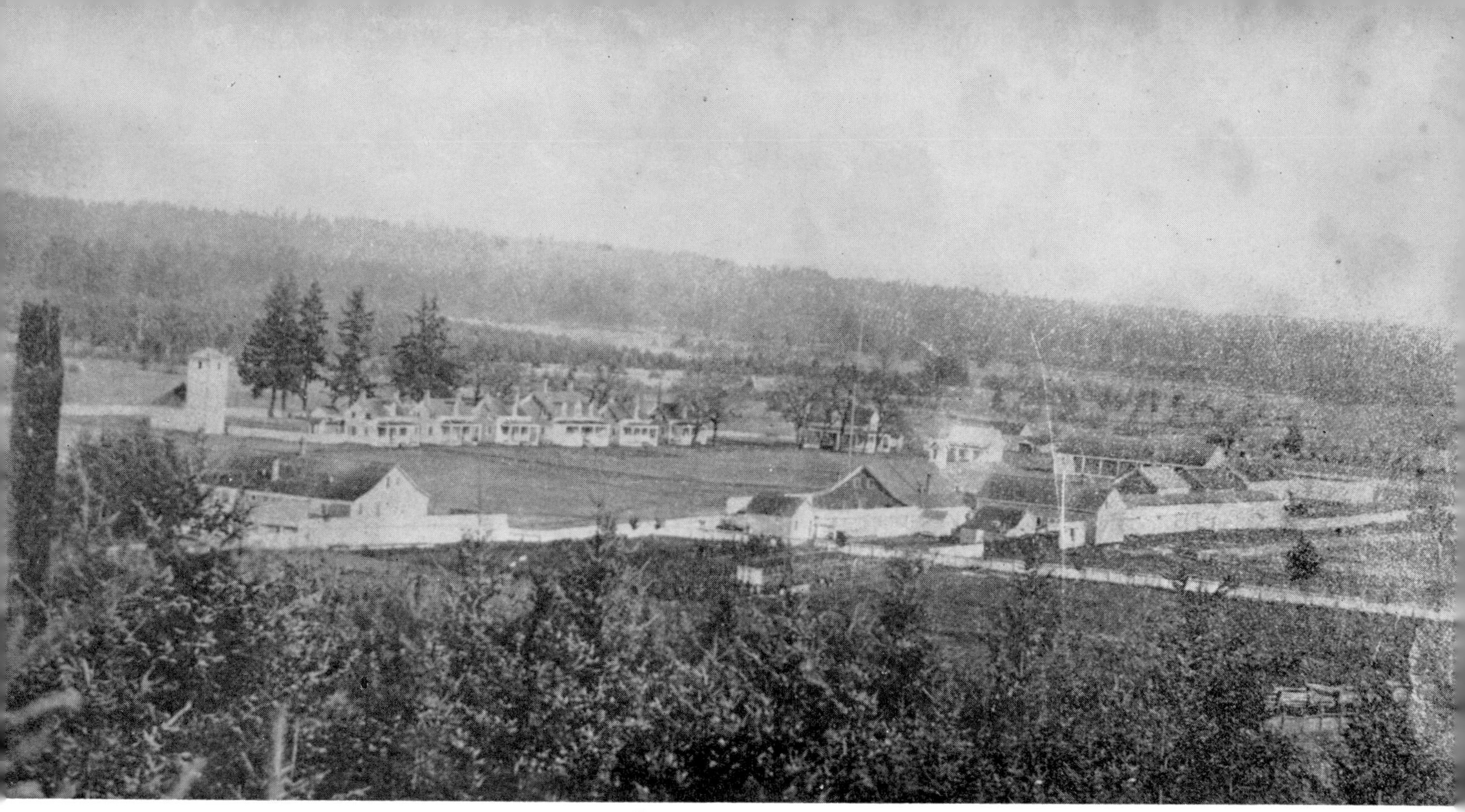

(Courtesy Dr. F. E. Shovlain, superintendent, Western State Hospital.)

ONLY OFFICERS' ROW remains from this 1857 view of Fort Steilacoom. The cottages were along left, or northern, edge of parade ground. Barracks were to southeast and south.

PARADE GROUND and officers' row of today indicates trees prospered after Army abandoned post in 1868. It was sold to the Territory of Washington for $850 for use as a psychiatric hospital.

(Courtesy Albert P. Salisbury.)

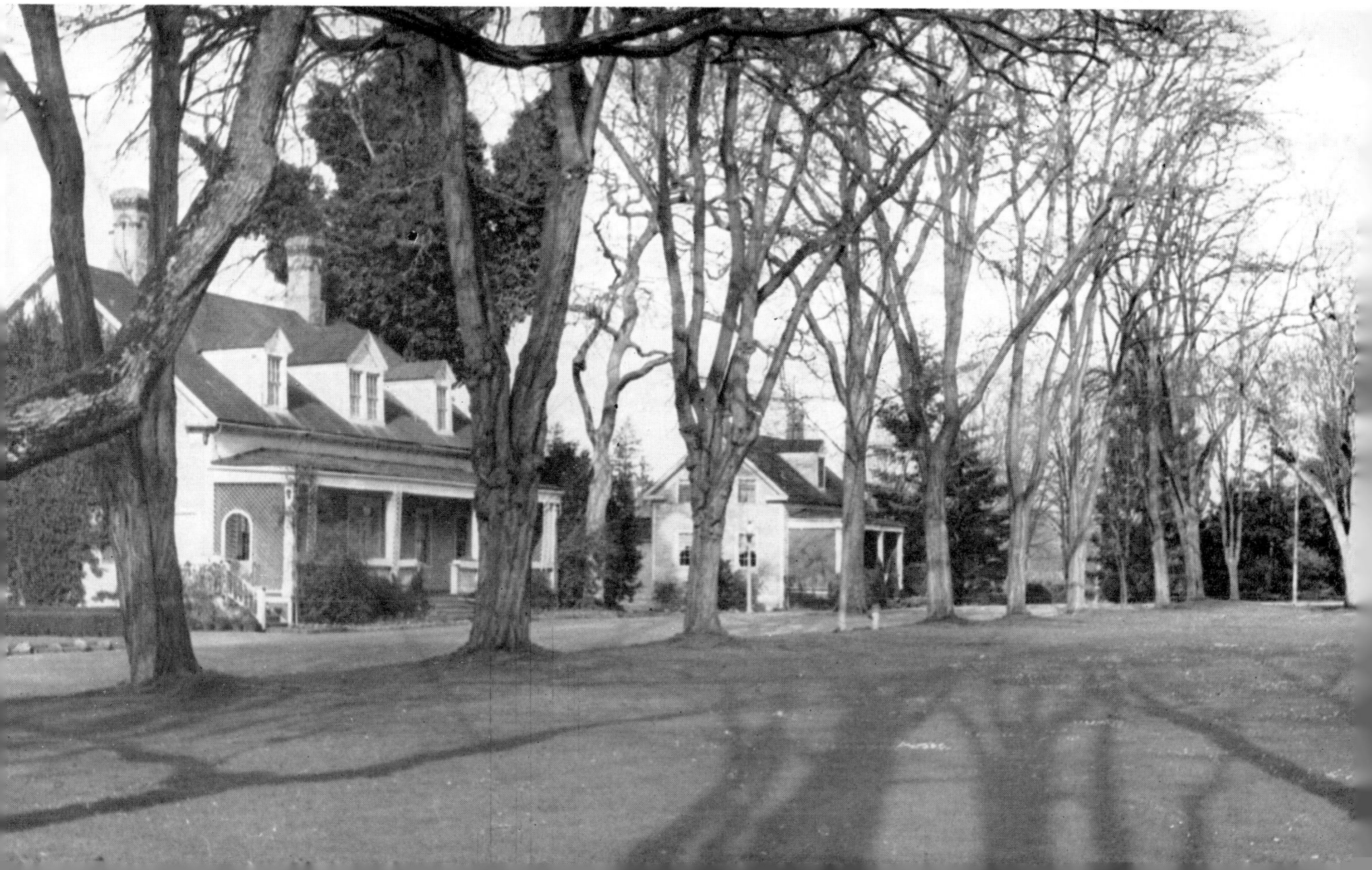

Fort Gaston, California

Fort Gaston almost was the scene of a Hollywood-type extravaganza back in 1861. That was when the District Commander decided to gather all of the Indians to the post, then stage a demonstration of drilling and firepower that would convince the redmen that they should be good Indians.

He planned to fire blank cartridges and the mountain howitzers. The idea fell through when he suggested to the Presidio that he would need six companies of infantry for the show.

This came at a time when troops were being pulled from the forts in the Humboldt. Gaston's commander protested that the transfer of any more men might have dire consequences.

"The excitement among the Indians has been great," he wrote. "Although I did not apprehend an attack from the Indians, I took the necessary precaution by issuing ammunition to my men and doubling my guards."

He said the local settlers were building a blockhouse, but would abandon their valley if any more troops were withdrawn. To complicate matters, he was the only officer at the post and was in such bad health he could not leave his room.

Gaston had its troubles from the day it was established in 1858. It was in the Hoopa Valley, a rugged deep slash in the redwood forests of Northern California, and the woods came right to the edge of the open fort.

Ambushes of mail carriers and stages were common. At least twice, the horses of the mailman and his escort returned to the fort without riders. Once a settler found a note left by the carrier that he was "shot and mortally wounded." When his escort was located, there was a knife through his neck and his nose and flesh cut from his face.

U. S. GRANT house, one of many in Pacific Northwest, was surgeon's quarters, supposedly used by Grant when he was at Gaston for short time in the fifties. Local legend, rather than fact, support the Grant connection.

On Christmas Day, 1863, a reverse type of battle with the Indians took place near Gaston. The Indians holed up in several log buildings, firing at troops from rifle ports, while the Army blasted them with the howitzers. Artillery accuracy wasn't too good and most of the first rounds went wild. By night fall the buildings were in ruins, but in the darkness the Indians were able to steal away.

Peace was finally signed with the Indians in 1865. Gaston, alternating between being called a fort and a camp, stayed in business until 1892 when it was abandoned.

TO GET THERE: *From Eureka, California, take highway 101 north to U.S. 299. Follow 299 for 41 miles to Willow Creek. Turn left. Road parallels Trinity river to Hoopa, nine miles. Fort site is on left at Indian Agency before arriving at town. Modern high school is next to road.*

FORT, OR CAMP GASTON, was built around parade ground 600 feet square. Buildings were of logs and adobe. (Redrawn from NA.)

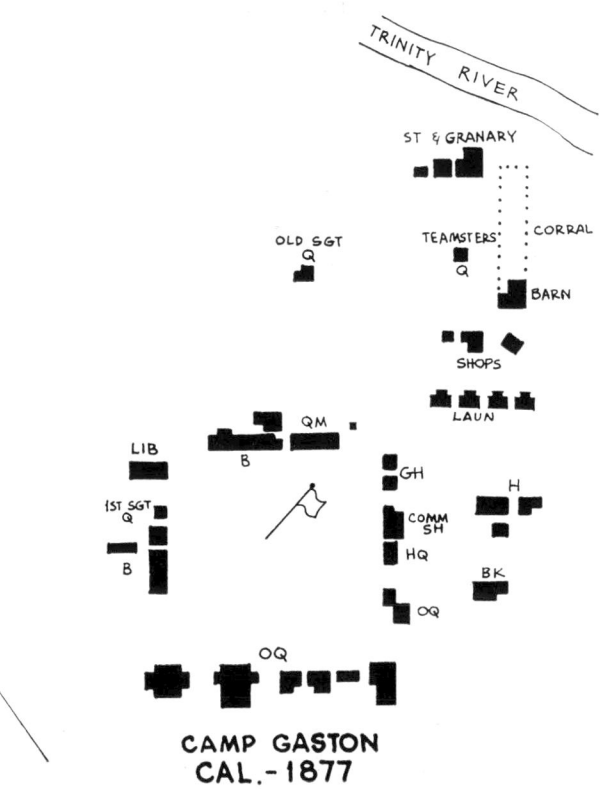

CAMP GASTON
CAL.-1877

(Courtesy Mrs. Eugene Fountain, Blue Lake, Calif.)

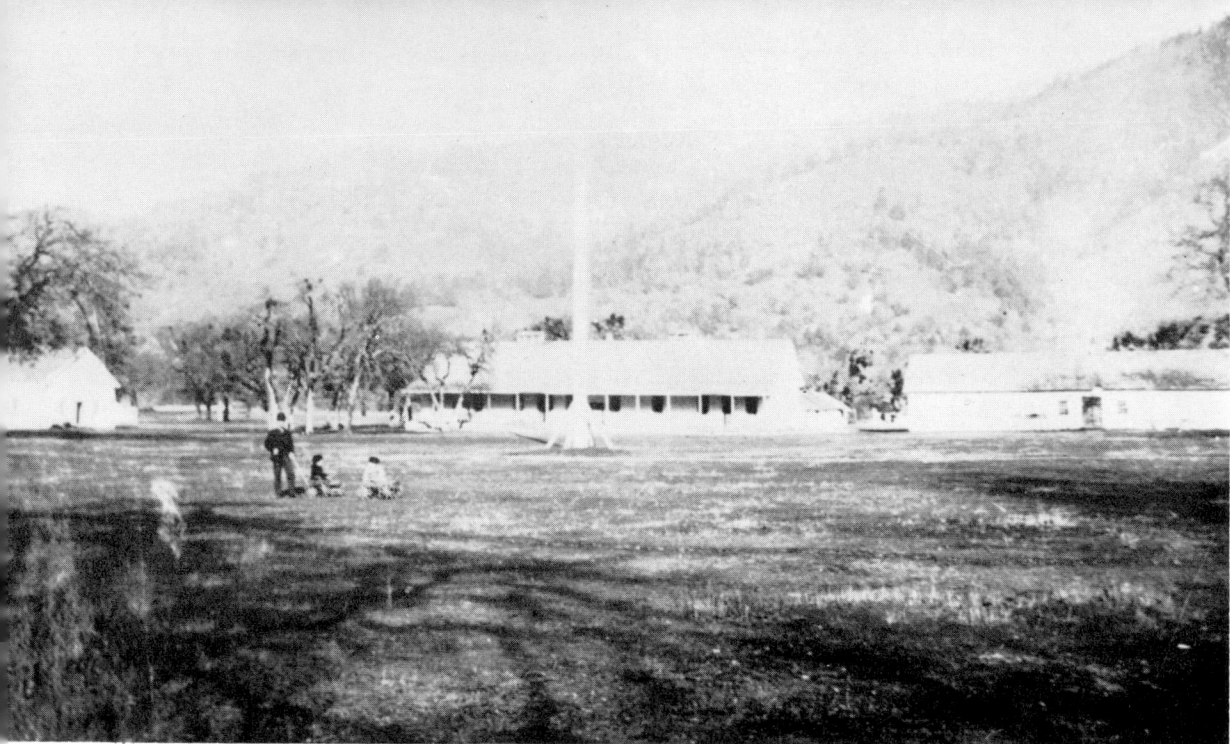

FORT GASTON IN 1882 was fairly calm, although woods and hills still came right up to edge of post. Theatre is at far left, cemetery in trees, barracks behind flagpole, commissary storehouse on right. Picture was taken from southwest corner in front of surgeon's house.

PARADE GROUND looking south. Officers' quarters are now occupied by staff members of Hoopa Indian Agency.

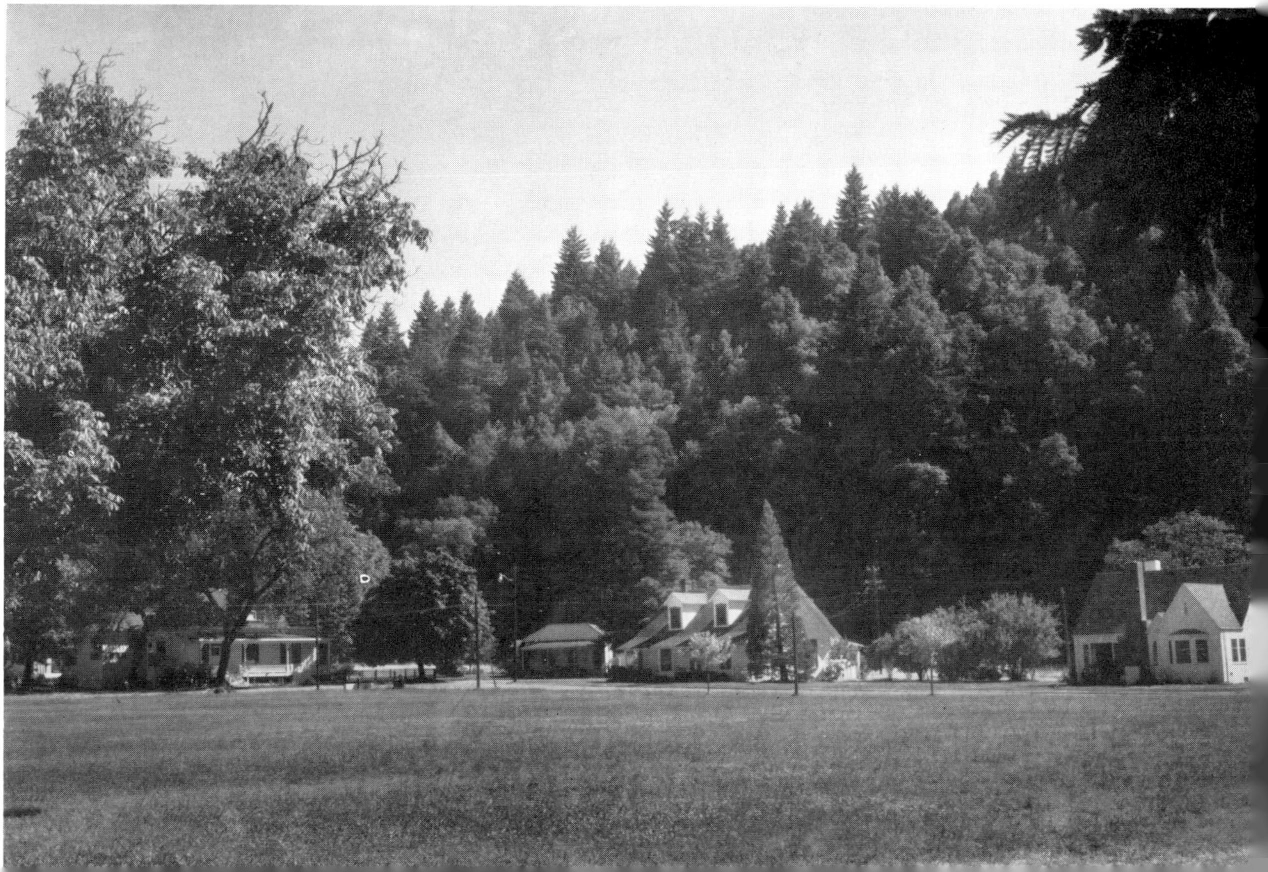

The Bloody Bozeman

"Great Father sends us presents and wants new road, but
white chief goes with soldiers to steal road before Indian
say yes or no. I will talk with you no more. I will fight
you. As long as I live I will fight for the last hunting
grounds of my people."

—Red Cloud to Colonel Carrington, Fort Laramie Conference, 1866.

THE SIOUX gathered at Fort Laramie in 1866 and signed a treaty that permitted a road
through their territory and forts to protect it. But only the old chiefs signed. They didn't
speak for the young braves, or the fiery Red Cloud.

The path was the Bozeman Trail, a shortcut to the Montana gold fields planned by John
Merin Bozeman in 1863. It wound from Fort Laramie across the eastern base of the Big Horn
mountains, passed the Big Horn river near the mouth of the canyon, went up the Yellowstone
valley and cut across southern Montana. After leaving 6,000-foot Bozeman Pass, its first
terminus was at the town of the same name, then it dropped into the valley to the west and
Virginia City.

The Army planned to build four forts along the route. They put up three, but that didn't
help the emigrant traffic. Red Cloud attacked the trains at will, and soon there was no traffic.
Bozeman himself was killed by the Sioux.

In 1868, the government decided there were better ways to get to Montana. The forts
were closed, the troops withdrawn. As soon as the Army had left, the Sioux moved in and
put the hated stockades to the torch.

Forts Connor and Reno, Wyoming

Fort Connor was a hasty cantonment built in 1865 during General Connor's Powder River expedition. It was manned by Indian volunteers and militia, and scheduled for abandonment when the Bozeman Trail forts were built.

Colonel Henry B. Carrington led the 500-man expedition that was to build and man the Bozeman forts. His wife later wrote of her first view of the "unprepossessing" Fort Connor on July 28, 1866.

"Expecting it to be abandoned," she wrote, "its ugliness and barreness did not so decidedly shock the sensibilities as if it had been gazed upon as a permanent home, or even a transient dwelling place."

Connor was an open post with barracks, officers' quarters, guardhouse, and magazine on a plateau above the Powder River. Carrington decided to rebuild the fort rather than relocate it, especially after he watched an Indian attack drive off the sutler's herd on his arrival day.

When the 80-man pursuit force returned the next day, Carrington saw their only catch was an Indian pony loaded down with presents that had been distributed at the Laramie conference. This suggested to him that Red Cloud meant business.

Carrington left a company to rebuild Connor and continued his march. A stockade was added and, on November 11, 1866, the post was renamed Fort Reno.

Indians hovered close and soldiers were prohibited from leaving the stockade to hunt without special permission. The simple matter of finding a hay field required a 50-man force, four days of rations, 40 rounds of ammunition per man, and 4,000 rounds in the wagons. The distance to be traveled: 25 miles up the bank of the Powder.

Reno was the supply base for the trail until it was abandoned on August 18, 1866. Eight years later, a new Fort Reno appeared along the Powder, but this one was three miles south and had an even shorter life.

Known as Cantonment Reno, it lasted officially nine months until it was moved 50 miles north on July 17, 1877, changing its name to Fort McKinney a month later. Built of huge cottonwood logs capped by dirt roofs, the cantonment stayed in operation as "Depot Fort McKinney" through part of 1878 until its stores could be moved. Many of its buildings were mere dugouts.

After the Army left, the depot became a town of 100 persons, saloons providing the bulk of the economy. Now only parched rectangles in the sagebrush mark the site of the depot. Of the first Fort Reno, ex-Connor, only a marker indicates that this was once an outpost of the Army.

TO GET THERE: *From Kaycee, Wyoming, take route 1002 east 17 miles to Sussex school house. A quarter mile east of the school, turn north on a gravel road. Fort Connor-Reno site is on right side of road, about 10 miles. Sign is beside road, site is private pasture. Second Reno site is on private property, also north of Sussex school. It is not marked and impossible to find without local inquiry.*

FORT CONNOR was to have a stockade according to this plan. "Barb" indicates it also planned a barber shop. (Redrawn from Hebard and Brininstool, "The Bozeman Trail," with permission of Arthur H. Clark Company.)

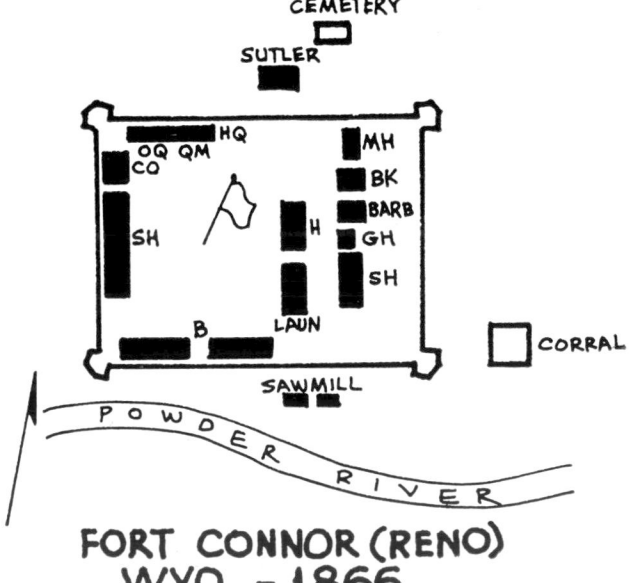

FORT CONNOR (RENO)
WYO. - 1866

MONUMENT is in center of fort site. Powder river is below bluff behind stone.

(Courtesy National Archives.)

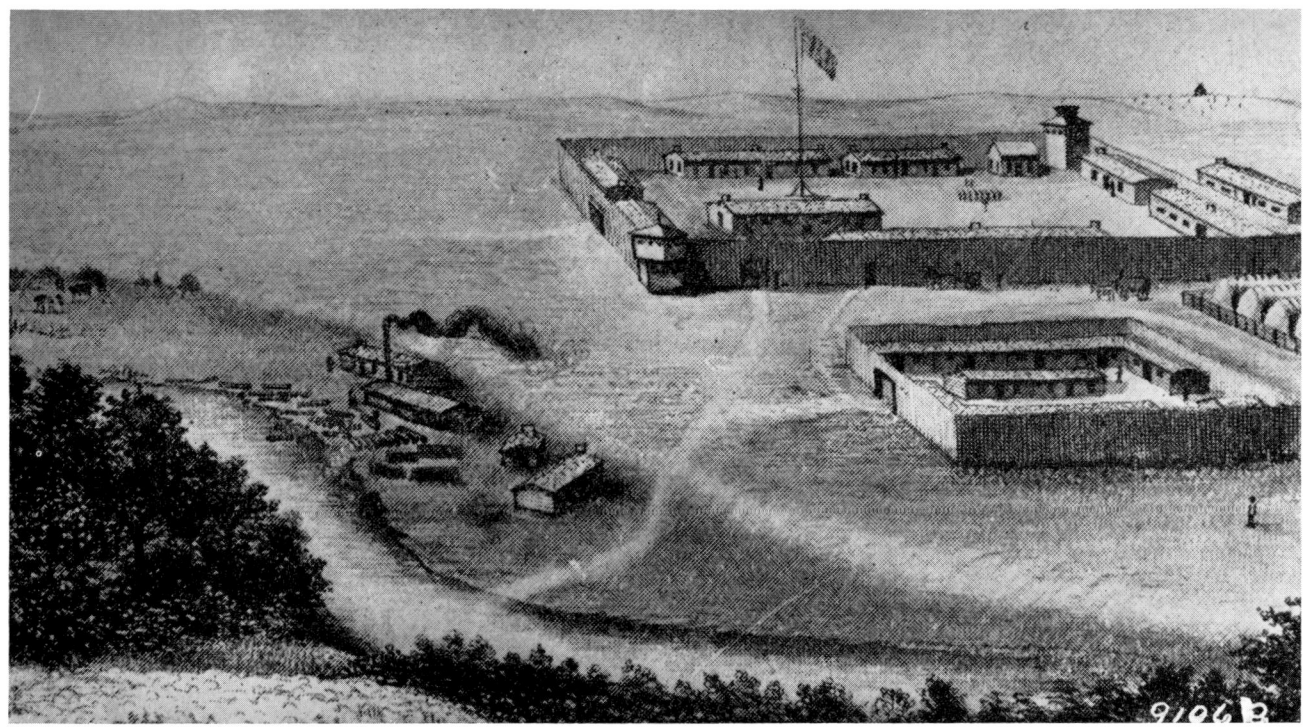

CONNOR WAS FORT RENO by the time of this sketch, though fort had not reached its final stage of completion. This is probably how it looked in late 1866.

CANTONMENT RENO'S dugouts are these rectangles in prairie flooded periodically by Powder river. Big Horn mountains are in the background.

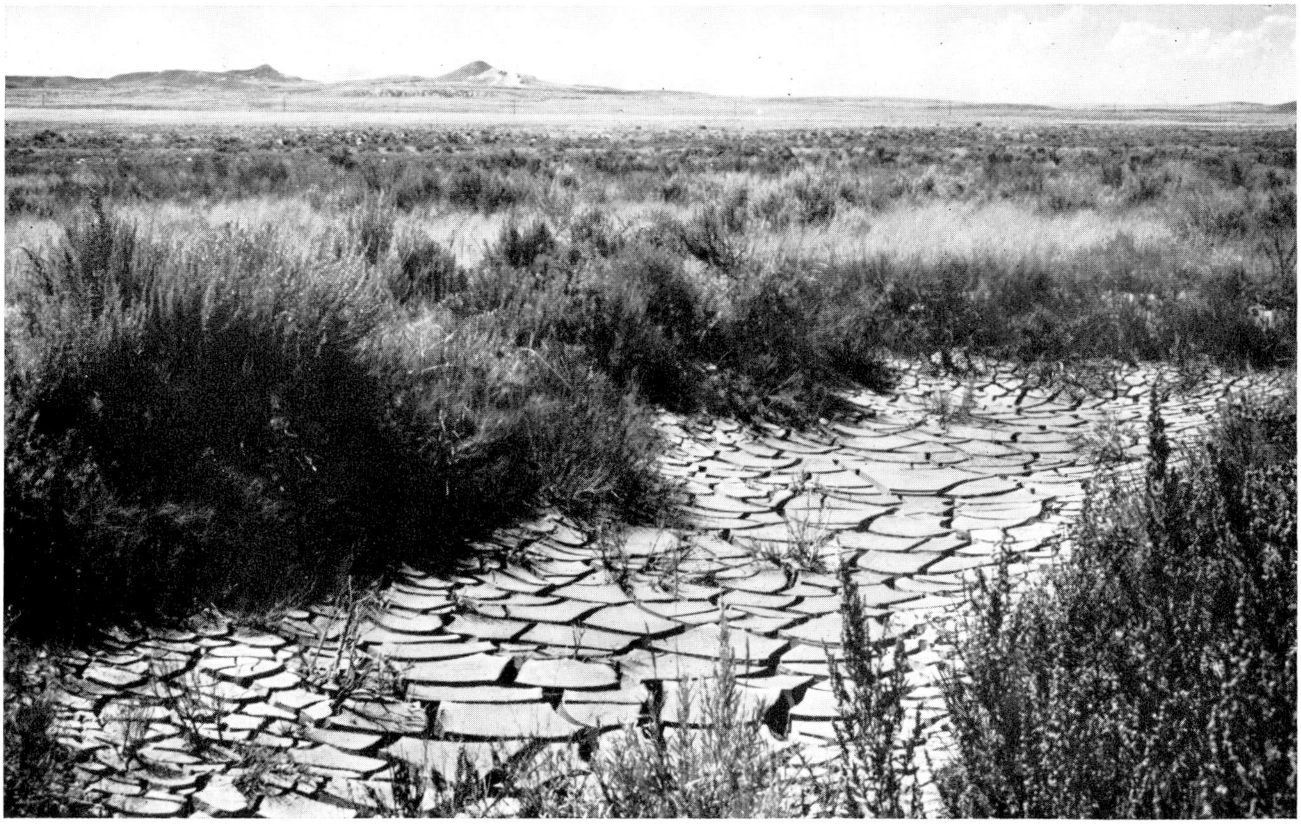

THREE CHILDREN killed in collapse of dugout roof are supposed to be buried near the wooden stake in foreground. This was Cantonment Reno site with Powder river in background.

FORT RENO (1866–68) site is marked by lonely stone. Local ranchers say rubble on surface was result of ranching, not remains of fort.

Fort Phil Kearney, Wyoming

When the Army's Inspector-General visited the completed Fort Phil Kearney, he said it was the best he had seen in the United States. It stood on a plateau 50 to 60 feet above the valley floor, measured 1,600 feet northwest to southeast and had 42 buildings within its log stockade.

Carrington built it after he left Fort Connor. He arrived at the site on July 15, 1866, and immediately had his big hay mowers put to work. Somewhat of a martinet, Carrington had dragged these machines all the way from Omaha. His next step was to place "Keep Off Of The Grass" signs on his new parade ground.

The next day, Red Cloud sent him warnings to leave, then Indians routed the horse herd. A hasty pursuit lost two men killed and three wounded. Within 10 days, five emigrant trains were attacked near the fort and 15 men killed. By the end of September, another 15 had been killed, 500 livestock driven off, and considerable property destroyed, including the precious mowing machines.

During six months, the Indians made 51 hostile demonstrations, killed 154 white men and stole 800 head of stock. Carrington made no effort to patrol from the fort, so every attack came almost as a surprise.

The worst disaster for Fort Phil Kearney was the Fetterman Massacre in which 67 soldiers were killed, the loss of a complete patrol. Lead by a glory hunting Captain William Fetterman, the patrol was sent out to aid a besieged wood train. Despite orders to remain on the near side of the ridge north of the fort, Fetterman pursued the Indians and was ambushed.

The disaster threw the fort into near panic. Portugee Phillips, a trapper, rode 236 miles through sub-zero weather to Fort Laramie for reinforcements. It was feared Red Cloud was going to attack the fort directly.

Carrington was relieved of his duties at Phil Kearney. Ultimately he was cleared of blame for the Fetterman fight, but not before the black mark had forced him from the Army.

Revenge was exacted by the garrison a year later in the Wagon Box Fight. Almost within sight of the fort, Red Cloud's warriors attacked a 30-man wood detail. This time the soldiers had formed their wagons in a circle, were armed with new breechloading rifles, and had plenty of ammunition.

Eight hundred Indians attacked and were driven off. Twelve hundred more charged. As soon as they came within 500 yards they were lashed by fire from the wagon boxes. They attacked for three hours until they could take the slaughter no longer.

The Army lost three dead and two wounded. Later a chief said the incredible number of 1,137 Indians had been killed or wounded.

TO GET THERE: *From Buffalo, Wyoming, drive north on U.S. 87 to Story, 14 miles. Turn left and go west on valley road, a short distance, following signs. Portugee Phillips marker is on north side of road. Fort site is on plateau south of road.*

FORT PHIL KEARNEY (1866–68) had a total of 42 buildings within the stockade, but only main ones show here. (Redrawn from Brady's "Indian Fights and Fighters" with permission of McClure Phillips & Co.)

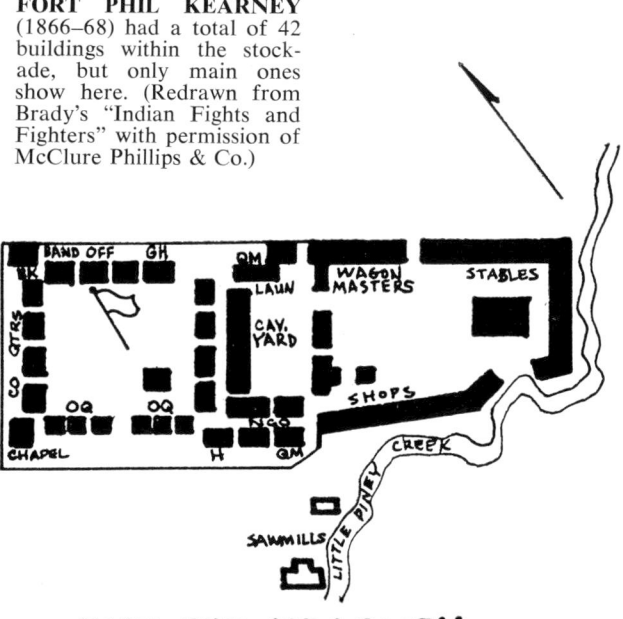

FORT PHIL KEARNEY
WYO. - 1866

PORTUGEE PHILLIPS monument commemorates heroic 236-mile ride. Phillips never recovered from freezing journey and was crippled the rest of his life.

EARLY ARTIST'S SKETCH closely resembles plat of Fort Phil Kearney. Indians burned fort as soon as Army left it on July 31, 1868.

FROM WITHIN FORT PHIL KEARNEY, caretaker cabin is to right, low fence in foreground. To north is site of Fetterman Massacre five miles away.

APPROXIMATE SITE of fort is marked by this reconstructed stockade wall and abandoned caretaker's cabin. Only one side of stockade is left from WPA work in the thirties. Nothing remains of original fort.

46

Fort C. F. Smith, Montana

Fort C. F. Smith probably was the most isolated military post on the frontier. From November 30, 1866, to June, 1867, not a single message got through to it.

Its commanding officer's resignation was approved on January 7, 1867, but he wasn't able to leave the fort until five months later!

There were 165 men and their families at this post that stood within the shadow of the towering Big Horn mountains. It was on a plateau that gave it a clear view of the entire area. A stockade, built by standing 10 to 12-foot logs upright in a trench, surrounded the fort, and cannon were mounted in the northwest and southeast corners. These corners were angled out from the walls so the cannon could sweep the forward face of the palisades in the event of attack.

The wife of Brevet Major Andrew Burt (later a Spanish American War general) kept a diary during her stay here.

"As quarters were crowded, we could only have two rooms and a kitchen," she remembered. "The latter had been hurriedly built of logs for occupancy by an officer when the post was built the previous year. The floor was of dirt beaten hard and covered with gunny sacks. The new rooms were of adobe and plastered walls and planed wood-work . . .

"The entire garrison was enclosed as a stockade. . . . Its two gates were closed at retreat and sentinels kept watch at its corner bastions. At each quarter-hour of the night would be heard their cry of the hour and 'All's well.' My husband always retired with his clothes on and boots close at hand, ready to put on at a moment's notice."

Fort C. F. Smith had its own version of the Wagon Box Fight. This was the Hay Field Fight three miles below the post. Using new rifles, 19 soldiers and 12 civilians held off between 500 and 800 Cheyenne for eight hours until help could arrive. Three men died and two were seriously wounded. While the Indian losses could not be counted, many bodies were dragged from the field, and the Indians even left some behind.

TO GET THERE: *From Hardin, Montana, take county route 313 to Xavier, 23 miles. From here, route is a fair weather road only to Yellowtail Dam camp. Within sight of camp and about a mile short of it, dirt road turns off to right. This road leads to fort site marker several hundred yards north. Local inquiry recommended.*

ROW OF BARRACKS is clearly marked by mounds that are several feet high. Trailer community of Fort Smith, background, houses personnel building the 200,000-kilowatt Yellowtail dam.

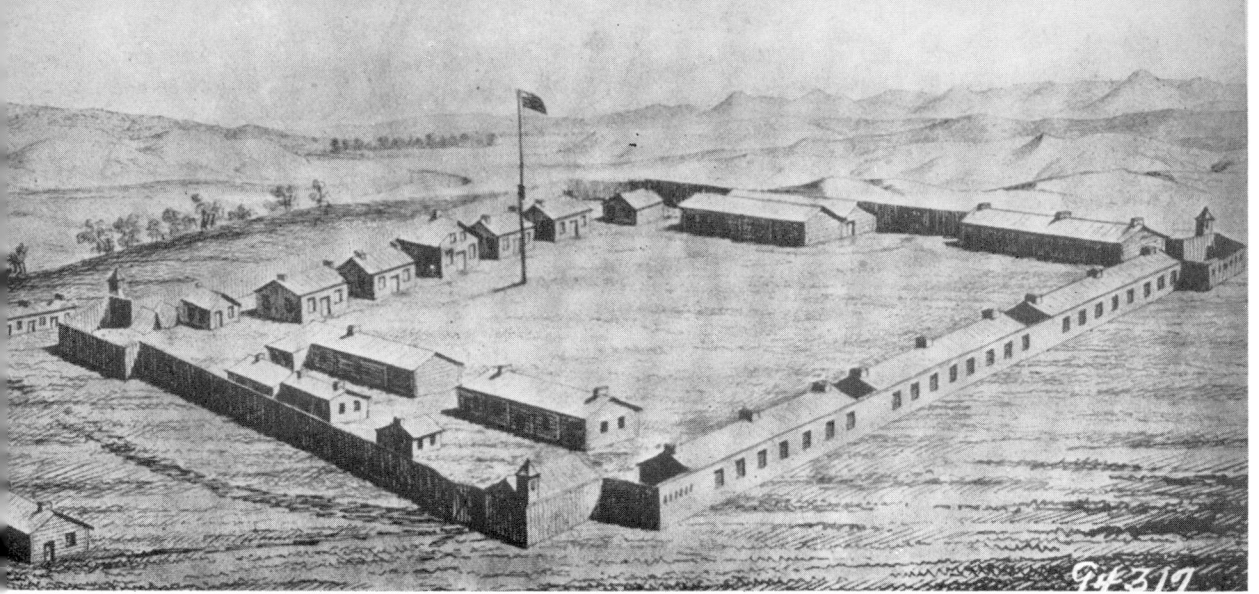

FORT C. F. SMITH'S adobe ruins could be seen almost to the turn of the century. Mounds still remain and match this sketch almost perfectly. Officers' quarters were the five buildings next to flagpole, barracks were the three long buildings in foreground. Fort was 300 feet square.

CENTER OF PARADE GROUND is marked by this stone. Mounds of the five adobe officers' quarters run along fence line in background. Big Horn mountains are in distance.

OFFICERS' ROW is the saddle-shaped formation in center. Picture was taken from left bastion location as shown in sketch. Post was abandoned on July 29, 1868.

Guardians of the River

"The steamboats on the Upper Missouri go armed. We carry on the forward deck two mortars, and in the saloon is a rack of guns and rifles,—not counting the revolvers that each male passenger is armed with as a matter of course."

—General de Trobriand writing of his trip up the Missouri in 1866.

THE WATER routes pioneered the western expansion before the trails and played major roles until surpassed by the railroads.

Navigation on the Columbia of the Pacific Northwest went as far as Fort Dalles, Oregon. With a railroad portage in operation, steamboats could go as far as Lewiston, Idaho.

General Connor was the first navigator of the Great Salt Lake of Utah and he sponsored a steamboat route between towns on its shores.

The Platte rivers meandered from Utah to Missouri. Neither deep nor dependable, nevertheless they provided water and a fairly level avenue into the west.

Most important water route was that of the Missouri. In 1832 the steamboat Yellowstone reached Fort Union, next to the Montana border, adding 1,700 miles of navigable water to the United States. As many as 30 steamboats at one time operated on the Missouri. One, the Luella, carried $1,250,000 in gold to Saint Louis from the Montana fields on one trip.

The last boat reached Fort Benton, Montana, in 1890. Now the Missouri plays a modern role of importance as the source of power and irrigation for the Dakotas. It is dotted with major reclamation projects which have inundated several forts once important to the west: Stevenson, Berthold, Brule, Thompson, Hale, Bennett, among them.

Fort Randall, South Dakota

Fort Randall was strategic from two angles. It was the last link in the chain of forts protecting the overland route along the Platte river, and was the first in the chain of forts along the Upper Missouri River.

In 1856 it was laid out on the second terrace above the western shore of the Missouri and just north of the Nebraska line. Soldiers ranged a parade ground with cottonwood log barracks, officers quarters, and a headquarters building. By 1860, the post had more than two dozen buildings, some from abandoned Fort Lookout upstream.

Before the Civil War, Randall's troops went from the Spirit Lake Massacre in Iowa, to the Mormon War in Utah, to distribution of Indian annuities at Fort Union far north in the Dakotas, and along the Yellowstone river and its tributaries on the expedition of 1859.

Randall was the base of operation of most of the expeditions against the Sioux in the Dakotas, including the 1,500-man Sully expedition in 1863,

his second in 1864, and the third in 1865. "Galvanized Yankees," former Confederate soldiers, were part of its garrison at the close of the Civil War. This was only poetic justice: most of its soldiers had deserted in 1861 to fight for the South.

Until 1871, a decrepit log stockade had surrounded most of the post. This was removed, and all of the log quarters were replaced by frame ones. In 1880, 12 new sets of officer's quarters were added, the water works, cemetery and commanding officer's house all renovated. A chapel was donated by the soldiers of the fort and the Odd Fellow's Lodge.

This chapel is the only ruin standing today, though many cellars and crumbled foundations lie half-covered by tangled brush and weeds.

In 1872, Brule Sioux came to Fort Randall to trade gold nuggets. Four years later, Randall troops fought winter blizzards to clear miners who had camped illegally in the Black Hills. In 1877, troops were sent to Chicago to keep order in the railroad strike. In 1879, Indian harrassment of the Black Hills routes caused Randall to establish a sub-post 28 miles west, Camp Keya Paha.

Sitting Bull and his tribe spent two years as prisoners at Fort Randall, after their surrender at Fort Buford. When he was sent upstream to Fort Yates, the soldiers were glad to see him go—handling the sightseers had become quite a problem.

In 1890, the Army abandoned Fort Randall. The frontier had passed it by and the steam boats no longer supplied the means of transportation along the Missouri.

TO GET THERE: *From Yankton, S.D., take State 52 for 14 miles to junction with State 50. Follow 50 for 40 miles to Wagner. Leave 50 and continue straight for 12 miles to Pickstown. This is the government city for the Randall Dam immediately to the west. Cross dam. Fort is below southwestern corner of dam. Follow signs to site, picnic and camping facilities.*

CHAPEL IS FORT RANDALL'S only remnant and was added after date of this plat. Location is within circle, lower left. River is to left of this plat. (Redrawn from data courtesy SHS and National Park Service, Omaha.)

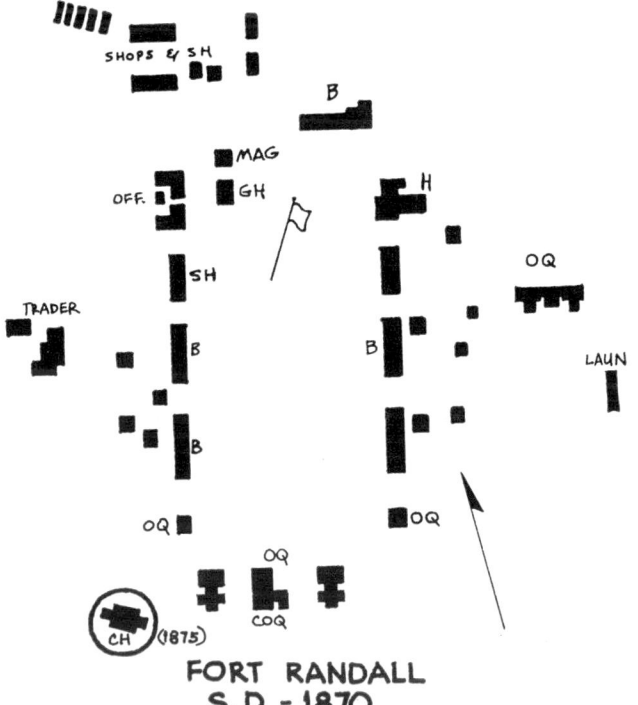

FORT RANDALL
S. D. - 1870

(Courtesy National Archives.)

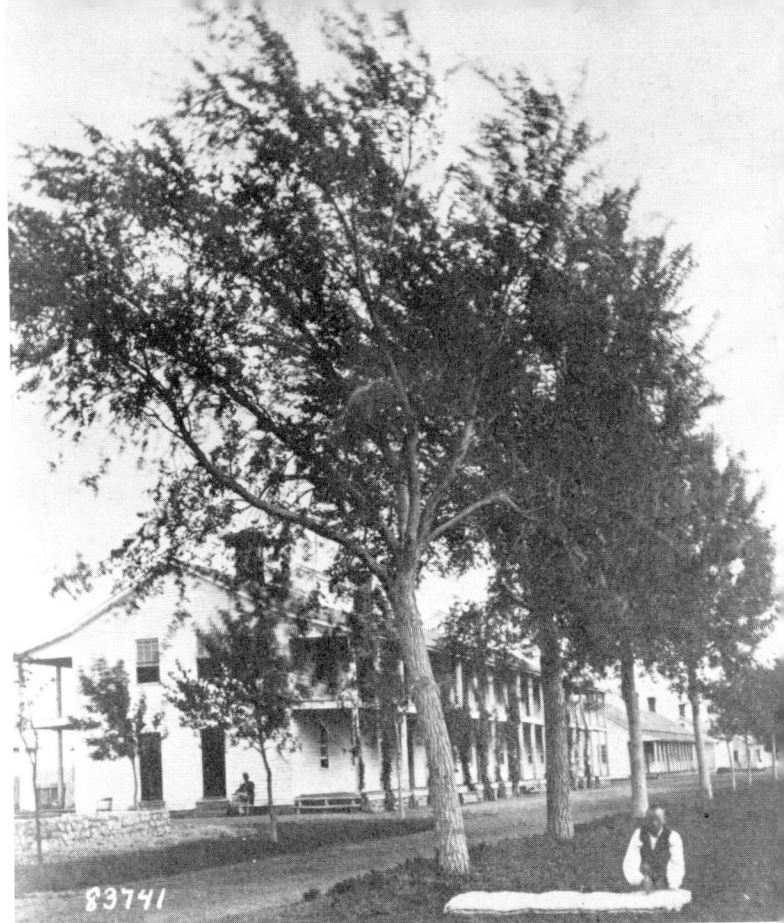

VETERANS WILL RECOGNIZE activity here. Airing bedding was as routine in 1880 as it is at posts today. Barracks probably is middle building shown on plat on left side of parade ground.

BARRACKS OF 1885 (old picture) might be the foundations in the foreground. If not, these are foundations of southernmost barracks.

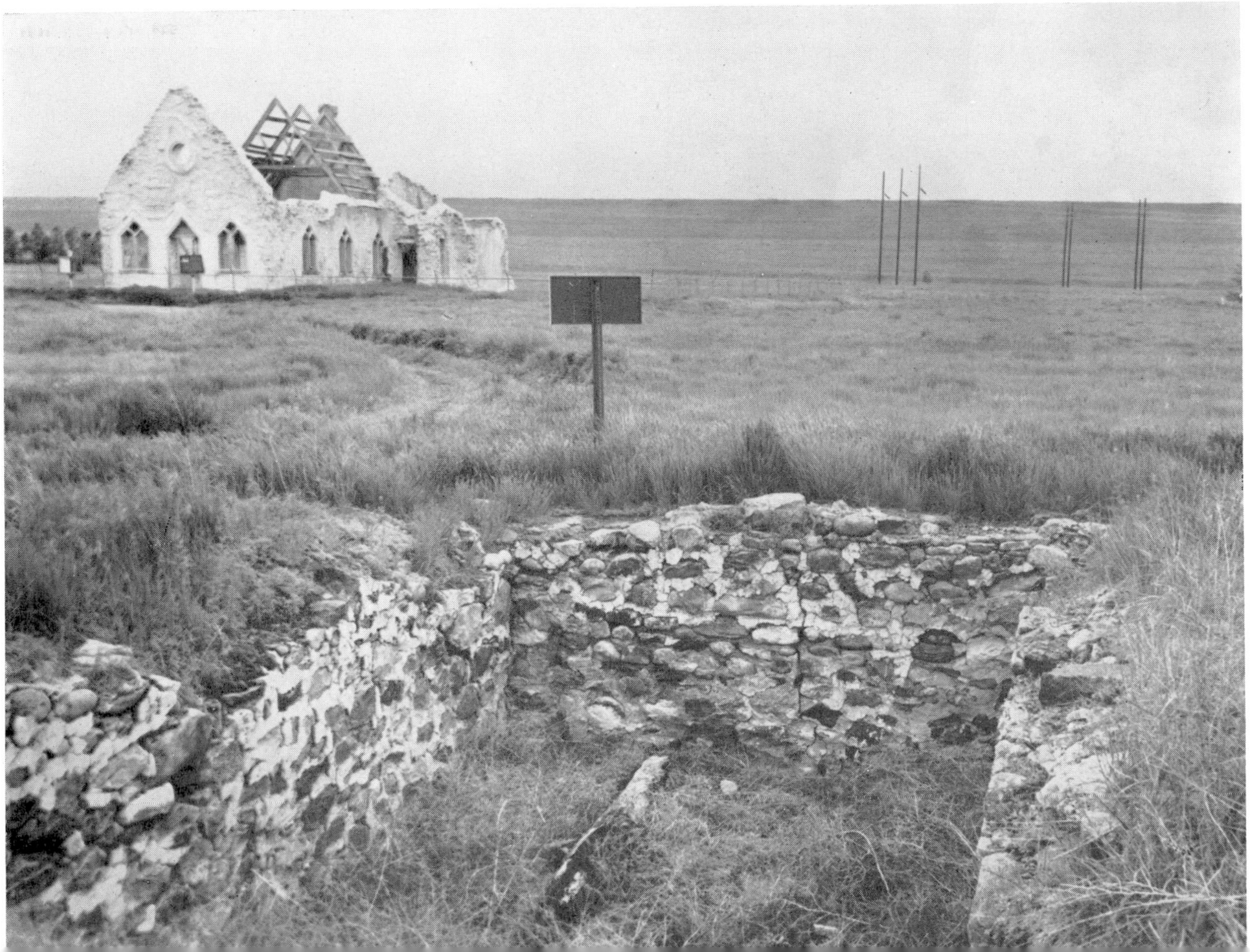

COMMANDING OFFICER'S QUARTERS once stood atop these foundations. Legend tells of militia major who claimed he was new commander, jailed fort's real chief in 1861. After imposter was forced to leave, real commander remained in guard house. No one seemed to have the authority to approve his release. Finally, higher headquarters had to order his freedom.

BELL TOWER and stairway have collapsed.

ODD FELLOWS built and donated chapel in 1875, used room at rear for meetings. Building has been stabilized and fenced by State Historical Society.

Fort Lookout, South Dakota

For a western fort of the fifties, Fort Lookout had all the earmarks of becoming quite an elaborate layout. Its parade ground was a quarter of a mile long and its site on the southern bank commanded all steamboat traffic along the Missouri river.

But a year and two weeks after it was founded on June 3, 1856, it was dismantled and moved lock, stock, barrel, and troops down river to the equally new Fort Randall. For years afterward, diaries and reports referred to "old Fort Lookout," but all traces of it had long disappeared.

Fort Lookout was the successor to Fort Pierre, the military post established at the fur post of the same name by General Harney in 1855. Although the government spent $45,000 to buy the old trading post, the troops found it in such a dilapidated condition that it would cost an additional $20,520 to make it livable.

Inadequate prefabricated houses of pasteboard were shipped up the river. The winter of 1855–56 was a rough one, complicated by scurvy and a lack of forage for horses. The next summer Harney decided to abandon Pierre. Its personnel and movable materials went to Fort Lookout and Randall, although some troops stayed until summer, 1857.

Captain Nathaniel Lyon built Fort Lookout, laying it out generously between small creeks at the north and south and the river bluff to the east. (It was the same Lyon who became the North's first Civil War hero after his 1861 triumphs in Missouri, coincidentally eliminating from the scene his former superior, Harney, who was thought to have Southern sympathies.)

When it was abandoned, the Army left behind the stone fireplaces, and married soldiers' cabins. The grave of a Sergeant Fiske remained on the hill to the west of the fort. Traces of the post rapidly disappeared, until the passage of time had completely obliterated even local knowledge of the exact site. The fact that three fur posts named Fort Lookout were in the area, further confused where the military post had been.

In 1950, the Smithsonian Institution investigated various possibilities, definitely establishing the military post's location by an accumulation of military debris in a probable dump on one of the slopes. At the same time, the locations of two other Forts Lookout (1823–25 and 1833) were determined to have been inundated by the Missouri, while one of the 1840's was spotted to the south of the military post.

TO GET THERE: *From Pierre, S.D., take U.S. 83 south 43 miles to Vivian and junction with U.S. 16. Turn left, follow U.S. 16 for 36 miles to Reliance. Dirt road, left, heading north from town should be taken to first right turn, 1 mile. Turn, stay on this road. After 11 miles it turns south at bluffs overlooking Missouri. Take primitive road that drops down into river valley. At end of road is marker for Lower Brule Indian reservation. Fort site is northeast, next to river.*

BARRACKS WERE LOG BUILDINGS, but officers' quarters in semi-circle were prefabricated pasteboard houses shifted from abandoned Fort Pierre. In 1856, river did not come as close as in plat. (Redrawn from research of W. G. Robinson, SHS historian.)

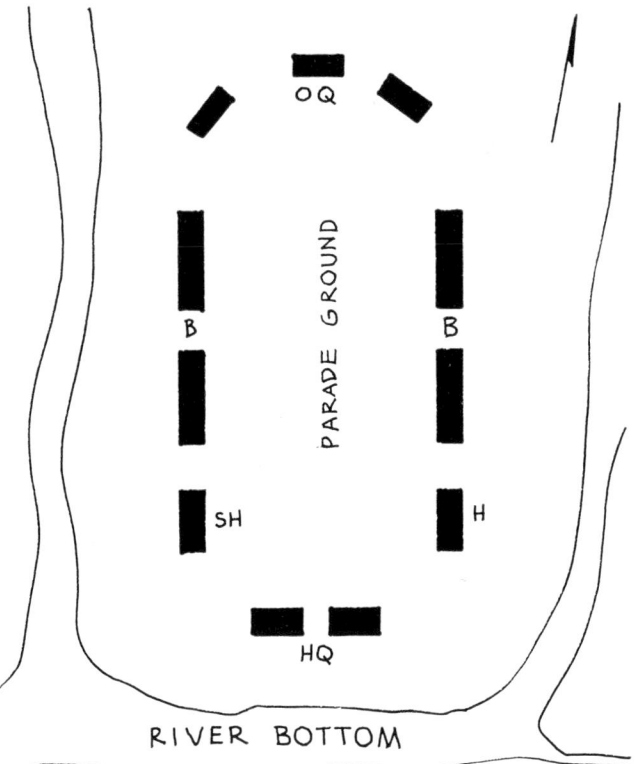

FORT LOOKOUT
S.D. - 1856

FORT LOOKOUT TODAY is pasture at southern edge of Lower Brule reservation. Row of trees borders creek along northern edge of fort site. Fort was on level ground in foreground, officers' row to left.

MISSOURI ONCE was two plateaus below Fort Lookout's bluff. Now it edges top of bluff. Water in foreground is backwater that has moved up the northern creek on fort site. Barracks were on level area in foreground.

Fort Sully, South Dakota

"Healthfulness" was the only item that gave Fort Sully a claim to being a desirable frontier post in 1875, according to its medical report. Construction of the Northern Pacific railroad made it, in company with Forts Buford and Benton, "the most inaccessible of the chain of posts along the Missouri river."

Elizabeth Custer visited it in 1873. She admired its gardens, poultry, cows, and social manners but added: "The thought of being walled in with snow, and completely isolated for eight months of the year made me shudder."

Isolated by the Oahe Dam flooding of the Missouri, Fort Sully is as inaccessible as it was in its heyday, if not more so.

More accessible is the site of the first Fort Sully, four miles east of Pierre. This was selected in 1863 by General Sully after the Battle of Whitestone Hill, N.D. His troops wintered in a stockade here. No one seemed to think the location very good since the 270-foot square stockade was on bottom land next to the Missouri. All buildings of the fort were within the palisades, many of them making up parts of the walls. Bastions stood on the northwest and southeast corners.

It was originally named Fort Bartlett, after its first commander, but renamed after the Sully Expedition's leader in 1864. In 1866, the post was abandoned because of its unhealthy location.

A report to Congress described it as "uninhabitable." It said "the buildings were broken and the floors consisted of mud. As elsewhere, fleas, rats, and bedbugs reigned supreme."

The new fort was 30 miles north and on a plateau above the river. General de Trobriand visited it enroute to his duties in North Dakota in 1866:

"The landing consists of only a half-a-dozen posts planted in the prairie, alongside which the steamboats moor," he wrote. "The post is a mile or two away on a point of bluff where not a shrub grows . . . There is no justification for calling it a fort, for the location is not even protected by a moat or a palisade. General Stanley (commanding the district headquarters at Sully) is of the opinion that with a despicable enemy like the Indian, the men should be trained to

EARLY STOCKADE was little more than a fence line by time of this plat. Soon the two barracks, 350 by 17 feet, became individual buildings and entire post was open. In years before abandonment in 1894, quartermaster occupied this hospital site and new hospital was built northwest of ice house. Flagpole was right of cistern. (Redrawn from NA Data.)

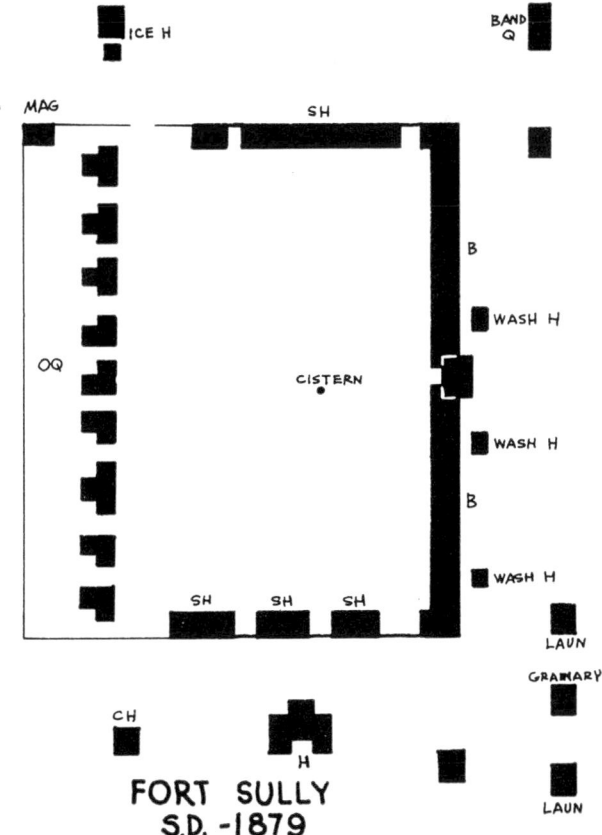

FORT SULLY
S.D. -1879

CHAPEL RUINS are within few inches of Missouri river. Main course of river is in background, but water has backed up Sully creek and within five feet of flooding site. In 1870 fort was 160 feet above low water mark.

FORT SULLY in later years was considered "finest and best built post on the Missouri river." Barracks are on left side of parade ground, officers' quarters on right. Top of chapel can be seen at far end of officers' row. Missouri river is in distance. New York's Fiorella LaGuardia played on this parade ground as a boy. His father was Sully bandmaster.

trust to their own vigilance and to their breech-loaders for their protection, rather than to the shelter of palisades which serve only to weaken their morale."

Fort Sully actually compromised on the matter of a stockade in its early stages. The various buildings were located around a long rectangle with high walls closing in the open spaces. By any other name it was still a stockade and that

WHEEL AND LOGS prevent visitors from falling into old cistern in Sully parade ground, noted on plat.

was what the surgeon's report of 1875 called it.

"The post is inclosed on its southwestern limits by a heavy stockade, flanked by bastions," he wrote. "The stockade is continued up to and adjourns the storehouses, and these, with the soldiers' barracks, take the place of the stockade on the northeast, thus inclosing the fort."

Fort Sully was probably the most active post on the Missouri. From 1863 to 1870 it was involved in frequent Indian disorders. Two of the six companies that escorted the 1871 Northern Pacific survey expedition came from Sully, and in 1874 it was called upon repeatedly to remove whites from the gold-filled Black Hills.

In 1876, it reversed the good-and-bad-man roles by recovering 62 horses stolen by a white wagon train from a band of peaceful Indians. It also supplied troops to keep "sooners" from jumping the gun when parts of the Sioux reservation were opened to settlement in 1889. A year later, Sully assisted in settling the Messiah Craze.

TO GET THERE: *First Fort Sully marker is four miles east of Pierre, S.D., on right side of State 34.*

Second Fort Sully can be reached from Pierre by route passable only in good weather. Take U.S. 17 north from downtown. At edge of city, bear left at asphalt road toward Snake Butte, three miles. North of butte bear right onto gravel road. Fourteen miles directly north, old hospital can be seen left of road in Okobojo Creek Valley. Three miles north turn left at junction with another gravel road. The Sully Buttes are visible two miles to northwest. When road turns sharply north (right) in five miles, stop. From here to fort is six miles southwest; vague trace of dirt road can be walked or jeeped through open rangeland. Except by boat, this is only approach. All others are underwater.

56

TWO FORTS NAMED SULLY are commemorated by these markers. Left shaft is in bottom land four miles east of Pierre and is only indication first fort was there. Right marker was placed in middle of parade ground at second Sully in 1929. Fearing site would be flooded, citizens moved it to county courthouse in Onida, S. D., in 1961. Pedestal without top still stands at second Fort Sully.

IT TOOK 120 HORSES to pull Sully hospital eight miles to ranch where it now serves as granary. Hospital is not the one shown on plat. It is of later vintage and is only fort building still standing.

Fort Rice, North Dakota

The men of Fort Rice might have been fearless against Indians—and they had plenty of chances to prove this—but when it came to women, well, that was another matter.

When General Custer came to Rice in 1873 for the Black Hills Expedition, the bachelor officers of Rice declined to invite the wives to remain until the expedition returned.

"Our officers hinted to them," Mrs. Custer wrote, "but they seemed completely intimidated regarding women . . . They added that there were but three on the post, and no two of them spoke to each other. They thought if we were asked to remain it might be the history of the Kilkenny cats repeated."

So Elizabeth Custer left Fort Rice, probably an appropriate decision considering that at the time it was in the heart of Indian country. Attacks on the horseherd and outbuildings were common as late as 1877.

Founded on July 11, 1864, during General Sully's expedition, Rice lost almost more of its men during its first year than the other years combined. Eighty-one men died from 1864 to 1865, 37 of scurvy and eight were killed by Indians.

THIS WAS NEW FORT RICE, rebuilt in 1868. Parade ground was 864 by 544 feet. Buildings were of frame or sawed logs with shingled roofs. Part of stockade next to river had been removed. (Redrawn from North Dakota State Park Board data.)

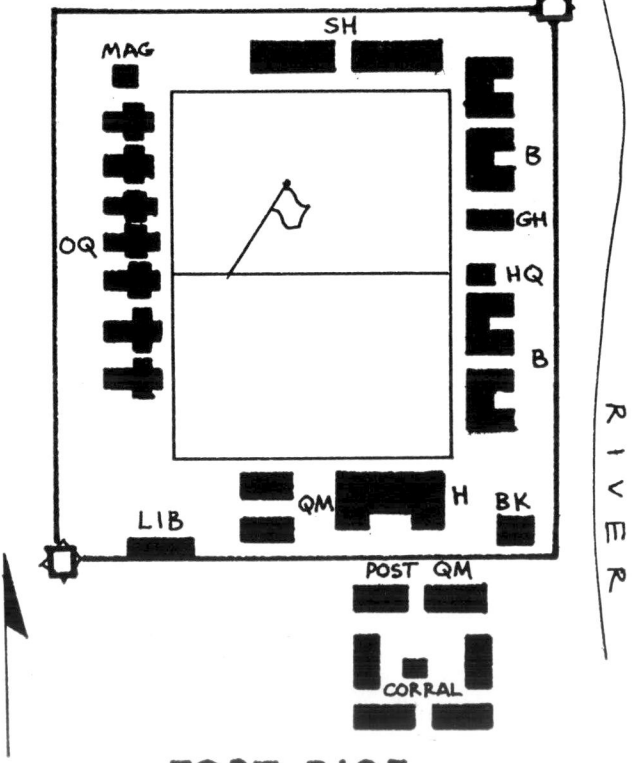

FORT RICE
N.D.—1868

The post was too small for the number of men cooped up inside it, and this shared the blame for the unhealthy situation. By 1874, the sickness rate was cut more than half by increasing the daily vegetable ration from nine to sixteen ounces.

In 1863 about 300 Indians routed the horseherd a mile from the post and others jumped the logging detail in the woods. At nightfall the Indians appeared on the hills overlooking the post.

"A few shells thrown among them soon made them disappear," reported the post commander. He sent two companies to try a night ambush, but no contact was made.

Apparently the Indians had a great fear of artillery in the early days. When General Sully landed at Fort Rice in 1865 for a peace conference, a cannon salute was fired in his honor. Runners had to be sent to recall the Indian conferees who scattered to the hills.

Early one morning in June, 1865, Indians appeared at five different points around the post. As troops approached, they fell back slowly, apparently trying to draw the Army into an ambush. When this failed, the Indians called out to the scouts to leave the Army's pay and join them.

General Sully's 1864 and 1865 Northwestern Expeditions used Fort Rice as a base, as did the Yellowstone Expeditions of 1871, 1872, and 1873. The Sioux treaty of 1868 was signed here, giving all the present South Dakota west of the Missouri to the tribes, though Sitting Bull was one of the chiefs who refused to sign.

Several companies of the 7th cavalry were stationed here. Two accompanied General Terry on the Big Horn Expedition in 1876 when their brother companies of the regiment died with Custer at the Little Big Horn. At this time its strength stood at 357 men, more than capacity for the small enclosure.

With the completion of Fort Yates, 32 miles to the south, and Fort Abraham Lincoln, 25 miles to the north, this number dropped to 61 men in 1878. On November 25, 1878, these men marched to Abraham Lincoln and Fort Rice was abandoned.

TO GET THERE: *From Bismarck, N.D., cross Missouri river into Mandan, take Fort McKeen road south. Pass through Fort Abraham Lincoln site, five miles. Road turns to gravel, continue south 25 miles to town of Fort Rice. Turn left, cross railroad tracks, bear right one mile to fort site.*

(Courtesy Minnesota Historical Society.)

THIS WAS FORT RICE in 1864, before remodeling. Rude cottonwood huts with earth roofs were whitewashed inside. Ten-foot high stockade surrounded post, blockhouses on southwest and northeast corners.

CANNON flanked fort marker after WPA reconstruction, but 1953 tornado collapsed sign and one cannon. Ten years later, this is how they looked in middle of parade ground, northeast blockhouse in rear.

MISSOURI RIVER is half mile behind trees, was only 300 yards in sixties. Looking from top of southwestern blockhouse, library is in foreground. Sites can be seen of storehouses, hospital, bakery, and barracks. Marker was placed by state; fort site was donated to park system by B. G. Gwyther in 1913.

59

HEADQUARTERS stood on this spot (right). Marker in center is for guard house, followed by two barracks and the northeastern blockhouse. Cellars were marked and blockhouses reconstructed by WPA in the thirties.

OFFICERS' ROW includes site of former residence of General Crittenden, ex-commander, hero of Civil War's Shiloh Battle. Fort cemetery was on slope 100 yards to right, had 163 soldier graves within first ten years. Southwest blockhouse is in rear.

Fort Buford, North Dakota

General Sully's 1864 Missouri river expedition had two important results for the strategic junction of the Missouri and Yellowstone.

Not only did it mean the end of Fort Union within a year, but from it came one of the important outposts, Fort Buford.

The timbers and other salvageable items from Fort Union were used to build the first Fort Buford, a couple of miles down river at the actual intersection of the two rivers.

In 1866, a one-company post was begun in a hasty stockade. The next night the 70 infantrymen on the site were attacked.

After daylight their cattle were stampeded. The new fort had to be built by soldiers carrying axes in one hand, rifles in the other.

Across the river, Sitting Bull made camp and was watching the construction. When the saw mill was finished, he attacked the post, made off with the circular saw, and used it for a tom tom.

On a small hill north of the fort, squaws gossiped and made bead necklaces. They were supposedly watching for the first sight of the steamboats that came up the Missouri. That hill is known today as "Bead Hill" and the colorful peas are still in evidence.

What can't be seen though, was the main purpose of the bead stringers: from here the squaws had a good view of the interior of Fort Buford and could relay reports to the braves.

The fort was under almost continual Indian harrassment. Favorite targets were the buildings and the stock. The 1866 cattle rustling might have been the first time, but it wasn't the last. In 1868, more than 240 head were driven off by between 200 and 300 hostiles. Determined patrols recovered only 40 cattle. Three soldiers were killed and three wounded in the skirmishing.

Eastern newspapers of 1867 were shocked by word of the complete massacre of Fort Buford's garrison. Printed first in Philadelphia, the account told how all of the soldiers had been killed, then the commanding officer burned at the stake. His wife was tied to a wild horse. All bodies were scalped, of course, and those of the officers carved up and eaten.

It was several weeks before the Army, and an unharmed Fort Buford garrison, could convince the East that the "massacre" was a hoax. The fact it first appeared on April Fool's Day, 1867, was probably coincidental, but appropriate. Before the rumor ran its course, it had been printed and embellished in major newspapers across the country.

The man who beat a tune on the fort saw mill in 1866, sang a different tune when he returned on July 19, 1881. With 187 followers, a ragged but still proud Sitting Bull presented himself before the headquarters building to surrender.

The chief and his main sub-chiefs were on their ponies, their squaws and children in three Army wagons. Twenty to thirty carts followed them, loaded with baggage.

His face covered with a blanket, Sitting Bull watched silently as his rifle was presented by his son to the commanding officer. No words were exchanged until he had arrived at his camp below the bluff near the river landing . . . and near that saw mill of 1866. While waiting to be moved downriver to Fort Randall, South Dakota, Sitting Bull had only one complaint: two many sightseers came to gawk at him.

Because of its location, Buford became the "holding place" for many surrendering Indian Chiefs. Gall, Chief Joseph, Crow King, and Rain-in-the-Face all passed through it, enroute to reservations or prison to the south.

FROM HASTY STOCKADE in 1866, Fort Buford built new one year later. It was twelve feet high, 330 by 200 yards, enclosed adobe buildings. By 1871, stockade was torn down and more buildings added. It had 100 at one time. When abandoned in 1895, 72 buildings were at post for four companies of infantry, two cavalry troops. (Redrawn from Surgeon-General Circular, 1875.)

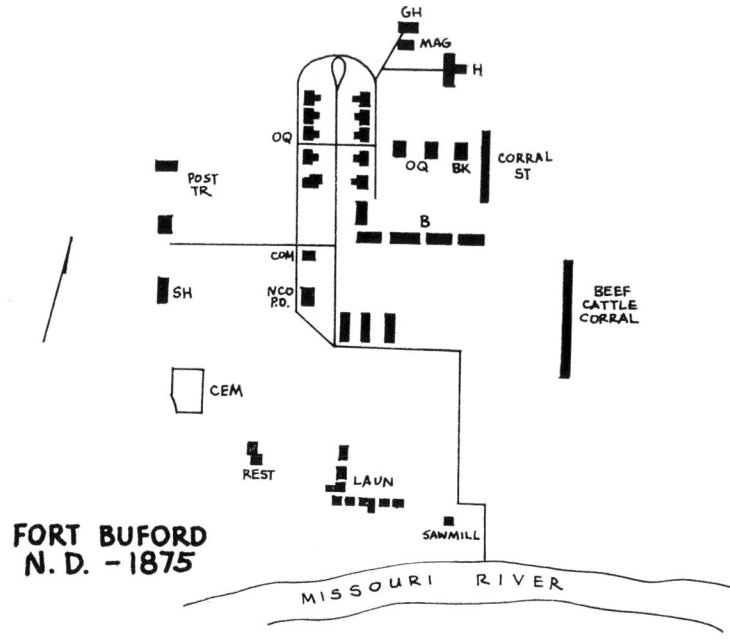

FORT BUFORD
N.D. - 1875

FORT BUFORD IN ITS HEYDAY, the Missouri river in left background. Barracks are long, double-storied buildings at left. Officers' row is at top center. Some of these buildings remain today, but have been shifted from former locations so that positive identification is difficult.

SOLDIER GRAVES in fort cemetery were moved when Army abandoned post, but civilian graves remain. This marker has been re-cemented but most old stones are legible. Cemetery is south of fort.

TO GET THERE: *From Williston, N.D., take U.S. 2 west for seven miles to left turn to Trenton, six miles. Road is gravel for the next 10 miles on to Buford town. At west edge of town, next to deserted double-story schoolhouse, turn left. Stay on winding road that ends at fort site directly south a mile. Information sign and parking area there.*

FOUNDATIONS are about where hospital is located on plat. Magazine is in background.

TOWN OF FORT BUFORD, now Buford, came into being after military abandoned fort and opened reservation to settlement. Remains of fort buildings helped build much of early Buford. This one was original with town, though, the former jail. Town is down to three families, but its post office, school and railroad station serve surrounding countryside.

MACKENZIE'S RAIDERS held forth here. Local legend says General Ranald Mackenzie fought off Indian attack on these two hills, overlooking Fort Buford. He led troops on left hill while a corporal commanded force on right hill. They're now known as Mackenzie and Corporal Buttes.

SITTING BULL surrendered in front of this building in 1881, local legend claims. Old magazine is at left. Other buildings are of recent origin. Former morgue stands 500 yards to right. Now occupied as farmhouse by John Melland and wife, previous use doesn't phase them a bit.

Fort Union, North Dakota

Laws prohibited importing liquor into Indian territory, but that didn't mean a thing to Kenneth McKenzie, fur trader supreme and founder of Fort Union.

In 1829 he had built the American Fur Company's model fur post on the Missouri up river from the junction of the Yellowstone and a scant 100 yards from what is today the Montana border. He located his own still somewhere about the premises, brewed his own portion of white lightning, and ran all competitors out of business. Some authorities estimate Fort Union averaged $300,000 a year in its lifetime.

Competitors there were, too. Down the Missouri where it joined the mouth of the Yellowstone, rival Forts Mortimer (1843) and William (1833) tried to fight the American Fur Company.

One tactic with temporary success was to send a parade of bandsmen and gift-givers to meet fur-laden Indians, detouring them away from any rival post. They would then be locked in a stockade, fed goodly quantities of whiskey, and left locked up and carousing throughout the night. With morning, upwards of several hundred Indians and squaws would awaken in the tiny stockade, head splitting hangovers being the only traces of the furs sold the previous day.

When General Alfred Sully toured the Missouri in 1864, he blamed the Indian troubles on the traders' use of whiskey. Soldiers were left at Fort Union, making it a military installation for the first time.

The fur trade had been dwindling, and this was its final blow. On August 15, 1865, Fort Union went out of business and its buildings were sold to the government.

TO GET THERE: *From Buford, N.D., (see Fort Buford) take gravel road west of town to Montana border. Fort Union site is on Dakota side, 50 yards south of road.*

(Courtesy National Archives.)

FORT UNION, 1835, measured 220 by 240 feet, included 34 buildings within stockade. McKenzie's house was double-story mansion in center. He observed all social graces, even required his guests to dress formally for dinner.

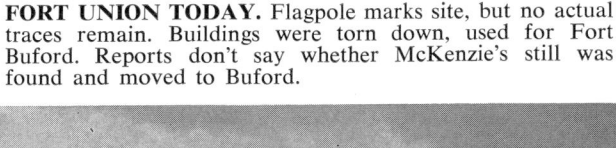

FORT UNION TODAY. Flagpole marks site, but no actual traces remain. Buildings were torn down, used for Fort Buford. Reports don't say whether McKenzie's still was found and moved to Buford.

Camp Cooke, Montana

A river named after a girl friend borders Camp Cooke, a fort site that had equal trouble from Indians, politicians, and rodents.

The river is the Judith, named on May 29, 1805 by Captain William Clark—one half of the famous exploring pair—for a Julia Hancock of Fincastle, Virginia. Captain Clark didn't know the damsel too well at the time. Her nickname was Judy and he just assumed that Judith was her real name. He got to know her better, though. He married her in 1808.

Judith's River, as the explorer termed it, flows into the Missouri at a sagebrush and cottonwood bottom about 60 miles east of Fort Benton. It was a gathering place of the Indians, and the Lewis and Clark journal reports traces of a large camp on what later became the site of Camp Cooke, the short-lived, but active post of 1866-69.

Because treacherous rapids threatened the steamboats 15 miles below and 3 miles above, a military camp was considered necessary, and the bountiful wood supply at the mouth of the Judith dictated the location. This disenchanted the merchants of Fort Benton and Helana, all of whom felt the Army payroll could be spent better closer to them.

Indians hit the post's horseherd on April 24, 1868, making off with 22 horses and nine mules. Nathaniel Crabtree, the herder, was left with nine arrows in his body, but lived long enough to tell what had happened.

A month later, 100 men went on a summer-long scout to temporary Camp Reeve, 25 miles east at the mouth of the Musselshell river. The Indians attacked undermanned Cooke. The cannon finally scattered them. When a pursuing party dashed after them unsuccessfully, the lieutenant in charge accidentally shot himself in the foot with a carbine. He had to play possum in the brush when some of the redmen doubled back.

If harrassment by Indians was bad, the internal harrassment of the rats was almost worse. An 1869 report suggested that all edible supplies had to be double-ordered just to insure enough to go around after rats had their share.

"The small garrison merely holds on in spite of the rats." the report continued. "The grain has now been put in fresh houses, but the rats are in it, and it will soon be going the way of the rest."

TO GET THERE: *From Lewistown, Montana, take State 19 north 15 miles to Hilger. Turn left on gravel road, go 23 miles to Winifred. Beyond Winifred, road becomes dirt. Go 13 miles to Lohse Ferry, free ferry across Missouri. Half mile short of ferry is Power-Norris trading post building, privately owned. Duncan's grave is half mile further south. Camp Cooke is accessible only by wading hip-deep Judith river, west of trading post, walking one mile (see aerial photograph). Beyond Winifred, route is passable only in good weather.*

CAMP COOKE TODAY can be seen only via aerial photographs. Indentations of camp (top right hand corner) are not visible on foot. Top of picture is south. Missouri river flows across bottom, Judith enters it at left.

(Courtesy U.S. Department of Agriculture.)

NEW YORKER Matt Duncan left steamboat to see an Indian in 1881. He did. This is where he was buried after Indian saw him. Camp Cooke site is in trees, center of picture. Marker is southeast of camp, below steep hill obvious in center of old sketch.

CAMP COOKE IN 1868 measured 500 by 600 feet. Officers' quarters and barracks ran in continuous rows, all facing parade ground. View is to southeast.

(Courtesy Montana Historical Society.)

TWELVE YEARS after Camp Cooke abandonment in 1869, Power-Norris interests built this trading post west of fort site, across Judith. Now a ranch stables, owner frequently finds invoices dated in 1880's. Building was combination store and warehouse, is only trace of river trade in Cooke area.

Fort Benton, Montana

Fort Benton was one of the most storied trading posts of the west. Founded in 1846 by the American Fur Company, it was first known as Fort Lewis and succeeded Forts McKenzie and Piegan, both burned by Indians.

It was from here that Lieutenant John Mullan ran his road to Fort Walla Walla, connecting the head of navigation of the Missouri with that of the Columbia. With the sixties and the gold boom, Benton was the logical northern base for the Missouri steamboats. Through it flowed millions of tons of cargo. During Red Cloud's war along the Bozeman Trail, steamers sheathed their pilot houses with boiler plate to ward off attacks.

By 1869, the gold business had slowed down. That year the Army bought the trading post, mainly as a forwarding point for supplies and mail to Forts Shaw and Ellis. Their arrival found the town had dropped from 500 to 180 citizens, but still had a courthouse, school, jail, brewery and, by official report, "about a dozen drinking and gambling shops."

The Army was located in the old adobe trading post 40 yards from the Missouri. As the surgeon reported in 1870, "Its capacity is sufficient for one superintendent and about 20 employees, but not for a company of soldiers."

The town and fort were involved in a second-hand manner with most of the Indian wars of the seventies. The Far West, a Benton steamer, carried Custer's wounded after the Little Big Horn. Chief Joseph and his Nez Perce crossed the Benton steamer line 150 miles down river, killing some freighters and burning the contents of one steamer.

The Army abandoned the fort on June 4, 1881. And the steamboats disappeared when the railroad crossed Montana.

To the west of the fort, near a hotel built in 1881, a steel bridge crosses the Missouri. It crosses at the head of navigation to which no one navigates by steamboat anymore.

TO GET THERE: *Fort site is immediately east of city of Fort Benton, 41 miles northeast of Great Falls, Montana, off of U.S. 87.*

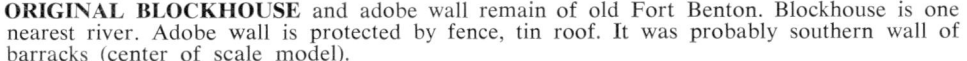

ORIGINAL BLOCKHOUSE and adobe wall remain of old Fort Benton. Blockhouse is one nearest river. Adobe wall is protected by fence, tin roof. It was probably southern wall of barracks (center of scale model).

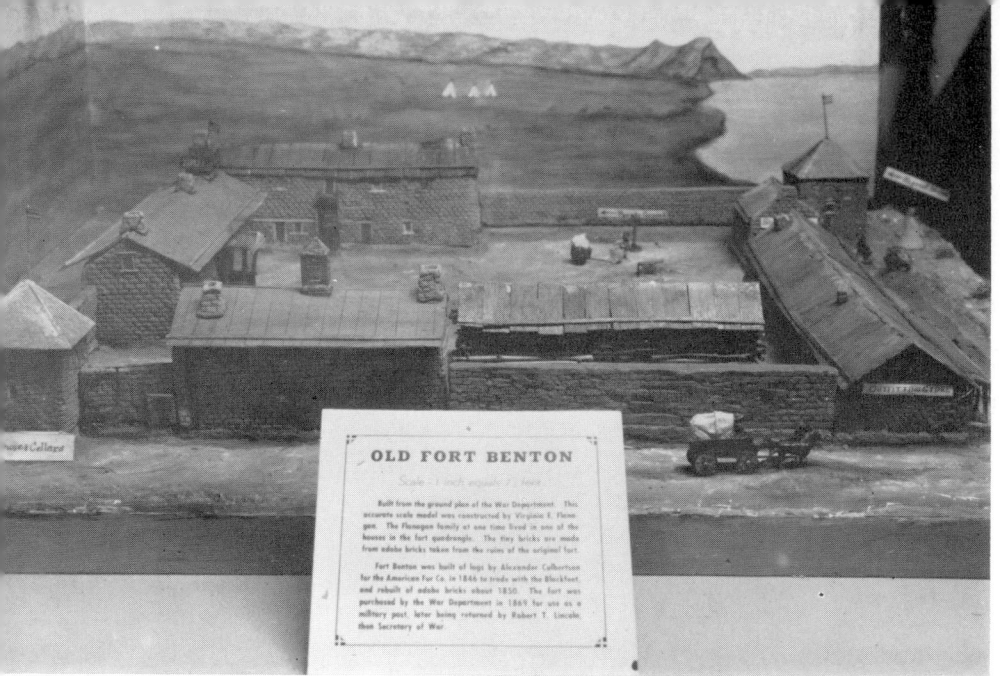

OLD FORT BENTON

Scale - 1 inch equals 2 feet

Built from the ground plan of the War Department. This accurate scale model was constructed by Virginia E. Flanagan. The Flanagan family at one time lived in one of the houses in the fort quadrangle. The tiny bricks are made from adobe bricks taken from the ruins of the original fort.

Fort Benton was built of logs by Alexander Culbertson for the American Fur Co. in 1846 to trade with the Blackfeet, and rebuilt of adobe bricks about 1850. The fort was purchased by the War Department in 1869 for use as a military post, later being returned by Robert T. Lincoln, then Secretary of War.

ADOBE FROM ORIGINAL FORT was used to make this scale model in excellent local museum. Army barracks were the two double-storied buildings at left, 85 by 18 feet. At time when War Department considered 600 cubic feet of air minimum per soldier in barracks, these permitted only 91. By 1875, most men lived in quarters rented in town.

(Courtesy National Archives.)

FORT BENTON, 1850, was surrounded by adobe stockade 250 feet square. Modern city of Fort Benton stands where wigwams are in this sketch.

HEAD OF NAVIGATION of Missouri river is crossed by this steel bridge. Old Fort Benton is few hundred yards beyond left end of bridge. Among goods brought up river were 30,000,000 pounds of supplies annually for Fort Macleod, Royal Canadian Mounted Police post founded in 1874 to control smuggling across border, 80 miles north.

Guardians of the Trails

"Will you please order the necessary force (probably one or two regiments) . . . to protect the Overland Mail Route; the number of troops to be employed is left to your discretion."

—General McClellan, Commander of the Army, to the Commander of the Pacific, November 13, 1861.

ACROSS THE continent they came, by foot and by horseback, by mule and by wagon train. Some destitute but energetic emigrants even came by wheelbarrow.

The trails that brought the East to the West cut through plains and forest, desert and mountain. Suspicious, then openly hostile, Indians watched as the paths became trails and the single parties became horizon-to-horizon trains.

Protecting this tide of emigration was the Army's main task in the West. Forts were located along the main trails, the Oregon and the Santa Fe, and many secondary routes. Army engineers built roads and stage lines erected way stations.

The Oregon Trail carried the bulk of the emigrants through the Northwest. More than 250,000 moved over it after the first wagon train of 80 made the trip in 1841. This 2,000-mile route generally followed rivers across the west, and had them at either end. As Captain John Fremont said in his survey of 1846, it was a route "commencing at the mouth of the Kansas in the Missouri river and ending at the mouth of the Wallah Wallah in the Columbia."

Most of these trails exist today. In the more desolate areas they are ruts visible when the light is right. The rest are under the concrete of modern great cross-country highways.

Fort Mitchell, Nebraska

When nineteenth century wagon trains rolled westward, civilization passed behind them as they crossed the plains of Nebraska. The gateway to the West opened to them and the Nebraska Territory began to blend with the Wyoming Territory when they climbed a slight rise and crossed Mitchell Pass.

To their right was 600-foot high Scott's Bluff, the first dominating butte to greet travelers along the Oregon Trail. Two miles to the northwest was a one-company outpost, Fort Mitchell.

This was a fort in the old tradition: stockade, a blockhouse, rifle ports and all. The wife of Colonel Carrington, of Bozeman Trail fame, described Fort Mitchell after passing it in 1866:

"This is a sub-post of Fort Laramie of peculiar style and compactness. The walls of the quarters are also the outlines of the fort itself, and the four sides of the rectangle are respectively, the quarters of officers, soldiers, and horses, and the warehouses of supplies. Windows open into a little court or parade-ground; and bed-rooms, as well as all other apartments, are loop-holed for defense."

The fort had been established originally as Camp Shuman in September, 1864. The name was changed in 1865 to honor General Robert B. Mitchell who was in charge of protecting the wagon trail.

The little fort lasted four years, 1864 to 1867. During that time, it became the prototype of the military frontier in many emigrant diaries. It also established a fighting record against the Indians, defending wagon trains from attack and reinforcing the garrisons at Fort Sedgwick, Fort Laramie, and others, when required. In true theatrical style, accounts always credit it with arrival in the nick of time, bugles blaring and banners waving.

TO GET THERE: *From Scottsbluff, Nebraska (the city is only one word!), take State 92 west across the North Platte river. Take the first left, head south about one mile. On west side, on top of rise, are markers for Fort Mitchell and Oregon Trail. Fort's site is on east side or road about where ranchhouse stands.*

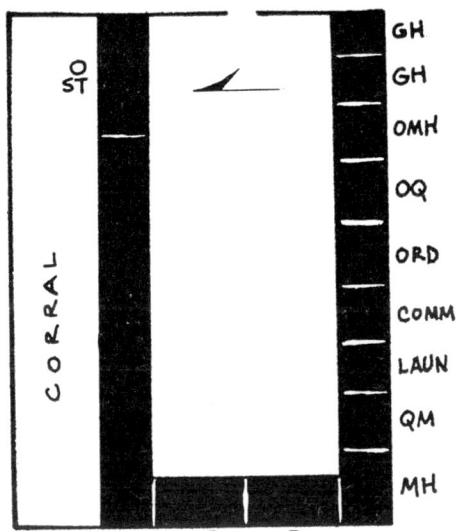

CAMP MITCHELL was a stockade 166 feet by 134. The long building on the left was the stable. A sentinel box was on top of the guardhouse room in the top right hand corner. (Redrawn from plat courtesy Earl Harris, Scotts Bluff National Monument.)

CAMP MITCHELL
NEBR.- 1866

FORT MITCHELL TODAY. This is approximate site of Jackson watercolor, but nothing of fort remains. Markers commemorate fort and Oregon Trail.

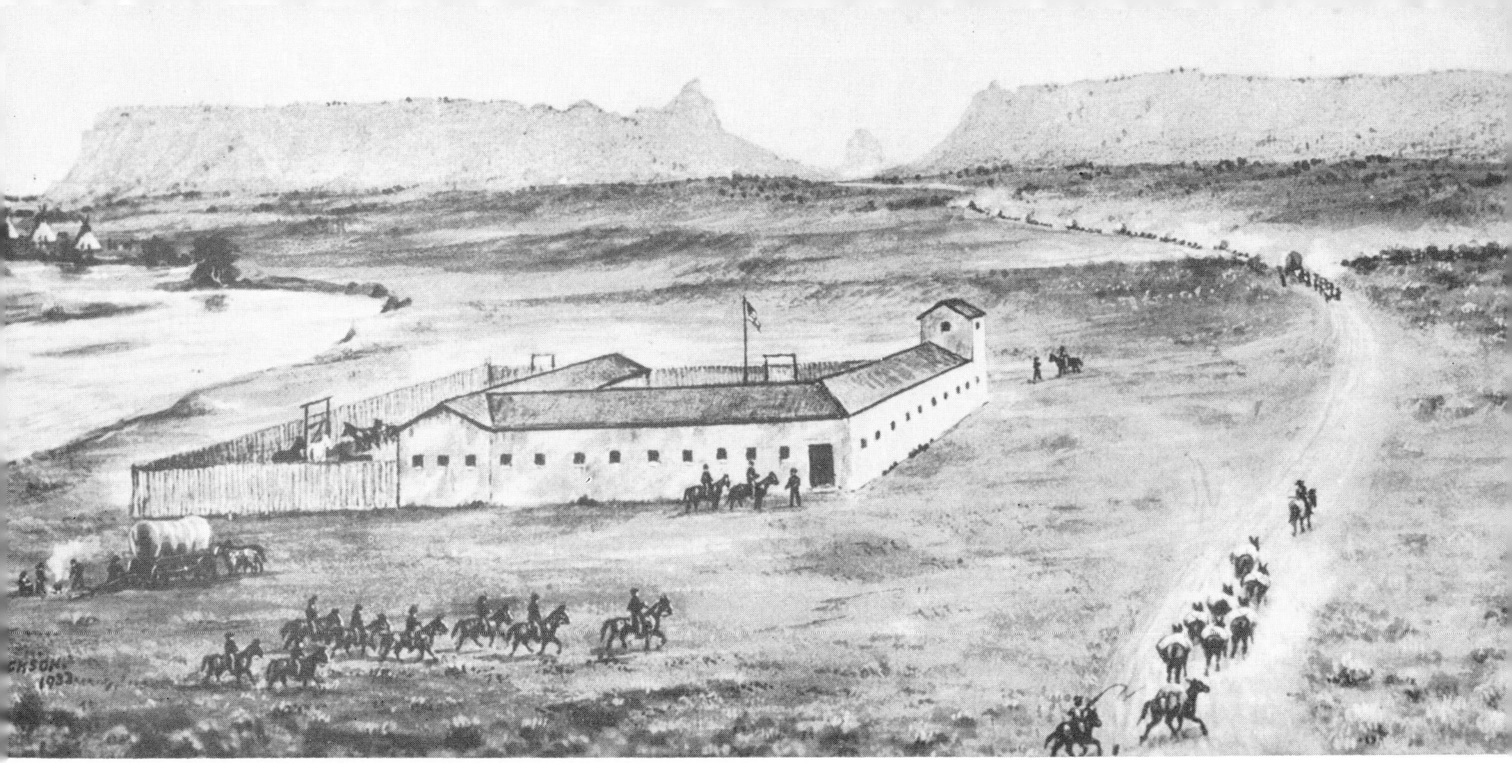

(Courtesy American Pioneer Trails Association.)

SCOTTS BLUFF AND MITCHELL PASS are behind the fort in this watercolor by William Henry Jackson.

DOORWAY TO THE WEST was Scotts Bluff. Ruts of Oregon Trail flank sign in foreground. Bluff was named for Hiram Scott, ill trapper who was abandoned by comrades in 1828. His bones were found near bluff a year later, 60 miles from where legend says he was left to die.

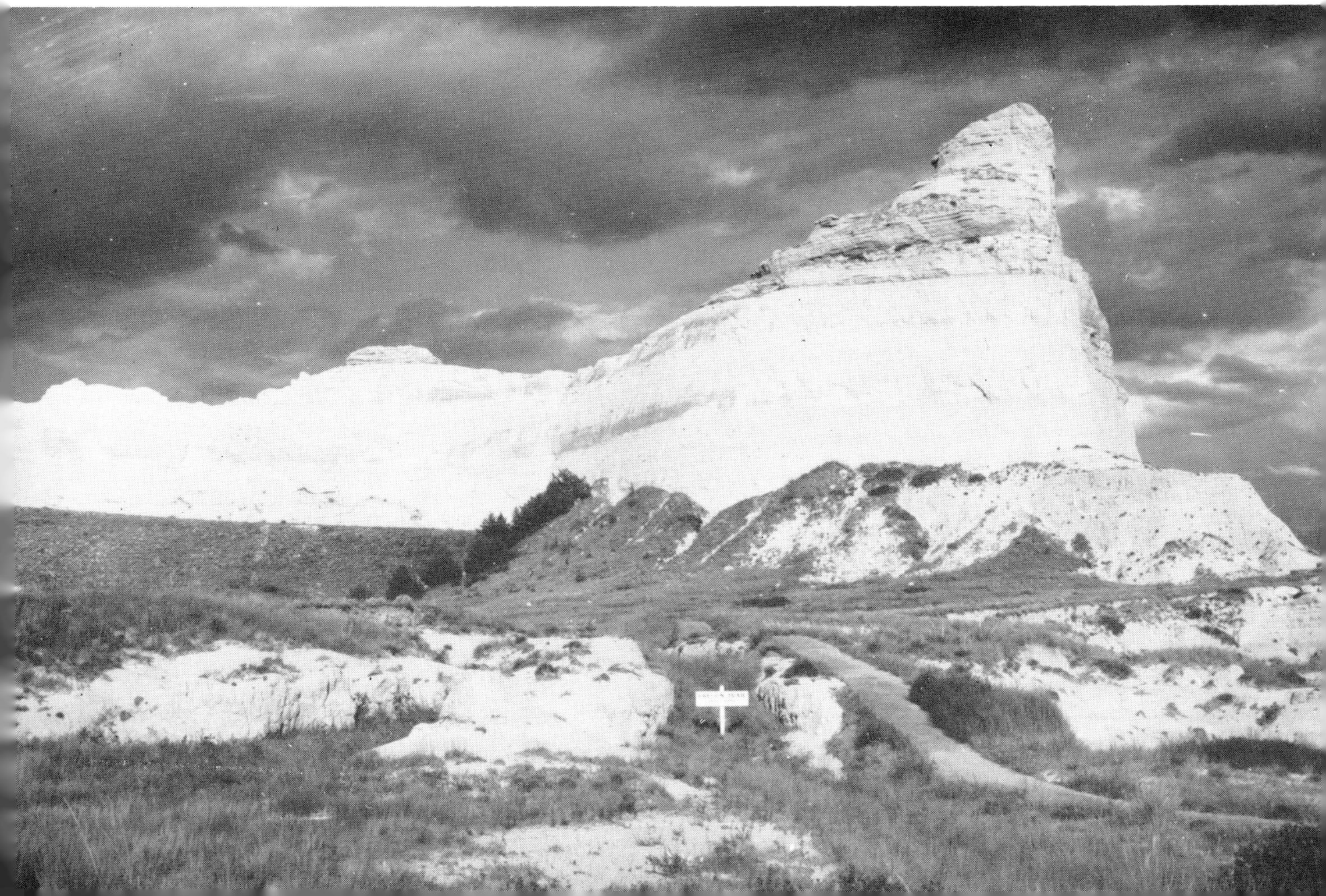

Fort Kearny, Nebraska

It might be said that Fort Kearny was so busy it never had time to look beautiful. In the ten years of the California "forty-niners," more than 200,000 emigrants rested here. In the sixties, it was a stop on the Oregon Trail, California Road, Pony Express, Denver Road, and Overland Stage Line.

There were to forts of this name. The first was a two-story blockhouse overlooking the Missouri river at the eastern edge of Nebraska. Started in 1846, it was never completed. The Army decided the site was poor and settled for temporary log settlers for the winter of 1847–48.

In 1848, a site was selected in mid-Nebraska, south of the Platte river, and 197 miles west of Fort Kearny. A four acre parade, surrounded by newly planted cottonwood trees, was laid out and the new post christened "Fort Childs."

On December 30, 1848, the Kearny name was officially shifted to the new post. Within six months, the fort records showed that 4,400 wagons passed the fort on the south side of the river; no estimate was given for those using the other river banks. Destination for most of the trains: California.

A member of the 1857–58 Utah Expedition described it. "It stands on a slight elevation . . . consists of five unpainted wooden houses, two dozen long, low mud buildings," he wrote. "Trees have been set out along the borders of the parade ground . . . Intermixed between these immature trees on the sides of the square are 16 blockhouse guns, two field pieces, two mountain howitzers, and one prairie piece . . .

"On the west side of the parade ground stands the house of the commanding officer. It is a large, ill-shaped, unpainted structure, two stories high, with piazzas along its entire front on both floors . . . On the other side of the square is the soldier's barracks, 70 feet by 30 feet, and two stories high. The barracks has never been finished and it is now in bad order."

These buildings, plus the wooden officer's quarters, hospital, and sutler's were described as not presenting a "very inviting appearance to the eye, but they are charming palaces compared to the spectacle of 24 long, winding, broken-backed, falling down mud buildings."

Kearny was abandoned in 1871 and hardly any trace remains. During its one Indian scare—there were many in the area but only one threat to the fort—two earthwork fortifications were thrown up. Named Forts Mitchell and Gilette, these never saw action, but their vague outlines were all that remained of Kearny in recent years.

Equally absent from the scene is the ever-present hog ranch: Dobytown, two miles west of the fort. So called because of its half dozen adobe buildings, it was a typical collection of saloons and dives patronized by the teamsters and soldiers.

Its reputation was so notorious that wagon masters arranged their routes to give it a wide berth. Not only was the whiskey bad, but arguments usually were settled by gunfire. Local legend says that the cemetery was larger than the town.

FORT KEARNY changed its appearance as old buildings collapsed and new temporary ones were built. Uses of buildings varied from year to year. (Redrawn from SHS data)

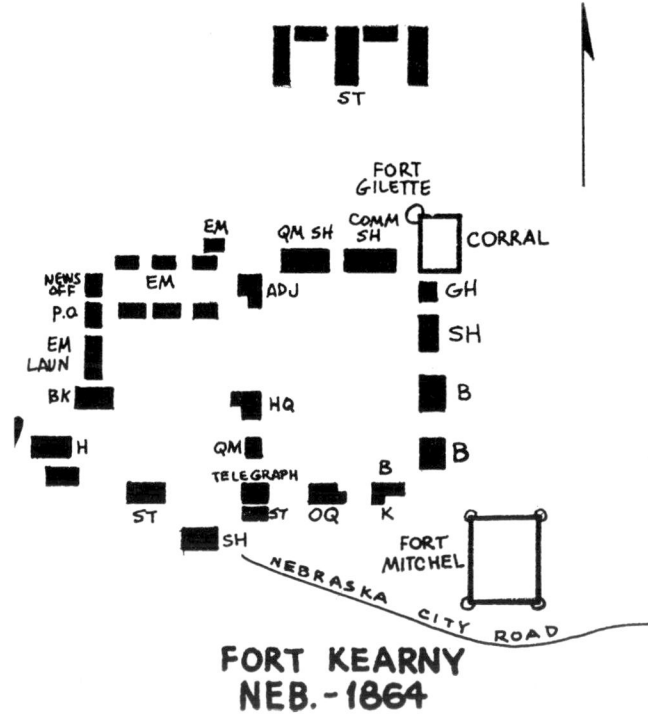

FORT KEARNY NEB.-1864

TO GET THERE: *The first Kearny blockhouse is on the main street of Nebraska City, Nebraska. Second fort is due to be a state park. From Kearny, Nebraska, drive south 3.8 miles on State 44. Turn left on dirt road, go 4.4 miles east. Monument is 100 feet from road, north side.*

NOT SHANTY TOWN but the back view of the commanding officer's quarters and parade ground at Fort Kearny in 1860.

THE FORT from the southeast shows slight trace of so-called Fort Mitchel, the slight mounds in center of picture.

SECOND FORT KEARNY was at this site in mid-Nebraska. General Sherman visited it in 1866, said "The buildings are fast rotting down . . . I will probably use it to shelter some horses this winter and next year let it go to the prairie dogs." Weeds and brush have all but obliterated even this marker for fort.

ORIGINAL FORT KEARNY in Nebraska City included this blockhouse, now reconstructed and used as a youth center.

Fort McPherson, Nebraska

The ghost bridge of the Platte is an eerie memorial to Fort McPherson, immediately south of Maxwell, Nebraska, and U. S. route 30.

In the nineteenth century, the Mormon Trail passed to the north of the Platte, the Oregon and Pony Express trails to the south. Three miles further south was a five-company Army post named Cantonment McKean in 1863 after its builder, renamed Fort Cottonwood in 1864 after the nearest settlement, Cottonwood Springs, and finally renamed again in 1866 to honor a Union general killed at the Battle of Atlanta.

To ease access to the fort from the north, the soldiers built a bridge across the Platte river by running old wagons and artillery caissons into the

shallow waters. Logs and brush were piled on top to form a rude bridge.

At low water, these old wheels have been seen occasionally, depending upon some unexplained circumstances that cause the wheels to appear one day, disappear for months, then reappear again. Local legend tells of a lost Army payroll bag thrown from the bridge into the Platte during an Indian attack, and of booty from a holdup similarly lost in the shallows.

The post was extremely active, especially in insuring safe passage for the emigrants. All wagon trains were stopped here and thoroughly inspected, special attention being paid to the proper weapons and ammunition for a cross-country trip. Some trains were held so they could be accompanied and protected by government trains bound for the west.

Not all of the groups were emigrants, though. In 1872, the Grand Duke Alexis of Russia used Fort McPherson as a base for a hunting expedition guided by Buffalo Bill Cody, and accompanied by Generals Phil Sheridan and George Custer.

Oldtimers say that broken champagne bottles—for the Duke provided the champagne during the hunt—were found for years between McPherson and Hayes, 30 miles southwest.

FORT McPHERSON's buildings flanked a quadrangle 560 feet by 844. In its heyday it had ten officers' quarters, five barracks, six laundresses' quarters, and five cavalry stables. (Redrawn from NA)

TO GET THERE: *From North Platte, Nebraska, take U.S. 30 east to Maxwell. Turn right, go 3.7 miles south to Fort McPherson National Cemetery, on right. Continue on dirt road, bearing left, one mile. Statue is beside road.*

CEDAR LOG BUILDINGS gave a permanent air to Fort McPherson, 1875, even though they didn't last long after it was abandoned in 1880. Only cemetery is left. Now Fort McPherson National Cemetery, it contains the dead of 21 abandoned frontier forts and 584 markers that say simply: "U.S. Soldier, Unknown."

(Courtesy Nebraska State Historical Society.)

A SOLDIER STILL STANDS
at the site of Fort McPherson.
Statue is dedicated to 7th Iowa
Volunteer Cavalry, the first
troops at the fort that "made
possible the first white settlement in Lincoln county, known
as Cottonwood Springs."

Camp Collier, South Dakota

The government may not have done a very good job of keeping miners out of Dakota's Black Hills in 1876, but it refused to deliver the mail there.

So Henry T. Clark of Sidney, Nebraska, was only too happy to peddle special envelopes for a dime, agreeing to deliver any U.S. mail inserted in them (one letter per envelope, if you please), anywhere along his route betwen Sidney and Custer, South Dakota, all 160 miles of it.

His riders had to pass Red Canyon in southwestern Dakota, a risky place, what with anxious Indians and equally anxious and assorted Dakota bad men. In 1876, two parties were massacred in the canyon with only a single April day to separate them. The Army moved in to quiet things down.

A small detachment erected a stockaded affair around 125 feet square, bastions on the northeast and southwest corners, and named it Camp Collier, after the officer in command. They kept peace for six months or so, until the stage lines decided to re-route up Beaver Creek Valley to the west.

Remains of this stockade lasted into the twentieth century, but in recent years only a single, man-high post marked the spot. That burned or rotted within the past five years. Now only its stump and a slightly raised table of ground, 125 feet square with two indentations at opposite corners, remain of this little post that back in '76 and '77 maintained the peace and kept the mails moving into the Black Hills of Dakota.

TO GET THERE: *From Edgemont, S.D., take U.S. 18 north one mile. Turn left at Red Canyon road. Camp Collier site is about five miles north on Bell ranch, private property, 50 yards east of road.*

ONLY REMNANT OF CAMP COLLIER is stump near Frank Bucher's right foot. It is on slight rise that follows trace of old stockade.

NORTHEAST CORNER of Camp Collier's stockade, from the southeast. Frank Bucher, born in 1889, stands on corner. Red Canyon is in background.

Fort Sedgwick, Colorado

As towns went in the early days, Julesburg, Colorado did not have an easy go of it. Nor did Fort Sedgwick, occasionally its neighbor, depending upon what dates are being considered.

In the northeastern corner of Colorado, where the Overland Stage and Pony Express trails dropped south from the North Platte and entered the route to Denver, the Army had a sod fort. Called Camp Rankin when started on August 21, 1864, it was a mile from Julesburg station on the stage route.

On January 7, 1865, the town and a small detail of soldiers were attacked by a thousand Cheyennes and Arapahoes. A rear guard action was fought to the fort, and the Indians withdrew only after the howitzers blasted them with grape shot. Fourteen soldiers were killed that day.

February 18, 1865, Julesburg was attacked again. One column of Indians hit the town, while two waited to cut off the relief force they expected would come from the fort, not knowing only a token group was manning it while the remainder was at Fort McPherson, Nebraska.

The Indians burned the town, one house at a time, watching for a reaction from the fort as each went up in smoke. When 15 men of the McPherson force appeared, their howitzer firing canister shot, the Indians pulled back slowly. After the troopers had reached the fort, the Indians beseiged it, firing blazing arrows in an unsuccessful attempt to set off the hay stack inside.

After dark, the hostiles broke into a liquor cache in the wrecked town, triggering a drunken orgy. Once a bonfire got out of control, spreading across the plains, their ardor cooled. By morning, all Indians had left.

Julesburg No. 1 was leveled by that attack. The telegraph line had been dealt a blow, too: 12 miles on the Denver line and 33 on the Laramie road had been torn out. The poles were cut off at the ground and carried away, the wire left in a tangled mass.

Later in 1865, the camp became Fort Sedgwick. No attempt was made to rebuild Julesburg, and a new and noisier town of the same name grew three miles away. In 1867, this was abandoned in favor of still a third Julesburg on the north side of the South Platte, providing "end of track" entertainment for railroad crews of the Pacific Railroad. At one time it boasted the reputation as "the wickedest little city east of the Rockies."

Modern Julesburg, Colorado, was founded in 1881 still further away in a curve of the South Platte river. It is the only one of the four Julesburgs of which any trace exists, and nothing of this clean, well-ordered city suggests the sordid past of its namesakes.

TO GET THERE: *From Julesburg, Colorado, take road from center of town (next to park). Turn right after passing picnic grounds south of river. About three miles west, stone marker is on north side of road. Fort site is half-mile north in privately owned pasture.*

FORT SEDGWICK looked like this at first, everything enclosed within a sod corral 240 by 360 feet. First winter buildings had no windows or doors and blankets were hung over the openings to keep out the cold. Later, magazine became guard house, sentinel box was hospital. (Redrawn from NA data.)

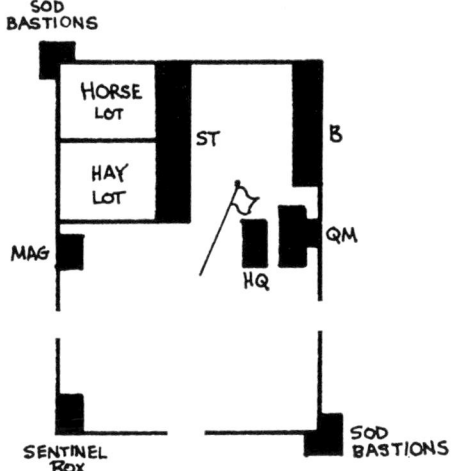

FORT SEDGWICK
COLO.-1866

BY 1870, FORT SEDGWICK had outgrown the sod corral. It had two adobe barracks, 100 by 25 feet with 10-foot high ceilings. Officers lived in four story-and-a-half quarters at right of parade ground. Flagpole is only remnant of fort; it is now at museum in Julesburg.

(Courtesy E. T. Hogue, Fort Sedgwick Historical Society.)

FORT SEDGWICK today. Nothing remains although buttons, shells, and other souvenirs usually appear whenever field is plowed.

FIRST JULESBURG's only inhabitants are four-legged today. Site of Fort Sedgwick is in midfield, marked by irregular line of trees.

Fort Lupton, Colorado

Today it might be called "psychological warfare," but in 1864 it was probably known simply as "scaring the Indians."

Because of it, a trading post north of Denver, Colorado, became for a short while an Army post. In the process it performed greater services than many official, but noncombatant, posts of later years of the Indian troubles.

The post was Fort Lupton, Colorado, 26 miles north of Denver and 80 miles south of Cheyenne, Wyoming, almost on a straight line. It had been built in 1836 by an Army Lieutenant, Lancaster P. Lupton, who was on some kind of detached service. At first it was called by his first name, Fort Lancaster. Later, things must have got more formal: it took his last name.

Kit Carson and John Fremont visited the fort in 1843. Later it became a stop for the Overland Stage.

In 1864 the Indian troubles caused settlers for 75 miles around to gather within the walls of Fort Lupton, and to call frantically for soldiers. Redskins were beseiging the stockade when the hollow boom of a cannon echoed across the valley. In true motion picture style, the Army had arrived at dusk and were a half mile away. By the next morning, the Indians had disappeared.

TO GET THERE: *From Fort Lupton, Colorado, take U.S. 85 one-half mile north. Turn left at marker, west side of road. Fort is within barn at end of this dirt road, one-quarter mile. Ranch is privately owned by Mrs. George Ewing, whose family has lived here since 1861.*

FORT LUPTON was a typical trading post, 100 feet by 150. Its adobe walls were four feet thick and 18 feet high. The tower at the northeast corner was ten feet higher. Part of the northern wall is all that remains today.

(Courtesy State Historical Society of Colorado.)

A FORT WITHIN A BARN is the fate of Fort Lupton. Note the rough sign by the door. This leads into addition built in 1955 to protect remaining adobe wall. Circular tower stood at this corner.

THROUGH THE dairy barn, original Fort Lupton adobe can be seen in background.

Fort Fetterman, Wyoming

Truly the end of the road and the edge of creation was the location of Fort Fetterman in the seventies. After the Bozeman Trail was closed only this outpost was left.

"No travels interrupt the monotony, there being no posts beyond, and no settlements in the vicinity," reported the post surgeon in 1874. "The graves of the inhabitants at the crossings of the creeks mark their former locations."

HIGH PLANK FENCE originally enclosed Fort Fetterman, but this was gradually taken down. There were four barracks, including double building at bottom left corner of parade ground. In 1875 they were adobe, 100 by 24 feet, had canvas roofs. It had seven officers' quarters, more comfortable than common for frontier. Theory was that commanding officer kept building himself a house, less senior officers getting the rejected but still highly desirable buildings. (Redrawn from NA data.)

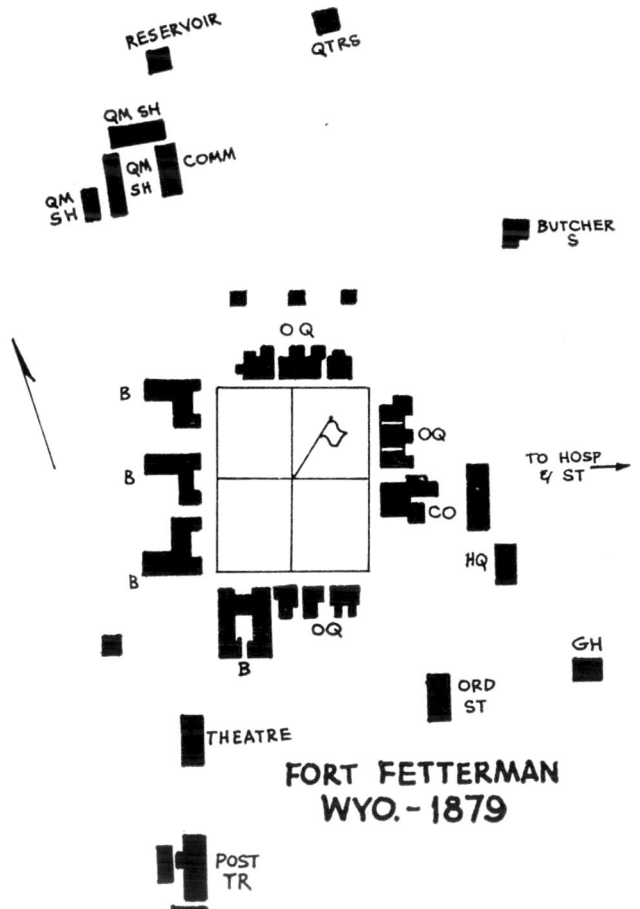

FORT FETTERMAN
WYO.-1879

With the Bozeman forts gone, Fort Fetterman was supposed to check the Indian depredations and protect the railroad. It was also base of operations for General George Crook's 1876 Yellowstone Expedition, and Colonel Ranald Mackenzie's campaign against Dull Knife and the Cheyennes.

The classic war correspondent of the Indian campaign, John S. Finerty, described it in 1876 as a "desolate fort grinning at us from the bleak hill on the other side of the Platte."

When Fort Fetterman was abandoned by the Army in 1882, it didn't just disappear as did most other posts. Cattlemen turned it into a riproaring, frontier town. Barns and warehouses became business houses, other buildings became residences.

Ex-soldiers, cow boys, trail hands came to blow their pay and in some cases, to wind up in an impromptu boot hill at the southeast corner of the site.

The new "town" wasn't as lively as it might have been, though. The Hog Ranch common to the edge of most Army posts appeared at Fetterman in 1882, and not to serve an abandoned fort, but a cattle town. This "recreational community" set up business seven miles north and across the river, providing new and old methods of relieving the sucker of his stake until the boom ended in 1888.

Sheep operations took over the fort site until 1961 when the State of Wyoming bought it. By this time only one of the officers' quarters and an ordnance storehouse remained, used as a residence and barn respectively.

Plans to restore the site are under discussion. In an area virtually untouched by other than agricultural operations since the seventies, Fort Fetterman still seems to fit the epiteph given it by the aforenamed Finerty:

"Fort Fetterman is now abandoned. It was a hateful post—in summer, hell, and in winter, Spitzbergen. The whole Army dreaded being quartered there, but all had to take their turn. Its abandonment was a wise proceeding on the part of the government."

TO GET THERE: *From Douglas, Wyoming, take U.S. 26 for 2.7 miles west to Wyoming secondary road 502, a right turn. Fort site is 6.8 miles, right side of road, overlooking valley of North Platte river.*

GENERAL CROOK'S 1876 expedition camped between Fort Fetterman and Platte river. Buildings on hill can be identified from plat. Single house, left is quarters at top of plat; group of buildings are storehouses.

CROOK'S CAMPSITE today is hayfield. Buildings are gone from bluff overlooking site, but abandoned officers' quarters can be seen behind this bluff.

BARE FIELDS remain where Fort Fetterman stood. View is from front porch of officers' quarters to east where headquarters and commanding officer's quarters once stood. Collapsing shed was a farm building of recent date.

OFFICERS' QUARTERS is only residence left at Fetterman. Building is at bottom right hand corner of parade ground in plat; this is back of building.

COMBINATION ADOBE and log construction of Officers' quarters can be seen inside building. Outside walls were of logs, covered with lath and plaster. Interior walls were adobe and plastered.

Fort Caspar, Wyoming

Second Lieutenant Casper W. Collins spent only one night at "Old Platte Bridge Station," but that was long enough for him to earn his niche in posterity.

He died while fighting Indians his second day at that post, causing it to be renamed in his honor, despite the poor spelling. When a town grew next to the fort, it took the Lieutenant's name, and spelled it correctly.

Fort Caspar, Wyoming, is that western outpost named after this second lieutenant. It was in 1865 that it all happened.

That was about the time the Indians decided that the Oregon Trail should be closed. Three thousand of them massed at the strategic river crossing at Platte Bridge Station, preparing an assault.

When they saw a 25-man patrol cross the bridge and near the foot of the bluffs, Indians appeared behind every sand hill. Six hundred Cheyennes hit the patrol's front and left flank; 1,800 Sioux attacked their other side. Hand-to-hand fighting ensued; the range was too close and the area too crowded for rifles.

Collins, the patrol leader, ordered a retreat and went to the rescue of a wounded soldier. His body was found the next day. It was mutilated almost beyond recognition, according to some records, untouched and unscalped out of respect for his bravery, according to other reports. Four other soldiers died with him.

His name was honored on September 28, 1865, when Fort Caspar was designated the new name of Old North Platte Station. The new name was short-lived, however. In August, 1867, the post was abandoned and the Army moved to Fort Fetterman, Wyoming.

TO GET THERE: *From Casper, Wyoming, take 13th street west one-and-a-half miles to Fort Caspar, owned and maintained by the City of Casper, even though the names are not spelled the same way.*

IT COST $60,000 to build this 1,000 foot bridge over Platte river. Pilings of bridge were found when fort was being reconstructed, but now are covered by dirt mounds to protect them from ravages of time and tourists. Top right corner of fort has been restored.

(Courtesy National Archives.)

STOCKADE wasn't necessary at Fort Caspar. Buildings were on line with the peeled-log backs facing the prairie. Windows are modern convenience for visitors to museum that now occupies barracks-telegraph building.

STABLES shared same building with officers' quarters and in modern restoration seem even more comfortable.

FORT CASPAR from north, almost duplicating old view. Officers' row is behind flagpole. Two buildings at left were shops. Stone commemorates Casper Collins' fight.

FORT CASPAR today was reconstructed on original site in 1938. This is view of parade ground from officers' quarters. Low building includes, left to right, squad room, mess hall, another squad room, storeroom, and telegraph operator's quarters and office. Office has original telegraph key, found in rubble during reconstruction.

Fort Abercrombie, North Dakota

Some 160 persons came to Fort Abercrombie when the Sioux went on the warpath in 1862. It didn't have a stockade at the time, so their protection was long rows of cord wood with gaps plugged by barrels of salt pork, flour, and beef.

Abercrombie had been a fort from 1857 to 1859, and was re-garrisoned in 1860. Its regular detachment was called away in 1861. Captain John Vander Horck's Minnesota Volunteers performed its mission of guarding the trails from Minnesota into the Dakotas and the river traffic up to Canada.

Thirty of his 70 men were at unofficial Fort Sanborn, near Georgetown, Minnesota, when the Sioux business started. He put the civilians to work patrolling. Fifteen miles away one detail came across the mutilated bodies of three settlers, and other patrols reported evidences of atrocities.

On August 30, 1862, the Indians drove off the horses. This put the garrison on a nervous alert. A shaky sentry wounded Captain Vander Horck before dawn on September 3, awakening the whole post. Although Vander Horck wasn't especially happy with his injured arm, it happened that was the dawn the Sioux tried a surprise attack . . . with everyone awake and ready for them.

Somewhere between 200 and 300 Sioux hit the fort. Rifles and grape-loaded howitzers met them. Fifty-four double barreled shot guns were found in a delayed train of government goods enroute to the Indians. The civilians made good use of them.

After the attack was beaten off, a startled Vander Horck learned he had only 350 rounds of .69 caliber rifle ammunition left. Before the attack he had 2,000. Without the resupply requested earlier by two urgent and unanswered dispatches, the fort soon would be defenseless.

Someone opened a can of howitzer canister shot, and noticed it contained .69 caliber metal balls, the Civil War version of shrapnel. This was a lifesaver. The balls were turned into cartridges, using powder from the government train. Scrap iron and other odds and ends were substituted in the muzzles of the howitzers.

Three days passed before another attack. At first, a force of Sioux demonstrated along the west side of the palisade. They hoped to draw off the soldiers, perhaps cause them to send a force from the fort. Then a three-sided attack came from the other directions. It took six hours to do it, but the fort finally beat back the assaults.

By September 26, the 160 occupants of the fort were getting tired of the constant threat of attack plus eternal sniping by the Indians at any force that showed itself. There was another attack that day.

The final action was on September 29, when Indians fired from logs across the river, trying to hit the horse watering detail. A few howitzer rounds discouraged any further action.

By this time, reinforcements had arrived. They came from Fort Snelling, Minnesota, organized so quickly that weapons had to be requisitioned from stores along the way. Once the Indian attacks had ceased, trees and brush were cleared from the edge of the fort, wiping out the cover that had protected assualts on the fort. By this time Abercrombie's war was over, however.

TO GET THERE: *From Fargo, N.D., go south on U.S. 81 for 45 miles to Abercrombie. Turn left at Abercrombie's main street. At its eastern end is Fort Abercrombie Museum; fort site is quarter-mile beyond. Blockhouses, guardhouse, building sites are within restored stockade.*

FORT ABERCROMBIE IN 1876 reflected changes from its 1863 appearance. It had a palisade 675 feet by 625, contained substantial buildings. Fort was abandoned in 1877, is now state park. (Redrawn from Division of Missouri Report, 1875.)

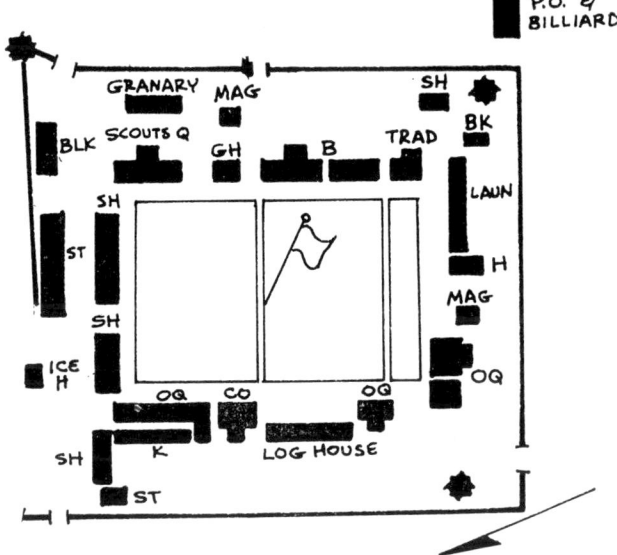

FORT ABERCROMBIE
N. D. — 1876

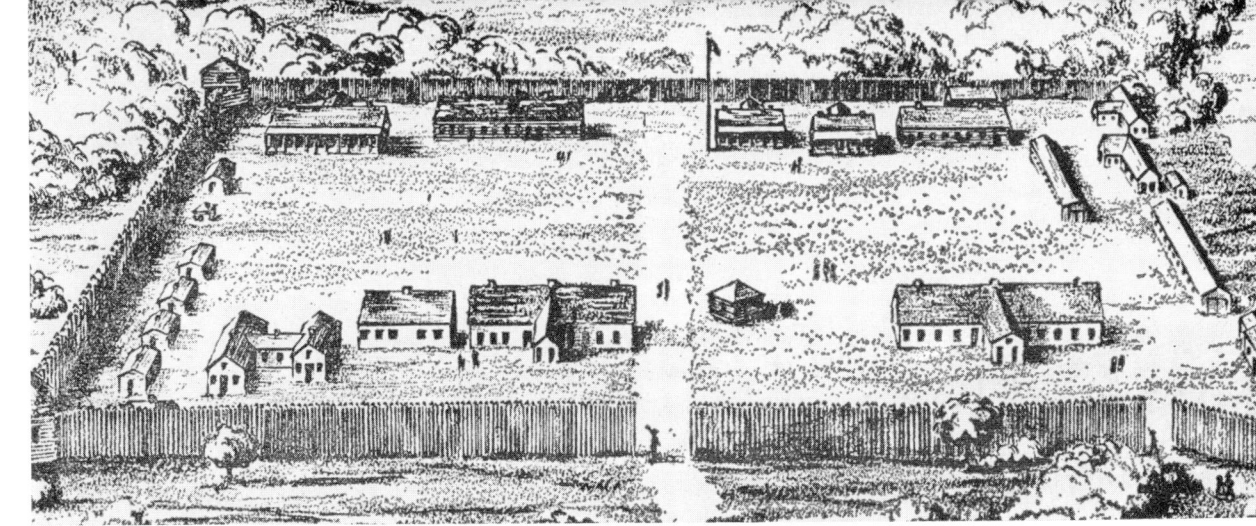

INDIAN ATTACKS proved need for 12-foot high stockade in this 1863 sketch of Fort Abercrombie. Sketch appears to be view from west.

SOUTHEAST BLOCKHOUSE was restored in 1938 in joint WPA-County project.

FORT ABERCROMBIE TODAY from center of parade ground, looking toward northeast blockhouse. Barracks and guardhouse were in row this side of stockade.

GUARD HOUSE and reconstructed stockade are next to Red River of the North. Guard house is original building, returned to Fort Abercrombie when it was restored. Bridge crosses river into Minnesota. Company barracks site is marked by sign to right of guard house.

87

Fort Totten, North Dakota

Hazards of being a mail man are many, especially in Indian occupied territory in the Dakotas after the Civil War.

The northern plains of North Dakota stretch from Montana on the west to Minnesota on the east, broken only by gullies, scattered boulders and rolling hills and punctuated on the east by Devil's Lake, 50 miles long and five to fifteen miles wide.

On the south side of this lake, the Army built a stockaded outpost in 1867 to protect an overland route cutting across the territory. "Fort Totten does not present exactly an enchanting aspect despite the fact that the lake serves as a setting," wrote the district commander, Colonel de Trobriand, of a visit in 1868.

Describing the original fort, 800 yards from the one whose remains can be seen today, de Trobriand wrote: "It is a long parallelogram formed by a palisade; at one end are the guard house, the prison, the saddlery, and the lodgings of the mule drivers; along the sides are the stables, the company barracks, the hospital, the warehouses and offices, and opposite the entrance at the back of the parallelogram, the officers' quarters."

The general didn't think much of the place. Stockades were getting out of style by 1868 and he said it gave the disagreeble air of a prison.

By the early seventies, this mud and log palisade had been abandoned in favor of a comparatively magnificent establishment nearby. That is what can be seen today, its 1875 appearance altered only by the shade trees lining the parade ground and splitting it into two equal parts.

It was about the time this new fort was being completed that the commercial mail scheme entered the Totten scene. Charles A. Ruffee, of Minneapolis, planned to "pony express" the mail overland from Fort Abercrombie to Fort Benton, Montana. He stationed two-man relay teams every 50 miles along the way who were to shunt the mail bags from station to station.

On paper, it looked fine.

But the first run out, the mail was overdue at Fort Benton, the tail end station on the line. Frank Palmer, the Ruffee man there, decided to head east until he came across the mailmen.

He went 300 miles, finally arriving at Fort Totten to be told that the riders had either been killed by Indians or deserted for less hazardous mail routes, and that he was out of a job.

Palmer stayed on at Fort Totten as a guide, leaving the mail carrying to the military which did it on a fort-to-fort basis.

TO GET THERE: *From Devil's Lake, N.D., take 20 south from city five miles to junction with state 57. Turn right to 57, take it about six miles to Fort Totten town and Indian Agency. Old fort is immediately south of town.*

IN 1870, FORT TOTTEN looked only a little like this plat. This was the plan, however. Today, fort actually looks like this with one exception. The second barracks from left, bottom row, was replaced by a gymnasium while Indian School used former post 1890–1960. (Redrawn from Surgeon-General Circular, 1870.)

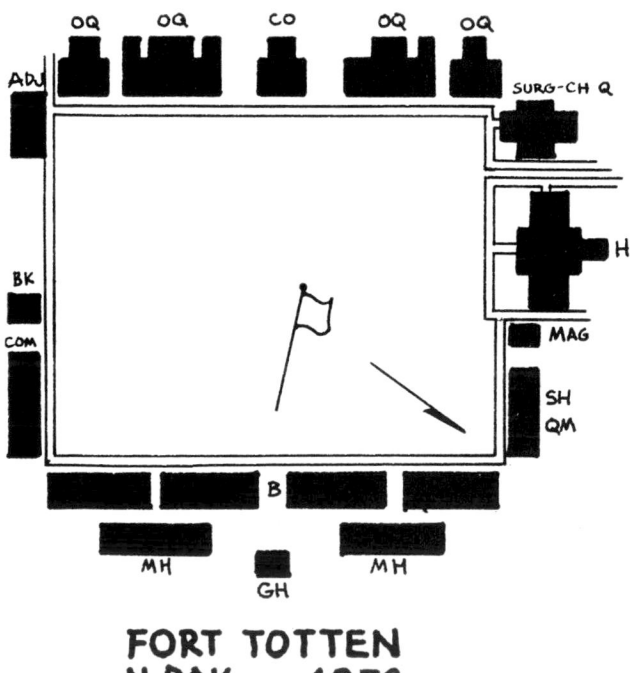

FORT TOTTEN N. DAK. — 1870

(Courtesy State Historical Society of North Dakota.)

IN 1871, DEPARTMENT headquarters directed that trees would be planted at Army Posts. Fort Totten had vague traces of them in 1878 (above), but by 1890 it had blossomed forth with trees existing today, though new bandstand is gone. In both pictures, officers' quarters are in row at left; hospital at far end, partly hidden in newer picture. Headquarters building is at left, front in older picture. Parade ground was 200 feet square, and almost all of these buildings remain today.

OFFICERS' QUARTERS were double storied, multiple-family affairs. This building housed four families. Two duplexes are at far end. Right set were reserved for the surgeon and chaplain.

SILENCE HAS SETTLED along piazza of barracks that once echoed to boots of soldiers. This is northeastern set of barracks.

EASTERN CORNER of fort included barracks, left, commissary storehouse, center, bakery. Bakery has bars on rear windows and tradition says it doubled as a guard house on occasion.

Fort Bridger, Wyoming

Part of Fort Bridger's attraction lies in its name, that of the most famous of the Indian scouts and fur trappers, Jim Bridger (1804–1881). He was the discoverer of the Great Salt Lake and the man about whom an Army colonel answered an economy order to discharge him as civilian scout: "Impossible of execution."

Bridger arrived at this spot in the southwestern corner of what is now Wyoming in 1842. He operated a mud and pole trading post and trapper rendezvous until Brigham Young's Mormons bought or forced him out in 1853. Originally the Mormons had set up a rival post 12 miles south for the emigrant trade, calling it Fort Supply.

At Bridger, they built several stone houses and enclosed them with a stone wall 400 feet square, 14 feet high. In 1857, they burned both Forts Bridger and Supply when Army troops were sent to enforce the laws of the United States on Brigham Young.

The troops wintered nearby, at a temporary Camp Scott, under mud and skin lean-tos. In the spring some soldiers were left behind to rebuild the fort, while the bulk of them went on to Salt Lake City, deserted by Mormons who had established defenses at Camp Floyd, 20 miles west of Provo, Utah.

The military stayed at Fort Bridger guarding the stage routes and serving as a base of operations for southwestern Wyoming and northeastern Utah. Its garrison was down to a sergeant's guard early in the Civil War, augmented by a volunteer company of mountainmen mustered by Judge W. A. Carter, post sutler.

Nevada and California volunteers and so-called "Galvanized Yankees" garrisoned Fort Bridger during the War, but did little to improve it. Three companies of ex-Confederate soldiers were there when the war ended. They celebrated their relief by regular Army troops in a questionable manner.

The regular troops arriving in 1868 found "grounds not policed, buildings out of order, flooring burned up, bridges burned, shade trees broken down," according to the Inspector-General's report. Although the commanding officer complained he had no men for maintenance, the report pointed out, "He had between three and four hundred men, with no duty but to care for the post."

Things were righted with not too much trouble, and soon the post took on an appearance still apparent. It was almost a square, with buildings facing the parade ground and a north-south branch of Black's Fork cutting the parade ground into two unequal parts.

Weeds, trees and mosquitos are abundant at the site now. In 1878 the fort was abandoned, reopened in 1880, and finally abandoned in 1890. Buildings were sold or allowed to deteriorate. Late in the twenties the state bought much of the property and the Carter heirs donated lots flanking the entrance. Gradual restoration is taking place, one barracks has been rebuilt as a museum, and all building sites have been posted.

TO GET THERE: *Fort Bridger is on the south side of U.S. 30 South, immediately next to town of Fort Bridger. It is 22 miles east of Evanston, Wyoming, 82 miles west of Rock Springs.*

FORT BRIDGER was a major post in the eighties. It had eleven barracks of various sizes, six double-set officers' quarters. The stockaded Trading Post served at various times as a station for Pony Express, Overland Stage Line, and Wells Fargo. (Redrawn from SHS data.)

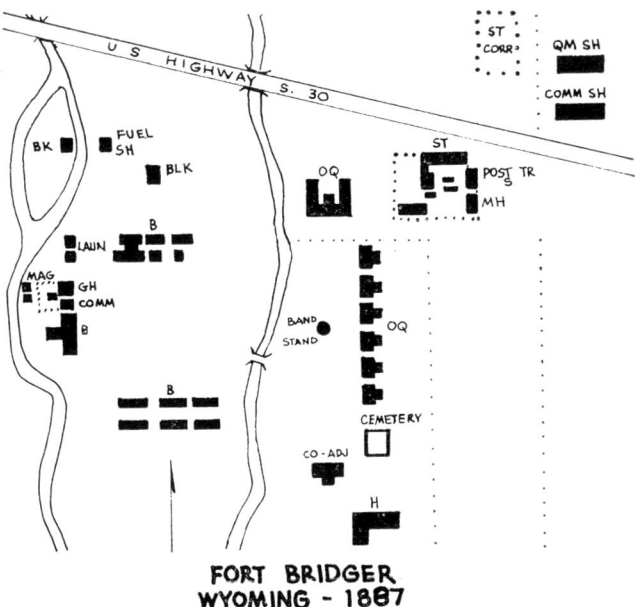

FORT BRIDGER
WYOMING - 1887

JUST BEFORE IT WAS ABANDONED, Fort Bridger looked like this in 1889. Plat's six southern barracks are in foreground. Present museum is restored building on site of large barracks to left of flagpole.

MORMON WALL, once 14 feet high, can be seen behind these crumbling buildings. On plat these appear as guardhouse and commissary.

POST MASCOT, Thornburgh, died in 1888, has fancier tombstone than many an early settler or soldier.

POST HOSPITAL was at this point, administration building beyond it on other side of the two trees. Post cemetery, right, has graves of Bridger's daughter and Judge W. A. Carter, Wyoming pioneer.

ONCE A BARRACKS, now a museum, building at left is completely rebuilt. Commissary and guard house, to right, are ready to collapse.

NEW GUARD HOUSE appears on plat as middle building, front row, north group of barracks. This is a complete restoration. Wagon on right was used on Wyoming-Idaho trails in eighties.

OFFICER'S ROW contains one original log building. It is protected from elements by modern second roof. View is from site of large officers' quarters next to post trader, looking south.

Camp Ruby, Nevada

It was a "frying pan into the fire" situation on September 24, 1862, for the 3d Infantry California Volunteers. That was when they volunteered to pay their own way to the battlefields of the East.

As Colonel P. Edward Connor, their commander, wrote the general-in-chief of the Army, "The men enlisted to fight traitors, and . . . will authorize the paymaster to withhold $30,000 of pay now due if the government will order it east, and it pledges General Halleck never to disgrace the flag, himself, or California."

As requests of this type always go, regardless of the war, the answer came back: you are needed where you are.

Connor and his men at this time were at Ruby Valley, Nevada. Just ten days before they had officially established Camp Ruby at the southern end of the valley and about 70 miles southeast of Elko, Nevada. Without attaching ulterior motives to the patriotic offer of the regiment, it just may be that the situation at Camp Ruby influenced them more than a little bit.

They had been in service a year, walked 600 miles, some of it in the 122 degree heat of the Nevada desert. Not long after they arrived at the site of the camp, winter set in and it became obvious that they would be at that point until spring.

Timber was cut and hauled to erect winter quarters, a store house, and other required buildings. Most of them were merely low walls and roofs over four-foot deep holes. As was common with these temporary forts, the work was done by soldiers.

Ruby was neither elaborate nor luxurious. In 1868 the hospital burned down and the commanding officer blamed it on a fireplace spark that ignited the "condemned sheeting on the 7-foot high ceiling."

Even before his arrival, Connor reported: "I understand Ruby Valley is a bleak, inhospitable place—no forage, nor lumber to build with, and, as far as the Indians are concerned, entirely unnecessary to keep troops there."

This last thought could have been wishful thinking. The troops were active throughout the seven year life of the post, especially against the Piute and Goshute Indians who were on the warpath for about a year. Shotgun riders were provided for the Overland stages, effectively cutting the ambush rate. And a small boy had to be rescued from two years of Indian captivity.

With the postwar days of expansion, transcontinental stage coach lines came to an end, and the need for Camp Ruby disappeared. The records indicate a strange contradiction, not explained or elaborated upon further.

It seems that in October, 1867, the commanding officer requested permission to destroy the liquor "and shut up the saloon" of a certain employee of the stage line "accused of selling liquor to soldiers and Indians."

Barely two years later, the same civilian petitioned for the custodian's job if the fort was to be abandoned. In his endorsement to the request, the post's commander called him "true, loyal, faithful, honest, upright, and a man of high integrity and I firmly think the care of the post could not be in better hands."

Obviously, the post had changed commanders in the interval between 1867 and 1869. It was abandoned on September 20, 1869, and the ex-saloon keeper became the custodian.

THIS IS ROUGH layout of how camp might have looked, based on traces remaining.

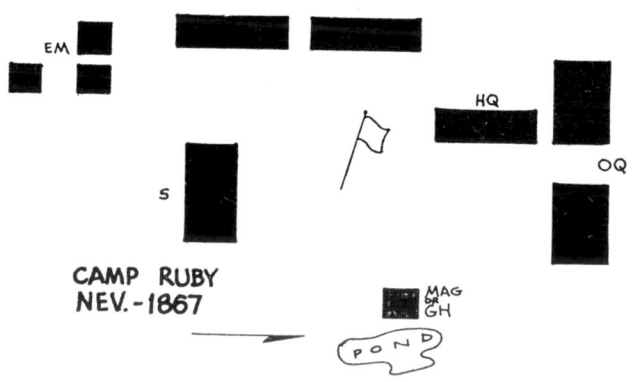

TO GET THERE: *Stock up on gas and water as route is long and dusty with only one gas station (regular 50¢ a gallon). From Wells, Nevada, take U. S. 93 south to state 11, 22 miles. Turn right, go 5 miles on 11, leave it by bearing left at first junction. In 7 miles, bear left again. Road turns to dust in 2 miles, stay on it about 30 miles more. Fort Ruby Ranch, privately owned, is set back from road on left. Alternate route from Elko and Halleck over route 11 is through Secret Pass (elevation 6,574), winding dirt road; route 46 from Elko through Harrison Pass (elevation 7,247) is no better.*

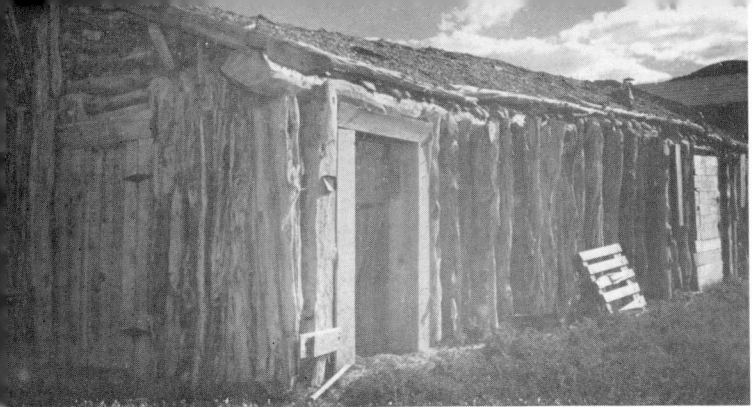

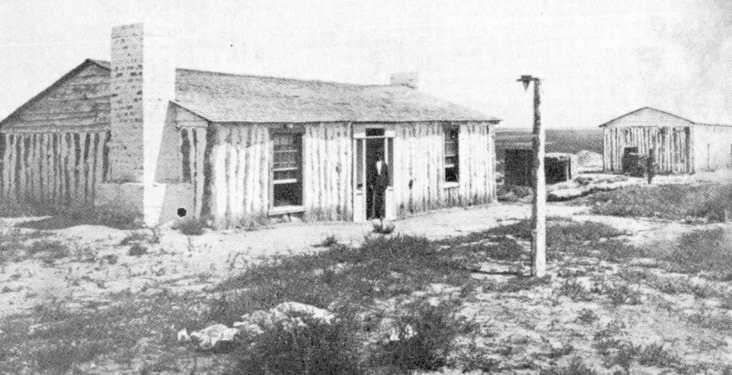

CAMP RUBY today retains traces of old buildings. This building is variously identified as officers' quarters, post office, and storeroom. It could be one of the buildings in old photograph, but is now a tool shed at Roy Harris' ranch.

(Courtesy James D. Horan Western Americana Collection.)

CAMP RUBY about 1867 was somewhat less than palatial. This was officers' quarters, probably a duplex, two rooms per family.

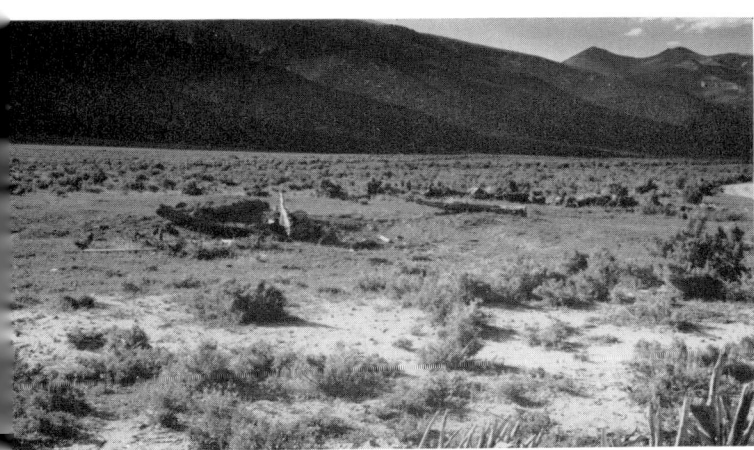

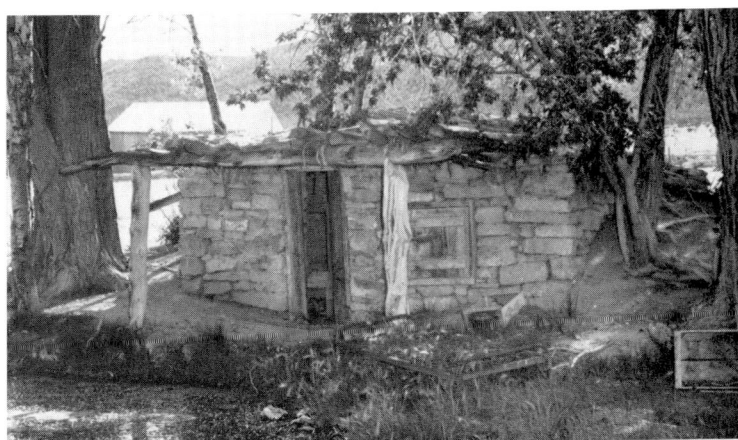

BARRACKS once were dug into Ruby Valley along line of slight indentations, center, Ruby Mountains are behind. Most of Ruby's movable material went to Camp Halleck upon abandonment.

SOLDIERS OR INDIANS built this stone shelter at Camp Ruby. Next to quarters' area, it could have been magazine, guard house, or living quarters. Spring in its front yard is almost an oasis in arid Ruby Valley.

SOUTH SIDE of supposed officers' quarters. Building to left is ranch house. Ruby Mountains are in background.

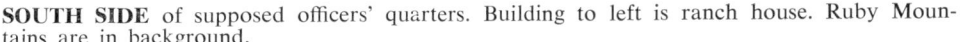

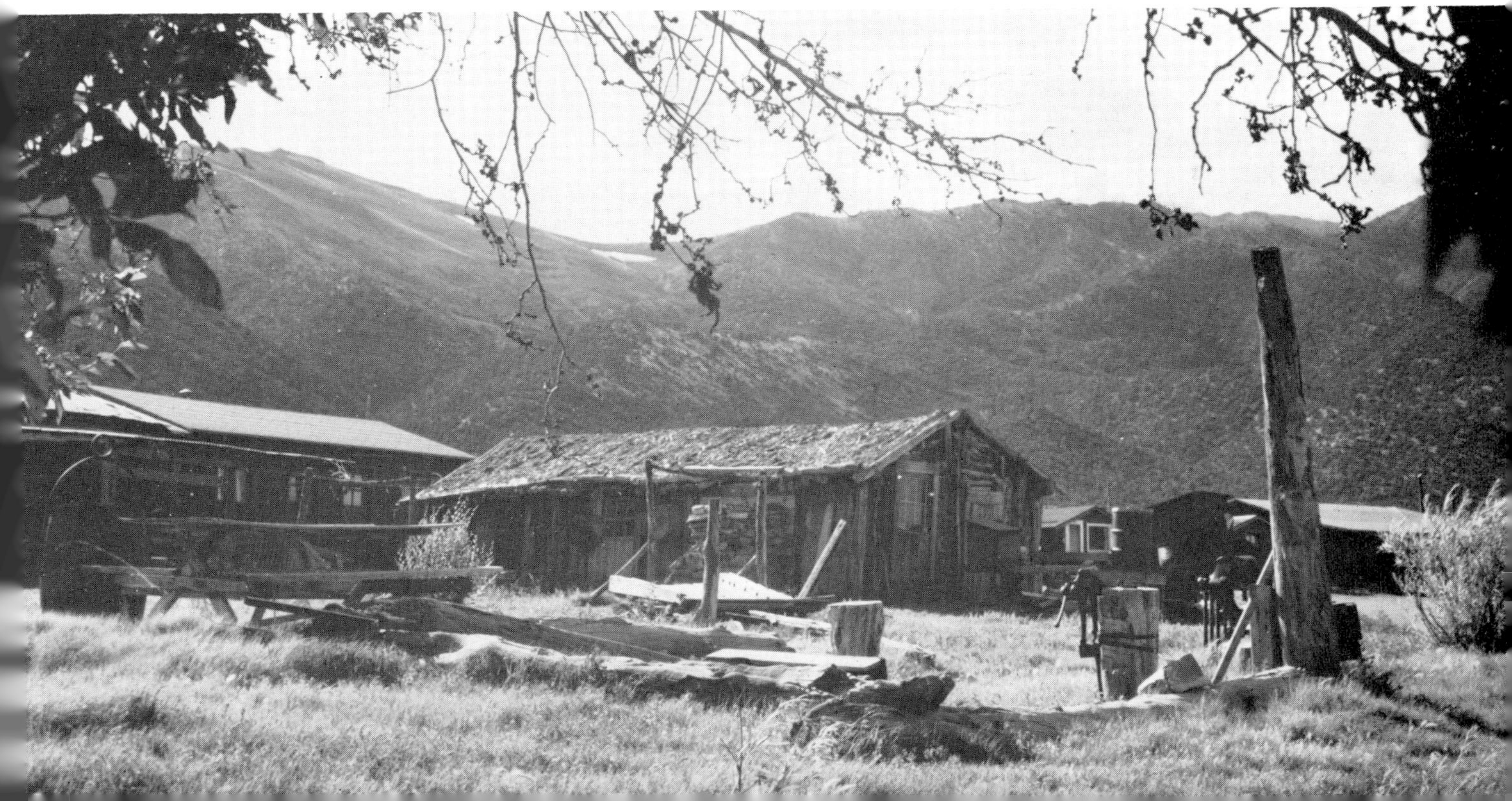

Fort Halleck, Nevada

Between the forces of nature, Fort Halleck didn't need any Indian wars to make things lively, but it had its full share.

At the foot of the eastern slope of Nevada's East Humboldt mountains, Halleck was established on July 26, 1867, by two companies of the 8th cavalry. They found a site beside a mountain stream with good grass land and plenty of timber, and protection from the elements from the north, east and west. On that hot summer day they didn't know that temperatures of 50 below 0° were encountered during the winter.

Halleck's 6,000 foot elevation presented a problem to the soldiers who were not used to the altitude. The surgeon reported that altitude sickness came from any type of violent exercise, but it can be assumed with safety that this was soon overcome.

In January, 1869, a smallpox epidemic hit the employees of the Central Pacific Railroad, claiming between three and five deaths a day near Halleck Station, 12 miles away. The soldiers had been vaccinated the previous fall, but this was repeated with all doubtful cases and a rigid quarantine was established, keeping out of the camp anyone from the infected district.

ADOBE AND LOG BUILDINGS, shingled roofed, surrounded Halleck's parade ground. Barracks were 87 by 25 feet. A frame commanding officer's quarters stood at bottom left corner of parade ground until it burned in 1873. Officers' adobes were 32 by 36 feet, occupied by two families. (Redrawn from NA data.)

A month later there was another calamity. Before dawn, hurricane strength winds blew off the roofs of the commissary, guard house, one of the barracks, and an officers' quarters. The storm lasted until almost noon, and was followed by a heavy snowfall. The uncomfortable and cramped winter of 1869 was long remembered by Halleck veterans.

Originally called Camp Halleck, the post was redesignated a fort on April 5, 1879. It averaged between 148 men in 1870 to less than 100 in 1875, and was down to 35 in June, 1877. That was when the commanding officer and all 58 able bodied cavalrymen left for Idaho and the Nez Perce War.

The fort was a busy one until it was abandoned on December 1, 1886. The rail, stage, and telegraph lines needed protection from both red and white marauders. Sometimes, though, it seemed that the Army needed protection, too . . . such as the climax of the 1882 Independence Day celebration. That was when a cowboy shot and killed a trooper at 1:30 a.m., July 5, in McKean's Saloon in Halleck Station.

TO GET THERE: *From Elko, Nevada, go east on U.S. 40 for 20 miles to state 11. Turn right to Halleck, Nevada, one mile. Continue south through Halleck on dirt road 17 miles to stone marker left side of road. Fort site was at back end of privately owned meadow, south of marker.*

COTTONWOOD CREEK

LODGE · LAUN · HQ · MH · MH · B · ST · OQ · GH · MAG · ST · OQ · COMM · COMM SH · BLK · H

FORT HALLECK NEV.-1879

COMMISSARY STORE HOUSE, northern corner of parade ground, is marked by large mounds amidst trees.

96

HEADQUARTERS BUILDING or officers' quarters stood here where only traces of rock walls remain. This is at top left hand corner of parade ground and part of parade ground can be seen to right.

PARADE GROUND, East Humboldt mountains in rear. Store houses were along row of trees at left, officers' row was along distant row of trees. Clumps of brush left of center trees mark mounds of guard house and magazine site.

Fort Boise, Idaho

Gold and silver fever beckoned, and adventurers followed, disregarding Indian threats and stories of bloody massacres. In Idaho Territory in the sixties, the idea was, move in and the Army will keep the peace.

Somewhere around 15,000 miners shared this belief. Disruption to the peace became so bad that the over extended Department of the Pacific had to take action.

On June 28, 1863, a troop of Oregon Cavalry made camp a few miles over the Idaho line and about 50 miles southeast of the American Fur Company's abandoned Fort Boise trading post.

Work began by locating a sawmill 10 miles away. On the Fourth of July the commanding officer, a brevet major with the unwieldy name of Pinkney Lugenbeel, celebrated the holiday by starting his troops to building barracks for five companies.

He lamented the difficulty of obtaining materials. "The very great loss of oxen, mules, and horses has driven many freighters from the road," he reported, "and we may find some difficulty in having all of our supplies brought forward this season."

For a start, then it was decided to get as much accomplished before the snows closed in. Then 25 men would remain at Boise, the rest spending the winter at Fort Walla Walla, Washington.

Trains of miners and emigrants increased the next year. So did the depredations by the Shoshone Indians of the Snake river. Lengthy patrols crossed the barren Idaho table lands, keeping the peace between the Indians and helping law officers in the mushrooming mining camps.

Fort Boise was centrally located for troops to move quickly to hot spots of activity. Between 1863 to 1879, it was almost a continual base of operations against Indians. During the Bannock Indian War of 1876, it was the field headquarters for the armies chasing the elusive Nez Perce.

In 1879, Fort Boise was renamed Boise Barracks. It maintained a small cavalry force until 1913. After World War I it was abandoned by the War Department, and is used by the Veterans Administration.

FORT BOISE could trace most of these buildings to 1864. Its five barracks were replaced by two that measured 90 by 30 feet, detached kitchen and mess room to the rear. Officers had three stone quarters, married soldiers used seven log buildings. (Redrawn from NA data)

GH   ORD SH

K B

LIB

OQ

OQ

K B

OQ

SH   QM

SHOPS   BK CH   QM OFF

POND

COTTONWOOD CREEK

LAUN   H

FORT BOISE
IDAHO-1877

TO GET THERE: *Fort Boise site is north of downtown Boise, Idaho, at 5th and Fort streets. Upon entering Veterans Administration center, turn right. Follow road that parallels fence one-quarter mile. Fort marker and building number 6, ex-paymaster's office, are on left. Two officers' quarters are on bluff behind, part of officers' row built in 1890.*

BARRACKS OR OFFICE built in 1864 is now used by Veterans Administration Loan Guaranty Division. A marker, only official trace of Fort Boise, is near this building. Building was used as paymaster's office at one time, somewhat similar to present use.

OLDEST BUILDING at old fort is this former officer's quarters, built in 1863. It stands on slight bluff above the 1864 paymaster's office. Director of VA center now occupies it.

(Courtesy of Idaho Historical Society.)

AT THE TURN of century, Fort Boise looked like this. Officers' row is in foreground, parade ground and barracks in center. City of Boise was slight distance from fort at this time; today city surrounds the fort site.

VARIOUS STAGES of construction can be seen in this 1870 building, now VA staff residence. Earlier construction appears to have been low wing on right, double story being later addition.

Fort Walla Walla, Washington

There were two Forts Walla Walla. One is now underwater. The other is a veterans hospital which can claim direct descendency from the original but with not much more authority than the original. The second fort was involved in just about every Indian War of the seventies and eighties. It may be that its namesake contributed even more to its country, and without knowing it.

To be specific, all the original Fort Walla Walla gave was dinner for a Methodist missionary and medical doctor named Marcus Whitman. Out of that dinner came a goodly portion of the Pacific northwest, however.

In October, 1842, Dr. Whitman was dining at the Hudson's Bay Company's Fort Walla Walla. Enroute to Oregon as a missionary, he had been the first American to take his wagon beyond Fort Hall, Idaho, also a Hudson's Bay post. The company had spread the idea that west of Fort Hall was impassable to wagon traffic, and he turned his wagon into a cart to get through.

ONLY THE OFFICERS' QUARTERS and post cemetery, to the south of plat, remain from Fort Walla Walla. Veterans Administration Hospital buildings now occupy sites of barracks and guard house. (Redrawn from NA data.)

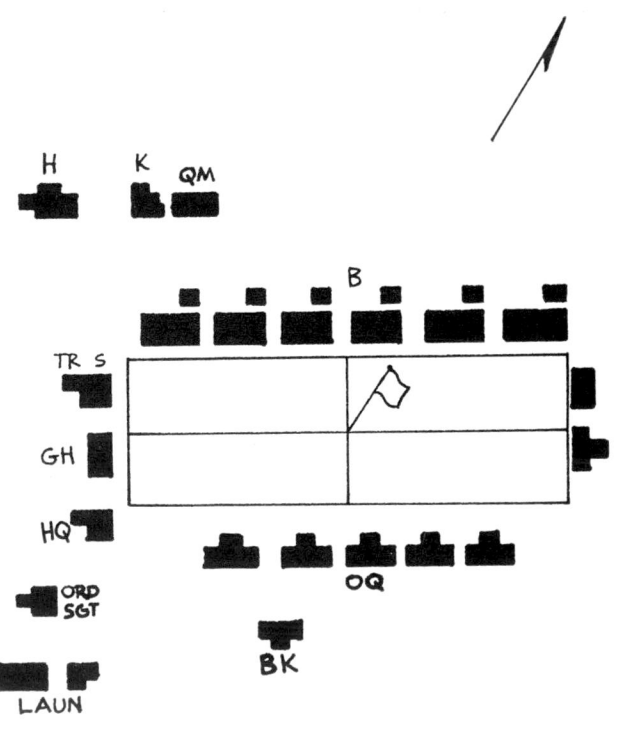

FORT WALLA WALLA
WASH - 1877

During dinner, someone announced that Englishmen had settled in the vicinity of what is now Okanogan, Washington.

"Hurrah for Oregon!" cried a Canadian, "America is too late, and we have got the country!"

Considering that an Englishman had uttered this, it was a battle cry for Dr. Whitman.

He decided to warn Washington, D.C., that Britain had designs on the Northwest. He took a roundabout route, to say the least. His road to Washington was through Colorado, New Mexico, and parts east, arriving at his destination five months later.

When he learned that the area was to be settled by a vote, it might be said that Dr. Whitman stuffed the ballot box. Through talks, articles and broadsides, he passed the word that an emigrant train was to leave from Missouri in June, 1843. This and other trains poured enough people into Oregon that when voting time came, the citizens selected an American, non-slave status, settling both questions.

But Dr. Whitman's dinner wasn't the only contribution made by Fort Walla Walla, nor was it his own. He and his family established a mission, only to be massacred by Indians in 1847.

The military fort was established east of the fur fort in 1858, lasting off and on until 1910. During that period, its troops were involved in the Modoc, Sheepeater, Nez Perce and Bannock Wars, plus just about every other Indian ruckus in the northwest. The matter of providing escorts for Lieutenant Robert Mullan, an engineer who was running a road from Fort Benton, Montana, sometimes occupied half the garrison.

TO GET THERE: *From center of Walla Walla go south to Veterans Administration hospital. Officers' quarters are along southern edge of old parade ground. Cemetery is within city park and camping grounds immediately south of hospital; return to highway and make two right turns to get to it as there is no direct road from hospital.*

(Courtesy National Archives.)

FORT WALLA WALLA in its heyday. Troops are formed in front of officers' quarters.

HISTORIC GRAVES are in old fort cemetery. Under shaft are buried 33 soldiers who died at Battle of White Bird Canyon. Their names are listed on the left block. Twelve of the Cottonwood dead are buried under right marker. Clearwater dead are unnamed, but also are buried in this cemetery. All three were Nez Perce fights. Walla Walla city plans to construct pioneer fort and town on rise behind cemetery, and now maintains area.

FORT WALLA WALLA was deactivated by Army in 1910, but the officers' quarters remain. These are same buildings seen in old picture; note the first-floor alcove and double windows, second floor, visible in both new and old picture.

Fort Dalles, Oregon

The Dalles, Oregon, started off with three religious missions, but within a few years it was one of the wildest river towns along the Columbia in northern Oregon.

Its location at the end of the 1,765-mile Oregon Trail had something to do with its active reputation, of course. This was the spot that wrapped up 100 days of dust, mud, snow and sun and here wagon trains were loaded on rafts and floated down the Columbia.

It was natural that the steep slopes perched above the rapids of the Columbia would be ready sites for saloons, outfitting and general stores, and the other less reputable attractions of a trade center.

And it was also a military center, serving in the 1850's as the headquarters for central and eastern Oregon. A detachment under Captain H. A. G. Lee came here in 1847 during troubles with the Cayuse Indians. They built a stockade and occupied the Methodist mission buildings, unofficially calling the whole business Fort Lee, after their commander.

On May 13, 1850, two rifle companies came from Fort Vancouver, Washington, to establish a supply depot at The Dalles (so-called by the Hudson Bay Company's French trappers who

said the basaltic walls of the Columbia reminded them of flagstones, "les dalles" in French).

A 10-mile square reservation was announced, forcing one trader to move his store, but this was soon cut to one mile. By 1851 the new post, Camp Drum, had a 124 by 20 foot log building as an officers' quarters and a 140 by 20 foot frame house for barracks. As of June 1, 1851, this presented only one problem according to the report of that date: both buildings needed ceilings to finish them.

A store house, stable, and sawmill completed the post. In 1853 the post became Fort Dalles, and in 1856 the log buildings were replaced by a semicircular layout to house a large garrison.

Eight infantry companies under Colonel George Wright were sent to Fort Dalles on March 28, 1856, arriving in time to rescue workmen who had been besieged in the Bradford store at the Cascades since March 26. A lieutenant named Philip Sheridan led a force from Fort Vancouver that assisted in this affair.

Some troops stayed at the post during the Civil War. The fort was abandoned in August, 1866. It was reoccupied for General Crook's expedition from December, 1866, to July 15, 1867, and then finally abandoned.

About this time the gold boom in Idaho and Oregon caused the federal government to build a mint at The Dalles. The boom ended after $105,-000 had been spent on construction. It was closed in 1868, still not complete and without having coined a cent.

TO GET THERE: *From downtown The Dalles, Oregon, take 15th street uphill (south) to Garrison street. Fort site is on southwest corner. A block away, 14th and Trevitt streets, is Colonel George Wright school on site of parade ground. Former U.S. mint is downtown at corner Second and Monroe streets.*

CLUSTER OF BUILDINGS made up fort by 1860. Two buildings north of flagpole probably were quarters for commanding officer and surgeon. Officers' quarters south of flag, the single building, actually was a set of five quarters. (Redrawn from approximate data in NA.)

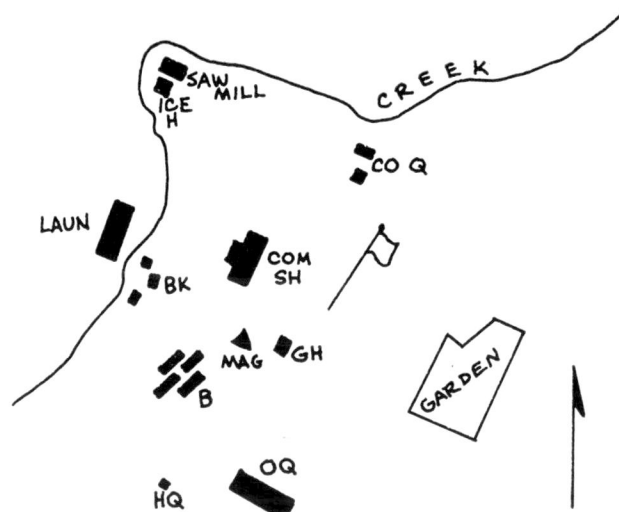

FORT DALLES
ORE.-1860

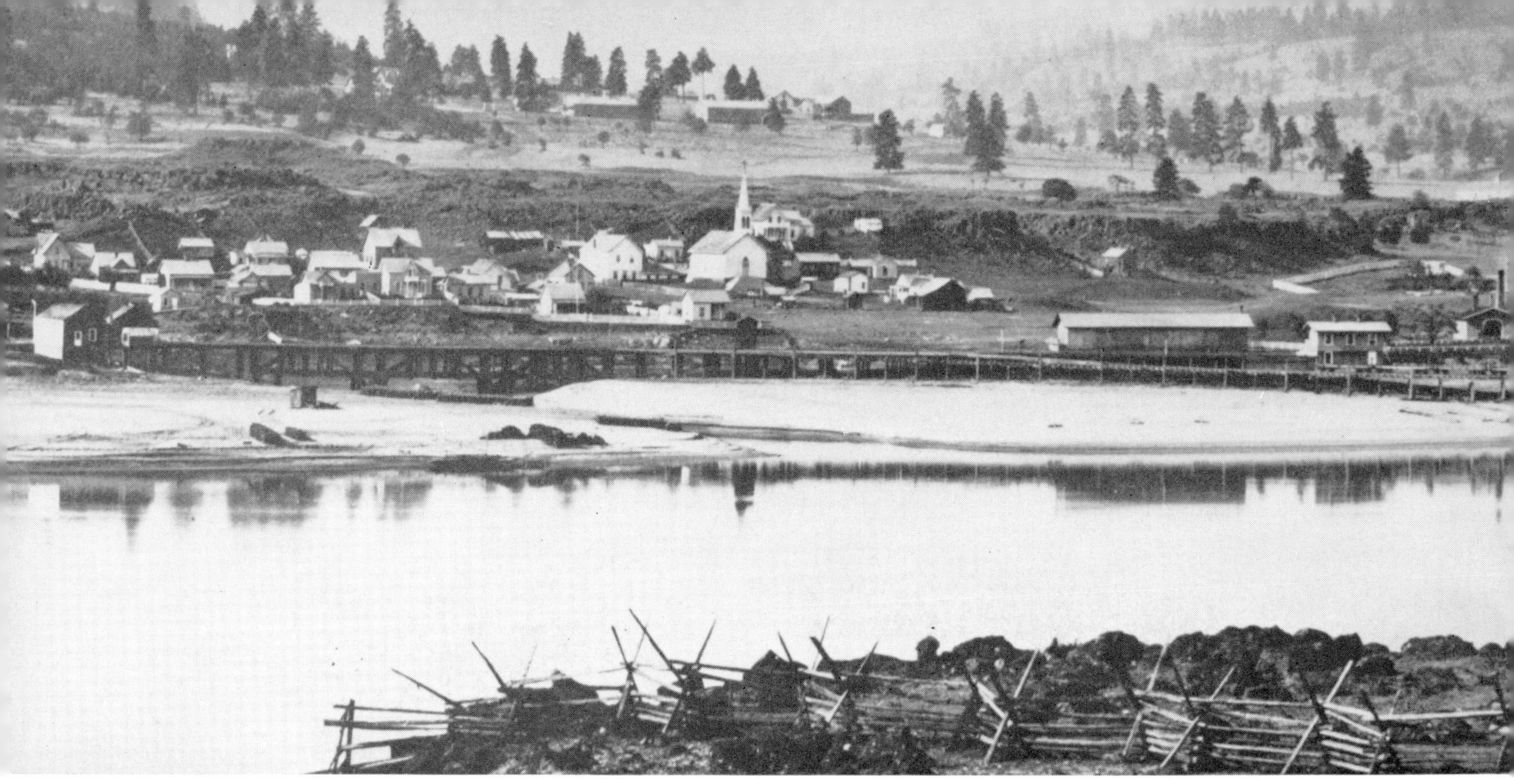

(Courtesy Oregon Historical Society.)

MOST PROMINENT BUILDING at The Dalles in 1860 was church, though town had more saloons than churches. Fort was re-built between 1858 and 1860 and new buildings can be seen on slopes above town. Barracks appear above church steeple. Infantry lived in one barracks, cavalry the other.

ONLY BUILDING LEFT at Fort Dalles is former surgeon's quarters, now a museum. Architect of Fort Dalles also designed Fort Simcoe, Washington. This building was next to commanding officer's quarters which burned in 1866.

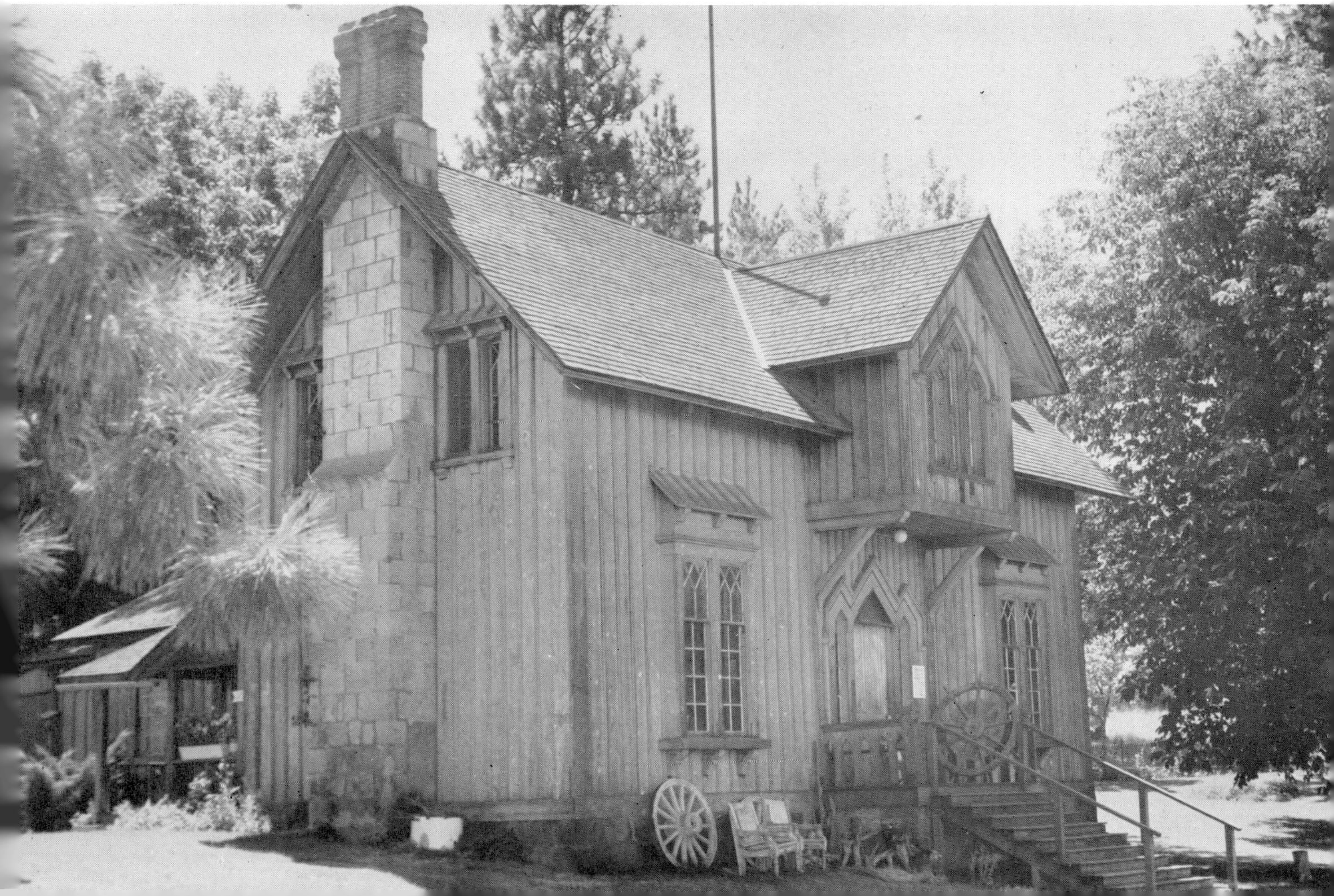

Guardians of the Rails

"I regard the building of these railroads as the most important event of modern times . . . A vast domain, equal to
two-thirds of the whole surface of the United States, has
thus been made accessible to the immigrant, and, in a military sense, our troops may be assembled at strategic points
and sent promptly to the places of disturbance, checking
disorders in the bud."

—General Sherman in his final report as General-in-Chief of the Army, 1883.

RUNNING THE thin ribbons of iron across plains and mountains and deserts was a task
undertaken by thousands of men in the last half of the nineteenth century.

With them, or within rifle range, were the soldiers of the Western Army. They spearhead-
ed the rails through Indian territory. And they kept the peace in the railroad camps—when
they weren't contributing their share of the disorder.

When the roads were built and the sooty engines came, the Army guarded against
the train robbers, both white and red. Some of their bases were adobe corrals shared with
telegraphers and agents. Others were large posts from which flying squadrons of infantry
and cavalry could be sent to restore peace.

The frontier truly was over when a rescuing Army no longer arrived with banners flying and bugles blowing, but aboard rattling coaches and boxcars, the engineer and fireman
in the lead.

Fort Ransom, North Dakota

Fort Ransom, North Dakota, was barely four months old when it was almost wiped out. And not by Indians, but by fire.

As described by Brevet Major George H. Crossman, the commanding officer of the new post, on October 10, 1867 "a most terrific prairie fire, accompanied by a perfect gale of wind . . . came upon us very suddenly, but owing to the fact that the full force of the fire did not strike us fair, we were enabled, with great exertion, to save the camp and post although both, and more especially the former, were in imminent danger.

Despite the loss of two civilians and 400 tons of hay and 200 cords of wood, the hearts of Department Headquarters at Fort Snelling were not stirred. Crossman wanted to buy hay from a local contractor, but was told: "The contractor ran a singular risk in putting up hay to sell, had the public hay not been burned, something sure to take place if desired."

It was suggested that he send most of his animals to other forts for the winter, keeping only the minimum at Fort Ransom, and "The animals then left may subsist on rats."

The immediate effect of this was a reduction in mail deliveries and wagon train escorts, the main reasons for locating Fort Ransom on the road between Forts Abercrombie and Totten. Before the fort went out of business in four years, its mission changed to protecting the railroad crews running the tracks through to Bismarck.

Ransom was a palisaded fort on the Sheyenne river at a place called Bear's Den Hillock. Rolling plains led up to it from the south. Low hills blocked its view to the north.

Indians were its prime concern and an 1869 order prescribed just what should be done during an Indian attack.

After the drummer sounded the assembly call, the troops were to line the rear of the parapet, the order declared. "As time is of the greatest importance in such contingencies, officers and noncommissioned officers will be held responsible that none is lost: timely action upon a scene of conflict is of vastly more importance than the personal appearance of the men, exactness as to which will not be required," it added generously.

Other orders during the fort's 1867-72 existence reveal housekeeping tasks that were probably magnified by the close quarters within the stockade.

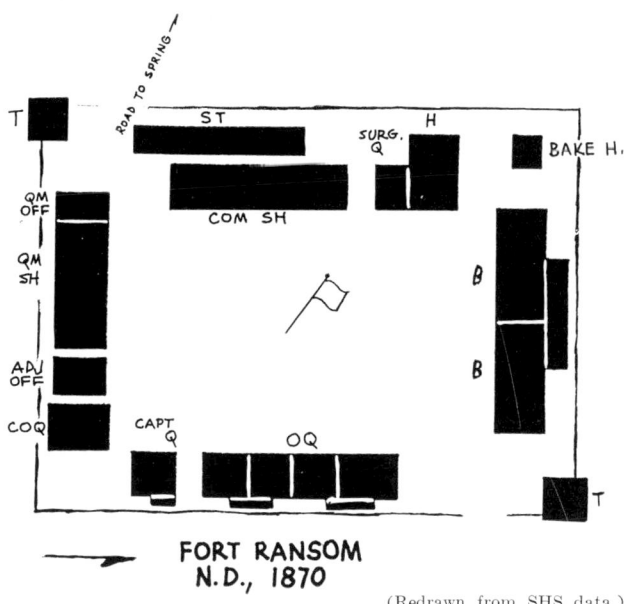

FORT RANSOM
N.D., 1870

(Redrawn from SHS data.)

FORT RANSOM was surrounded by this moat and a stockade 350 by 400 feet. Blockhouses were at this corner, the northeast, and opposite at southwest. Officers' quarters were single story high except two: the commanding officer's and that of Captain who commanded other company. All were in row to left of and facing flagpole.

Walking on the parade ground was prohibited in 1869 so the grass would grow. This probably didn't reduce either the drilling or jay walking.

Throwing ashes and garbage "upon the parapet, into the ditch, and even to some extent upon the parade" was noted in March, 1869. This was to end, an order directed. Instead, trash barrels were to be used.

Stray dogs were the next targets of general orders. On November 26, 1869, the order was: "No dogs will be allowed to run loose within the limits of the breastworks of this post and sentinels will be instructed to shoot every dog loose in violation of this order."

It is assumed this order was properly published to all dogs.

Department Headquarters also got into the housekeeping act. On February 15, 1871 it directed all posts to plant trees if they had not already done so. The absence of much foliage at the abandoned sites today indicates either this order wasn't followed, or the trees were carted off along with everything else when the forts were abandoned.

By 1872, many of Fort Ransom's soldiers were away from the fort. The railroad crews required continual protection, and several outposts were established along the tracks.

When the commanding officer had to spend more time at these outposts than at the fort, it appeared the fort was being left behind. It wasn't long before it became obvious that Ransom's value had ended, and it was abandoned on July 31, 1872.

TO GET THERE: *From Fargo, N.D., take Interstate 94 west 48 miles to state 32. Turn left follow route 32 for 50 miles to Lisbon. (A secondary road, left turn at Tower City from Interstate 94, cuts 11 miles from this route). At Lisbon, turn right on state 27, go 12 miles west to junction with secondary road that deadends here from north. Turn right, go north five miles. Fort Ransom is off road to right, south of Sheyenne river. State has placed information sign, parking area, reconstructed cabin at site.*

OPPOSITE VIEW OF fort site shows cellars of officers' quarters, foreground, and probably storehouse. Barracks faced north side of parade ground. Log building in background was reconstructed by State Park Board, is outside of stockade.

Fort Sidney, Nebraska

Sidney, Nebraska, was an "end of track" town long after End of Track did away with itself at Promontory Point, Utah.

Like the "life of the party" who is the little boy who hasn't grown up, Sidney continued to carouse and roustabout until its momentum finally was stopped by its own Vigilante movement. By that time, things were so bad that even the railroad, the instigator of the whole thing, wouldn't let through passengers alight at Sidney.

Sidney Barracks was established in 1867 at a point midway between the two Platte Rivers and 101 miles east of Cheyenne, Wyoming. It was a sub-post of Fort Sedgwick, Colorado, following the track crews of the Union Pacific.

The typical nomadic hangerson that followed the rail head poured into Sidney, the boom town that settled next to the Barracks. A year later End of Track had left, and with it much of the new town's population. The Barracks continued to protect the rails and the citizens, and in 1870 became Fort Sidney, independent of Fort Sedgwick.

Sidney might have met the fate of many other railheads towns, but the Black Hills gold discovery placed it in a strategic stage-railroad connecting point. In 1876, the Black Hills were opened to gold seekers. Daily freight traffic of a million pounds and 1,500 passengers passed through Sidney. Twenty-one saloons lined Front street, backed by the inevitable allied entertainments of the frontier.

Things got so boisterous that the firing of a 101 gun salute on the Fourth of July, 1877, drew the comment from the Sidney Telegraph: "Let it be stated for once that more than a hundred guns were fired in Sidney without an accident."

The fort's soldiers were active in keeping the peace at the same time some were active in breaking it. The activities at a roadhouse dance in 1881 were only slightly curtailed when a soldier shot himself dead; they merely moved the body to the corner so the music could continue. Two more bodies joined the first before the festivities ended.

Early another day John Mathews and his wife each emptied a six-shooter at a group of soldiers, wounding six or seven. The pair then barricaded themselves inside their roadhouse while the troopers riddled it with bullets. The soldiers blasted from the hip and shoulder, the couple dropped flat on the floor and the only thing hurt was the roadhouse.

Other than the routine patrols and peacekeeping activities, Sidney did not figure prominently in the history of the west. Some say its men were on the tail end of the post Little Big Horn expeditions. In the 1891 Battle of Wounded Knee, they arrived in time to clean up the field but not to fire any shots in anger.

Sidney's settled down now. The fort finally was abandoned, despite political opposition, in 1894. Today the site is broken up by shaded residential streets with only a couple of buildings, the old magazine, a converted stable, and the rifle range mounds to mark where once the advance of progress stopped momentarily . . . and then moved on.

TO GET THERE: *Sidney, Nebraska, is in western Nebraska, on U.S. 30, 117 miles west of North Platte and 101 miles east of Cheyenne, Wyoming. Site of Fort Sidney is one block south of highway immediately after entering city from east.*

EARLY SIDNEY BARRACKS had few buildings compared to the sketch ten years later. At this time only a small force was stationed here. (Redrawn from plat courtesy Robert Rybolt, Sidney, Nebraska.)

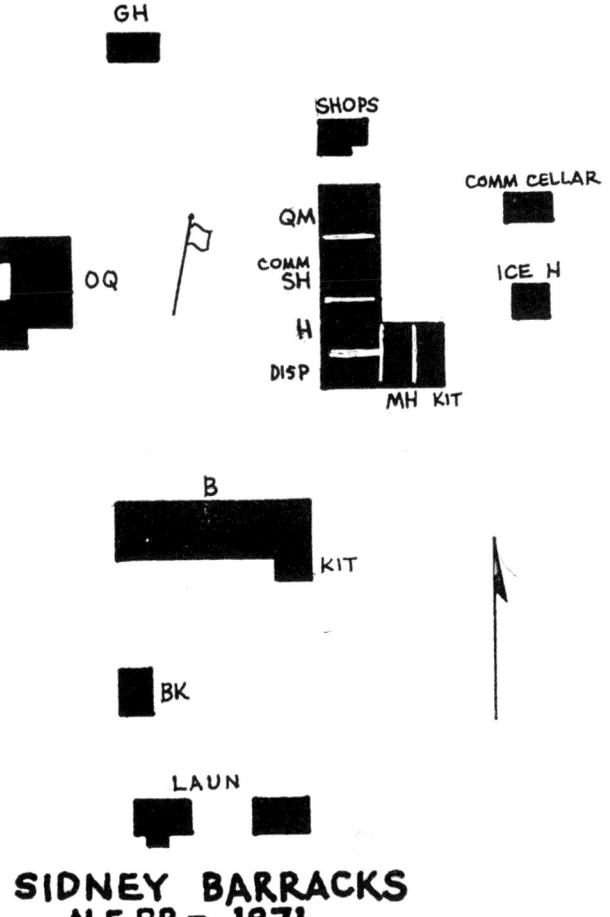

SIDNEY BARRACKS
NEBR.- 1871

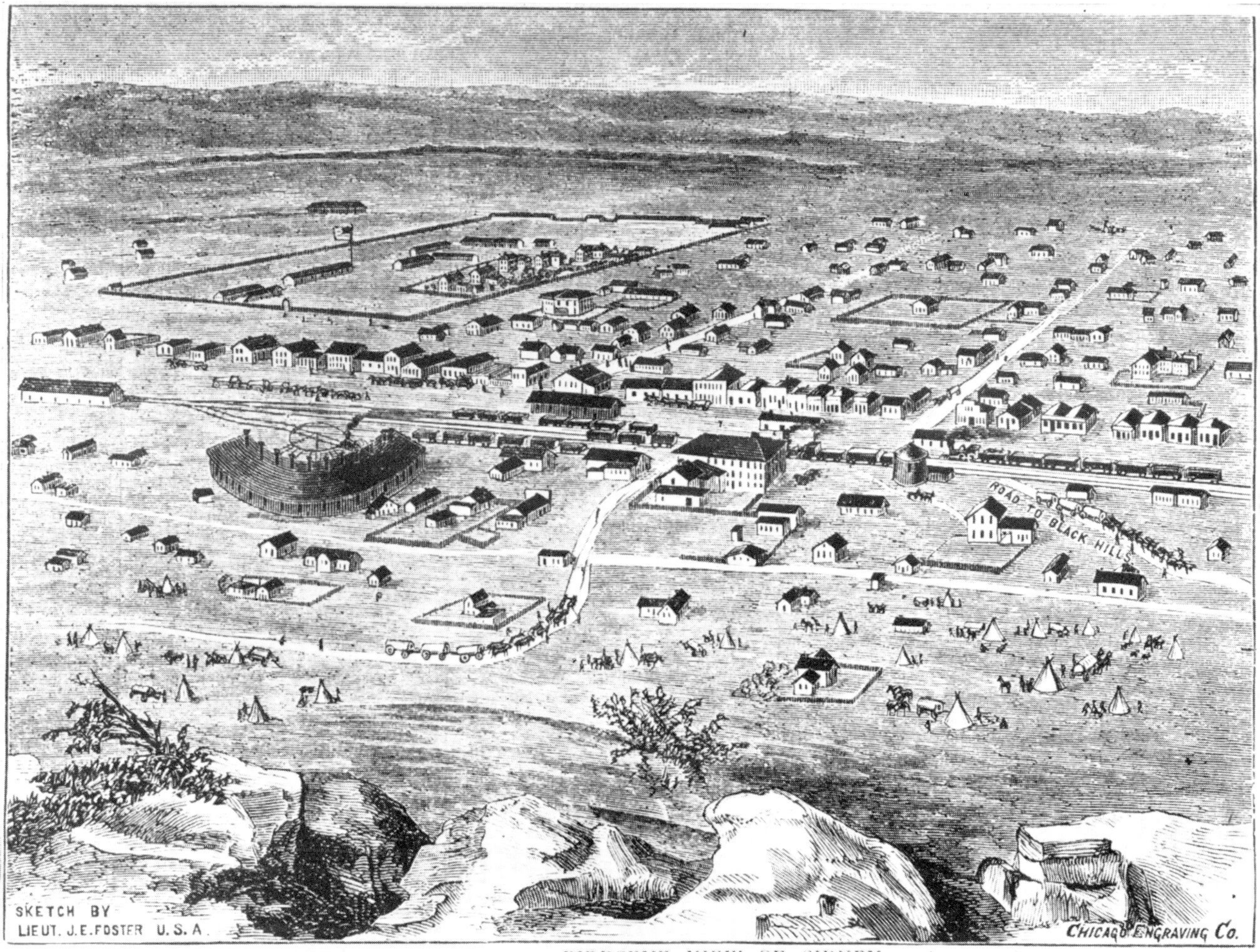

SKETCH BY
LIEUT. J.E. FOSTER U.S.A.

SIDNEY BARRACKS.   BIRDSEYE VIEW OF SIDNEY.   CHICAGO ENGRAVING Co.

(Courtesy Nebraska State Historical Society.)

FORT SIDNEY in the eighties was a rectangular affair 433 yards by 200, surrounded by picket fence. Five officer quarters were along the west side. Four were double sets. Rifle range was east of post and mounds can be seen today. Early sketch shows fort, also notorious Front street, along railroad, where the 21 saloons operated all night long.

MODERN DAY VERSION of early sketch. Fort Sidney was about where building roof appears in trees to left of near pole. Railroad can be seen straddling north-south street. Large building to right is believed to have been stable from fort. Picture is from bluff north of city on which Sidney Barracks had a blockhouse in the sixties.

HAUNTED OFFICERS' QUARTERS are on Sixth Avenue. Local legend claims officer's wife died from fall down stairs one October night. Now, she walks stairs every October, though current owners deny any face-to-face meetings.

MAGAZINE NOW serves as bedroom of modern house two blocks from old officers' quarters. When fort was abandoned, buildings were sold. Some were shifted, others converted on the spot. Soldier graves were moved from cemetery to Fort McPherson in early 1920's. While locating those of military, Army found "sunset to sunrise" graves, unofficial burials made after dark. Some still had ropes around their necks and one had barbed wire.

Fort D. A. Russell, Wyoming

Fort D. A. Russell started life with a bustle in 1867, and never really settled down. Even today it survives actively as a segment of Warren Air Force Base, only a mile from the capitol of Wyoming at Cheyenne.

But when it was founded as the Post on Crow Creek on July 21, 1867, to protect the Union Pacific railroad crews, the post was the only thing around. It didn't take long for the "end of track" types to arrive, even though the rails were still at Julesburg, Colorado, 100 miles away.

The U. P. had announced that Cheyenne was to be a division point. That signalled ready cash to the speculators, gamblers, and other assorted characters. On August 8, 1867, the army post was officially named after the Civil war hero of a battle near Opequon, Virginia. The same month, a quartermaster depot was built next to it, named Camp Carlin after, to a certain misspelled extent, a Captain Carling.

While the citizens of new Cheyenne were settling their townsite claims, soldiers set to work on what was to become one of the most elaborate posts of the Indian wars. It became so extensive, in fact, that when the troops were deployed every

spring to guard the railroad, a report complained that left behind were "hardly enough men to perform the guard duty and other necessary work for so large a post."

When the Indian trouble of 1868 got hotter, a company of volunteers was organized in Cheyenne to protect the fort—and perhaps to convince the War Department that Cheyenne had a definite need for the soldiers (and their payroll).

Camp Carlin became Cheyenne Depot or "Quartermaster Depot at Cheyenne" in 1871 and was absorbed into the fort in 1888. This had a single barracks for the 42-man company, a set of quarters for the married enlisted men and three sets for the officers. It depended upon D. A. Russell for hospital services and, unfortunately, according to an 1875 report, for water.

The latter came from Crow Creek, shared jointly by D. A. Russell and the QM depot. It flowed past Russell first. "Receiving the drainage of that post," the report complained, it "becomes the receptacle of the slops from the laundresses quarters, as well as the filth from its cavalry stables."

Troops from D. A. Russell were involved in most of the Indian scrapes of the Dakota and Wyoming area. Frequent changes of the garrison and commanders became the rule rather than the exception.

Next door in Cheyenne, "end of track" arrived in November 1867. The first train was piled high with shacks, furniture, building segments, and people.

"Here's Julesburg!" was the announcement as the train pulled in. Parts of buildings were thrown off even before it stopped. No delay was brooked in raising the roof, both literally and figuratively.

The Army was called out occasionally to calm matters, but vigilantes usually settled things. At times, it was only a matter of semantics that determined what vigilante action was an execution and what mob action was a murder.

TO GET THERE: *From capitol in Cheyenne, Wyoming, take Randall avenue west one mile. Obtain pass at gate of Warren Air Force Base. To reach Camp Carlin site, continue on Randall avenue, turn left at First street. Granite monument near railroad crossing marks site. Fort D. A. Russell diamond parade ground is at end of Randall avenue.*

UNUSUAL DIAMOND SHAPE made possible for all eleven barracks to edge parade ground without requiring unreasonable size. Parade ground measured 1,040 feet from north to south, 800 feet east to west. Barracks were 30 by 80 feet. Wooden barracks were replaced by brick construction in 1880. (Redrawn from Surgeon-General Circular, 1875.)

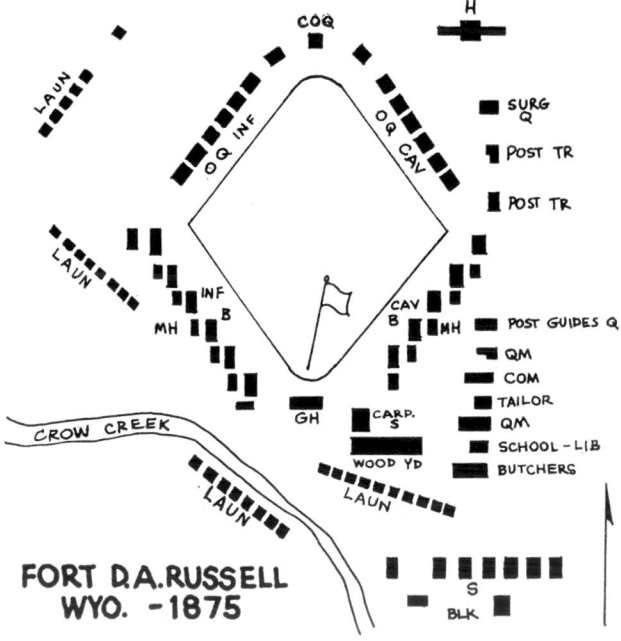

FORT D.A. RUSSELL
WYO. -1875

(Courtesy National Archives.)

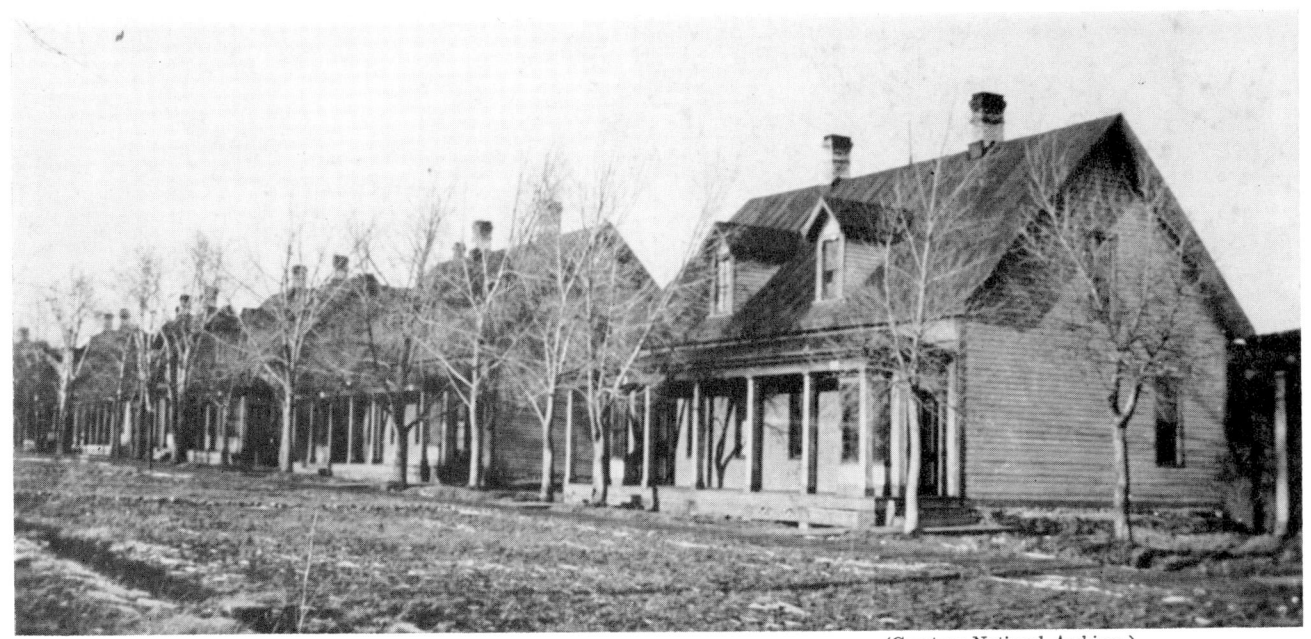

OFFICERS' QUARTERS, 1875, had ulterior motive in mind: one side of double set was for captain of company, other side was for his two lieutenants. Records don't say how wives liked this. Fort was renamed Fort Francis E. Warren in 1930 after Wyoming senator whose daughter married John J. Pershing when he was stationed at post.

ORIGINAL ENTRANCE TO FORT D. A. RUSSELL is flanked by trees planted in 1870. View is almost like old picture. Officers' quarters, behind trees, are now brick but have same basic plan. Former commanding officer's house is at left of center in picture. Stone marks old main gate; on plat this is near post trader's building. Modern Warren Air Force Base's main buildings are immediately east.

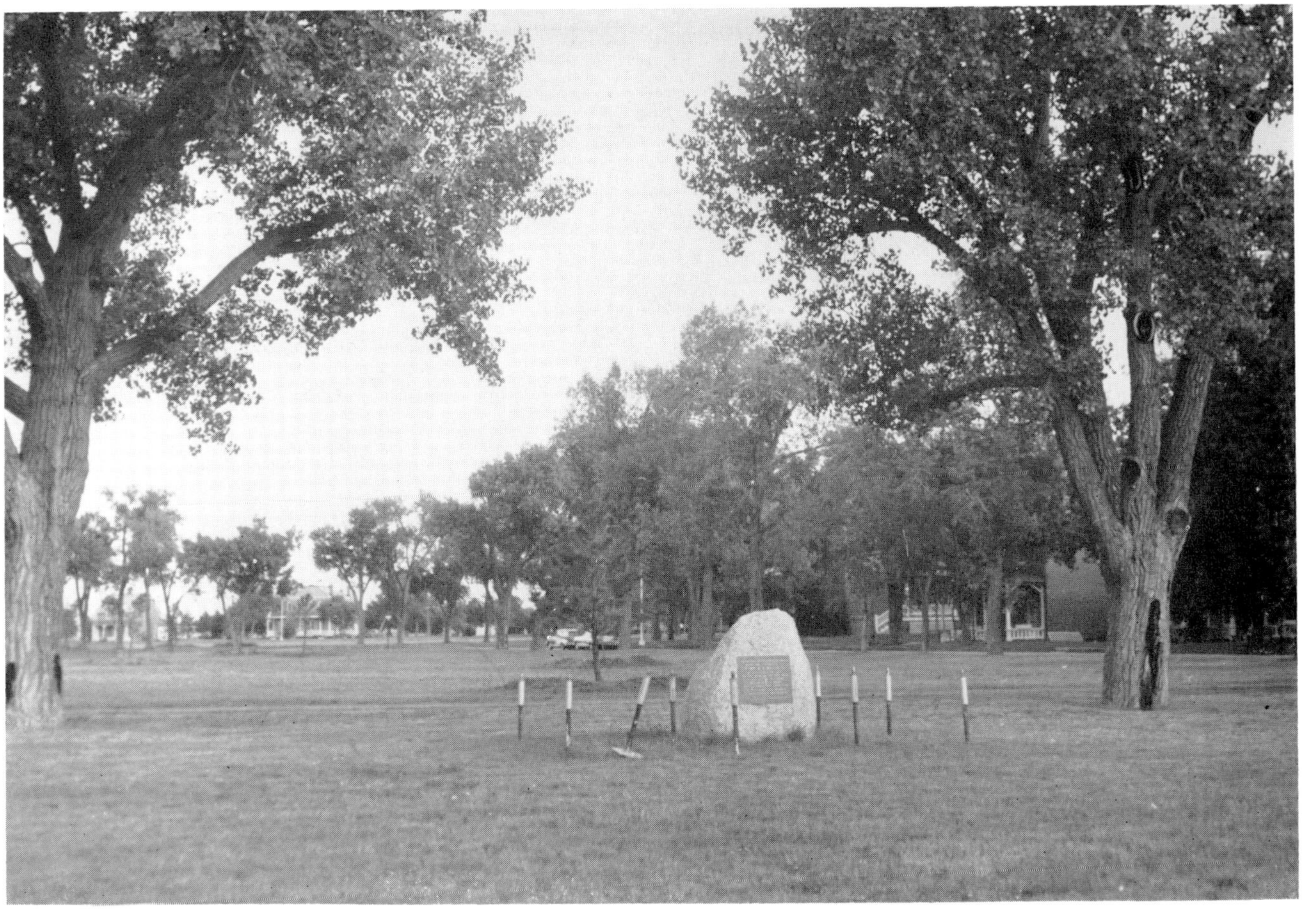

PERSHING'S HOUSE when he was at fort in 1912 stands along row of infantry officers' quarters. This view is across parade ground from barracks. Before World War II, post was third largest in country, had largest maneuver area.

OLD CEMETERY is still in use. It holds graves of dead from many abandoned forts and has outgrown original boundaries. Can be located to northeast of hospital on plat.

Fort Sanders, Wyoming

October 29, 1868, was a night to remember in Laramie, Wyoming. That was the night when Fort Sanders' post town declared war on the outlaws. Five hundred vigilantes swooped down on the gangs' hangouts—the Belle of the West dance hall, in particular—and the grandest gunfest in Laramie history took place.

Beside it, the Army battles from Sanders looked like Saturday afternoon marksmanship practice. Most of the town wound up in the fray, especially after simultaneous raids didn't quite come off on schedule. The scoreboard the next morning: five dead, 15 wounded.

But a temporary peace had come to Laramie. It calmed to a quiet roar the "hell on wheels" town that came with the railroad earlier that year. The usual assortment of sordid characters had poured in to start the town after it became definite that the Union Pacific would establish shops here, the edge of the vast plains to the west.

The Army had arrived with the building crews earlier, establishing a small post as Fort John Buford on July 4, 1866. Troops from Fort Halleck, Wyoming (not to be confused with the Nevada fort) started it. On September 5, the name was changed to honor a cavalry general who died in the Civil War Battle of Campbell's Station.

At times, the fort was the only stable influence in the area. Ranches were scattered throughout the range, and in Laramie the lawless elements controlled the county government. Finally the legislature dissolved the county charter, placing the town under federal court control until 1874. This period signalled a first in the woman's suffrage movement: six women served on a jury, finding a man guilty of manslaughter after a hotel duel. They passed judgement on other offenses that ranged from disturbing the peace to cattle rustling.

Laramie's first newspaper was published in a railroad car at the fort in 1868. Known as "The Frontier Index," it moved with the tracks. At Beartown, Wyoming, a mob destroyed its presses after the editor's comments became too critical.

Generals Grant, Sherman, and Sheridan, met at Sanders in 1868 to discuss the railroad with Union Pacific officials. In 1871 and 1872, Calamity Jane was at Fort Sanders as a scout, according to her memoirs.

Fort Sanders was abandoned on May 18, 1882, its buildings meeting the same fate as other western forts. Many were auctioned off and moved to Laramie, others just stayed and rotted. A three-story officers' quarters wound up at the

A FOUR-COMPANY POST in the 1866, Fort Sanders had parade ground 400 feet by 235. It became six company post in 1875, and parade ground was enlarged to 600 by 500 feet. Large barracks at bottom left ran 200 feet along south side, 170 on west. (Redrawn from NA data.)

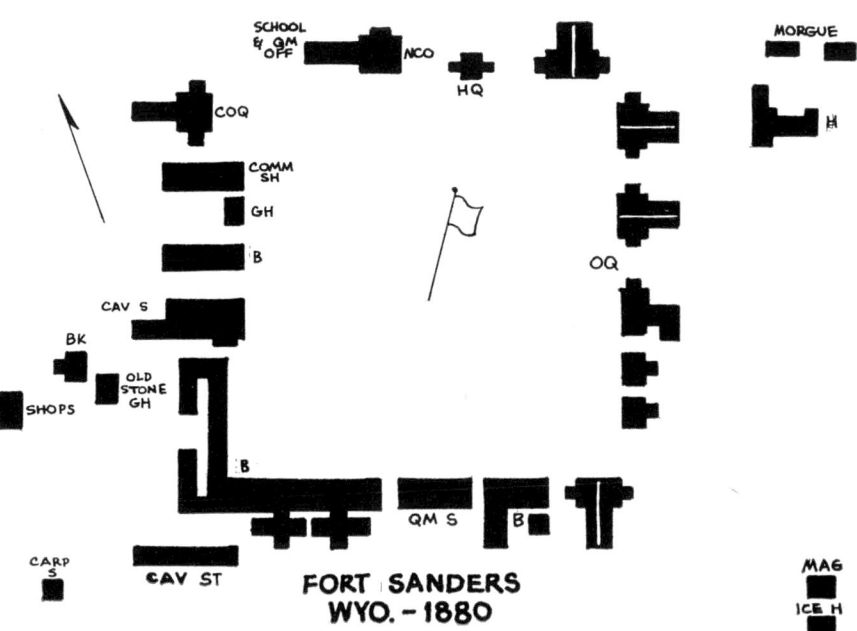

FORT SANDERS
WYO. - 1880

113

MAGAZINE is one of two buildings left at original site. It stands almost in front yard of Laramie Country Club.

University of Wyoming as the Kappa Kappa Gamma sorority house—a far cry from its military origin. That, too, has been replaced by a modern building.

The old guard house and the magazine, both stone buildings, are all that remain at the Sanders' site. One small quarters building has been moved and is a private home to the west. Otherwise, the Laramie Country Club's golfers putt across the parade, while a new transcontinental highway cuts through the near-center of the site.

BOTH RUINS OF FORT SANDERS can be seen here. Magazine is in distance, looking through window of stone guard house.

PARADE GROUND is bare today, crossed by transcontinental highway that splits it in two (dust follows trace of highway.) Stone guard house, note bars, is left, root cellar or tornado cellar, right.

TO GET THERE: *From Laramie, Wyoming, take U.S. 287 south from center of city, two miles. Fort site is on left of highway. Stone marker is at junction of highway and dirt road; guard house is 100 yards east.*

(Courtesy Wyoming State Archives and Historical Department.)

FORT SANDERS, 1875, was enclosed by board fence that not only added to its appearance but, its surgeon reported, "keeps out the stock, which is scattered over the plains." This view looks from east over officers' row toward commanding officer's quarters, right, and mammoth barracks, left. Buildings were built of planks, lathed and plastered.

OLD STONE GUARD HOUSE can be found on old sketch across parade ground, in second row of buildings left of flagpole. Door and windows seen here are as obvious in sketch.

Fort Fred Steele, Wyoming

About 45 miles east of the Continental Divide, where the North Platte and the Union Pacific meet, the remains of Fort Fred Steele straddle the right of way.

A modern bridge has replaced the Platte river ferry of J. W. Hugus, post trader for the old fort. Transcontinental trains do little more than sound long blasts on their horns as they wind into the valley, across the Platte, and rush through the site—the engine leaving before the caboose has even entered.

On June 20, 1868, Fort Fred Steele was a tribute to a general who distinguished himself in the Civil War. When it was established, it was designed to protect the Overland Trail. Arrival of the railroad altered its mission only slightly.

Routine events kept it busy until September, 1879, when the commanding officer, Major Thomas F. Thornburg, took 150 men south to Colorado. What was to be known as the Meeker Massacre started when Agent Nathan Meeker attempted to turn Utes into farmers overnight.

When it didn't work, the Indians revolted. Thornburg rushed aid, but was stopped by an ambush. A four day fight ended when the Ute chief, Ouray, learned of the revolt and ordered it stopped. After the Utes withdrew, the Army counted Thornburg and 12 other men dead, 47 wounded. The Indians admitted to six dead.

Abandoned in 1886, Fort Fred Steele today lies in ruins scattered along the railroad and the river, two miles north of U.S. 30 and nine miles east of Sinclair, Wyoming. A few frame buildings are rapidly falling down, the old magazine is now a granary, and only a couple of families man this outpost for the Union Pacific.

To the southeast of the fort, within sight of the speeding streamliners, are strewn the broken and half buried tombstones of the cemetery. They cover a small hillock that overlooks the fort site. The soldier grave sites are marked but the bodies have been moved by the government. Civilian bodies remain, dating from 1868. A toppled stone dated January 22, 1883 bears a simple eulogy to a man and a life's work: "James Jones—13 Years Bridge Tender at Fort Steele."

TO GET THERE: *From Sinclair, Wyoming, take U.S. 30 nine miles east to North Platte river. Northwest of bridge is small park and dirt road. Turn left on to road. Fort is at end of road (2.5 miles).*

TOMBSTONES are scattered through old cemetery. This one was for a 26-year old civilian who drowned crossing the river in August, 1872.

RAILROAD SPLIT FORT FRED STEELE in two. Ruins or sites of almost all of these buildings still are evident. Road passes between saloon and trader's buildings. Round object next to station is water tank, evident in old photograph. Chief of police of Sinclair, Wyoming, still has the giant key to guard house lock. (Redrawn from NA data.)

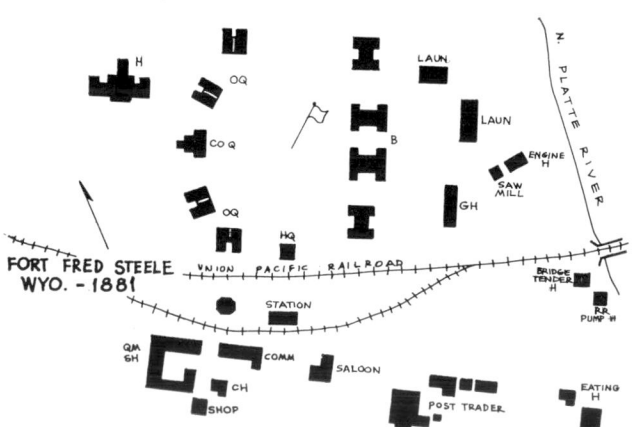

STONE RUINS are southwest of fort, probably were civilian's house in later years of military activity.

FORT FRED STEELE about 1880 can be identified easily from plat. Storehouses are in foreground, parade ground and flagpole behind. North Platte river is to right.

COMMANDING OFFICER'S residence still is used as home. Chimney from southernmost officers' quarter (see plat) is at left. This is all that remains of western side of parade ground.

FORMER BARRACKS, later general store, are on eastern side of parade ground. These two buildings can be seen in the old picture to the right of flagpole.

RAILROAD BRIDGE and few houses of present day Fred Steele, Wyoming, can be seen in this view from southwest.

MAGAZINE now is granary. Building is southeast of fort, does not show on plat. Tin silo attached to it is less-picturesque modern addition.

The Peacekeepers

"Eleven miles from wood, nine miles from water, two miles from hell. God bless our home. A woman wanted."

—Sign on miner's camp 60 miles from Fort Peck, Montana, 1870.

Rᴇɢᴀʀᴅʟᴇss ᴏғ where they were, or why, the citizens of nineteenth century America felt they deserved protection from the Army. If their claims were loud enough—or backed by sufficient political strength—they got a fort, or retained one that the Army wanted to abandon.

The Army was too small to put forts everywhere they were requested. It did its best to keep the roads open, the Indians quiet, and give what protection it could to the settlements.

When Major General H. W. Halleck took command of the Pacific Division in 1865, he outlined his policy:

"Keep the troops in advance," he proposed, "retain them in rear of the white settlements, and to make the posts as temporary and cheap as possible. These should be maintained as depots of supplies for expeditions against the Indians and the temporary camps which may be established in their country. As these camps will be continually changing, they should be of the most temporary character. Tents and huts constructed by the troops will usually be sufficient."

FORT ELLIS, Montana, guarded gold fields of southwestern Montana between 1867 and 1886. Originally stockaded post 390 by 485 feet, it was one of the most important forts in Northwest. Montana State College now uses site, roadside marker is only evidence of Army's former use.

(Courtesy Montana Historical Society.)

Fort Ridgely, Minnesota

"Once an artilleryman, always an artilleryman" may or may not be an old adage of the Army. In the case of Fort Ridgely, it would have been appropriate, though.

Founded in 1853, it was 15 miles from the Lower Sioux Agency. It was primarily for infantry, but it had a few ex-artillerymen and four cannons for ceremonies.

Forty miles away on August 17, 1862, Indians massacred three farm families as they were sitting down to Sunday dinner. And all along the Minnesota river, Indians turned on the whites in a blood bath that ended with 757 dead, 644 of them farmers, shop keepers, families and other civilians.

Refugees streamed to the fort. A 48-man relief force from the fort was ambushed before it got to the agency. Half the men, including the captain in charge, were killed.

More than 250 refugees and 150 men, mostly recruits, were in the fort when the Indians attacked the morning of August 20.

The first defense line fell and the second line was penetrated. Indians got into several buildings. It looked like massacre was imminent.

As the Sioux mustered for another attack, the ex-artillerymen manhandled a cannon into place. Fired point-blank into the surging waves of red men, it stopped the charge. Another group came up a ravine from the southwest. They were met by a miscellaneous collection of old cannon balls, shot and grape.

A final attack was halted before it reached the parade ground.

The day was saved, but not the battle at that point.

Friday, August 22, the Sioux tried again. Shortly after noon, 1,200 hit the defenses and captured the sutler's store and barn.

Then a strange alliance came into being: Sergeant Jones and the sutler's wife. A cannon was wheeled into position, and a signal given to the sutler's wife. She pulled a rope that opened the door to the barn and red hot cannon balls roared through. The place was put on fire, the Sioux were routed.

A defeated Sioux nation tried to save face that weekend by pillaging New Ulm, 15 miles southeast of Fort Ridgely. The New Ulm Massacre still lives in the memory of Minnesotans, probably because of the 269 prisoners taken by the Sioux and held for a month.

TO GET THERE: *From Minneapolis, Minnesota, take U.S. 212 (Lake Street) west to Hector, 64 miles. Turn left (south) on asphalt road, center of town. Fort site is 25 miles south on right side of road. Follow signs into Fort Ridgely State Park.*

FINAL ATTACK ON FORT RIDGELY came up ravine south of officers' quarters, along trace of the north arrow. Cannon were located at the four corners of post. Parade ground was 300 by 350. Post was abandoned in 1867. (Redrawn from SHS data.)

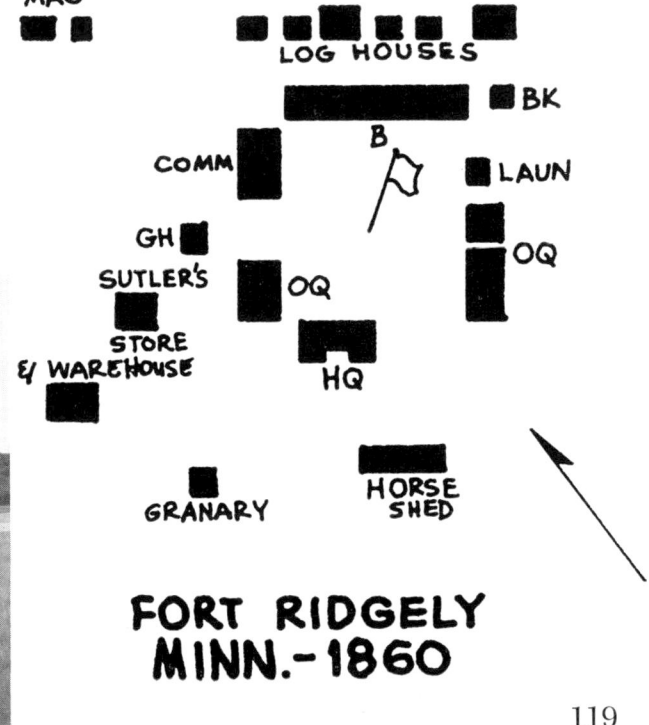

UP THIS RAVINE Indians tried final attack. Sign in foreground tells how cannoneers saved fort.

FORT RIDGELY IN 1863. Not all buildings shown in plat appear, although commissary (left rear) serves to orient. Officers' quarters flank parade ground, barracks faces flagpole in center.

COMMISSARY building has been reconstructed at Fort Ridgely, now houses museum. Excellent presentation describes siege of 1862. Foundations of officers' quarters and headquarters are in foreground; magazine is in background, left edge of picture.

OFFICERS' QUARTERS at southeastern corner of fort exist today as preserved foundations and cellars. Ravine in background was route of Indians' final assault.

Fort Sisseton, South Dakota

Back in 1866 Sam Brown rode 150 miles through driving rain to alert the countryside to an Indian attack on Fort Sisseton.

But Sam Brown earned no niche in posterity for that accomplishment.

The last half of his trip was a return ride to cancel his first warnings. As he said later, "My great adventure had turned out to be a wild goose chase, a false alarm."

Brown, the fort's Indian agent, had been told of Indian tracks near this fort in the northeastern corner of what is now South Dakota. He assumed they were from hostiles. The memories of the New Ulm and Fort Ridgely fights of '62 were still fresh in this area that bordered Minnesota, and he wanted to take no chances.

Off he went on a 60-mile, 5-hour ride, passing the word as he went. At Elm River he was told the tracks must have been from friendly Indians enroute to Fort Sisseton as peace messengers.

It was after midnight and pitch black when he tried to retrace his route. A driving rain storm turned to sleet, then hail, then snow. At daybreak he found he was 15 miles off his course and 25 miles from the fort.

When he finally reached it, "I rolled off the pony in a heap," he wrote. "I staggered toward the stockade gate and fell head long through the door of a house where I lay in a stupor for hours."

Sam Brown's ride, and his devotion to duty, cost him dearly. He was almost completely paralyzed for the rest of his life.

The fort he wanted to save was the peacekeeper of the Dakota Kettle Lake region, nestled since 1864 on the rolling plains next to Rose Lake.

Although the fort never underwent an Indian attack, it was prepared. An emergency tunnel ran to Rose Lake from the northwestern corner of the moat, and it was planned to keep the post supplied with water through it.

Outside of the northern gate, the post trader had his buildings. These were popular places for off duty hours, especially around pay days. At least once, pay day was too long in coming and troopers broke into the cellar, cleaning it bare of whiskey.

In 1876 Wadsworth's name was changed to Fort Sisseton, honoring the Indian band in the area. By this time, its main activities were more social than military, and Dakotans still tell of champagne suppers and colorful balls sponsored by the officers of the post.

Fort False Alarm had one more to go before being abandoned in 1889. In 1888, homesteaders rushed to its protection when a band of Sioux were spotted. After a worried night, they were told the Sioux were more interested in fishing than fighting.

TO GET THERE: *From Watertown, S.D., take U.S. 81 north to Sisseton, 57 miles. At Sisseton, turn left on state 10 and go west 25 miles. At gravel road six miles west of Lake City, turn left, go nine miles south. Fort is large building on right.*

BREASTWORKS SURROUNDED FORT, were 12-feet high. Six-foot deep ditch was outside of it. Sisseton occupied nine-and-a-half acres, had sentry boxes atop three corners, cannon at all four corners. (Redrawn from Division of Missouri report, 1875.)

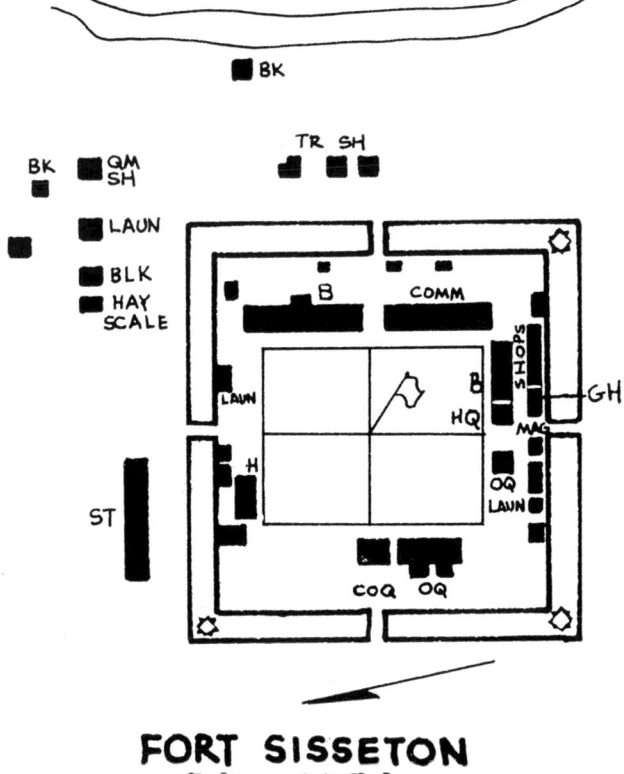

FORT SISSETON
S.D. -1874

MAGAZINE AND HEADQUARTERS BUILDING show only slight ravages of time at south edge of parade ground. Posts in foreground were placed by state to keep automobiles from driving into fort.

FROM HOSPITAL TOWARD PARADE GROUND shows where wing collapsed. Breastwork can be seen through window. Guard house is across parade ground.

(opposite page)

CANNON AND COMMISSARY greeted commanding officer when he walked out front door of his residence each morning. This is view from front hall of eight-room house assigned to fort's commander.

(Courtesy of Minnesota Historical Society.)

FORT SISSETON IN 1886 no longer had sentinel boxes, prominent breastworks. Barracks are left of flagpole, hospital to right.

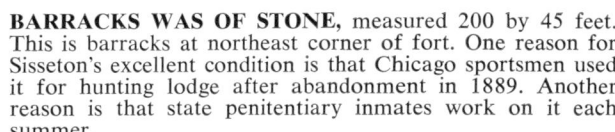

BARRACKS WAS OF STONE, measured 200 by 45 feet. This is barracks at northeast corner of fort. One reason for Sisseton's excellent condition is that Chicago sportsmen used it for hunting lodge after abandonment in 1889. Another reason is that state penitentiary inmates work on it each summer.

HOSPITAL was prominent building at first, now is most imposing. Years have treated it kindly and, except for collapsed wing, it is in fairly good condition. Guard house, in immediate foreground, fared less well.

Fort Hartsuff, Nebraska

For the settlers around Ord, Nebraska, the 1874 construction of Fort Hartsuff was a lifesaver having nothing to do with Indians.

Of course, it was because of the Indian raids that Congress had appropriated $50,000 to build the post. But it was because the grasshoppers cleaned out the crops in '74 that the settlers were glad to work for the government as carpenters, masons, haulers and builders.

By the time the fort was built and the completion celebrated by a fancy, full-dress ball, the need for a military post had ended. The Indians were appropriately cowed. The show of Army force was sufficient to keep them on the reservation.

The one "battle" in the fort's history ended when the Indians snuck back to the reservation.

The fort consisted of two officers' quarters, a barracks and kitchen, guard house, office, hospital, and barns and stables, all fronting around a square parade ground. A tunnel led from one of the officers' quarters to a small hill behind the fort where the water supply came from a spring. The spring was surrounded by a circular stockade. It was planned to defend the fort from here if the Indians attacked—which they never did.

After the post was sold in 1881, farmers occupied some of its buildings. The absence of souvenir-toting tourists contributed as much to its present condition as did the sturdy stone and cement construction.

Many of the buildings still have roofs, interior plastering and floors. Some others are mere shells. An Ord optometrist, Dr. Glen Auble, owned the site for several years and tried to prevent further deterioration until he could present it to the state of Nebraska.

In 1960 the state accepted it and plans to turn it into a park with a resident superintendent. Fort Hartsuff's main claim to posterity is not the Indian battles fought near it, as there were none, but the prosperous countryside made possible because the fort was here to keep the peace.

TO GET THERE: *From Grand Island, Nebraska, take U.S. 281 to St. Paul, 23 miles. Turn left to state 11 to Ord, 41 miles. Continue on 11 past Ord to Elyria, 7 miles. Dirt road leads from center of Elyria north to Fort Hartsuff, about 3 miles by winding road. Signs mark turns from Elyria.*

TRACES STILL EXIST of all of these buildings. Infantry officers' quarters will be museum when restoration of fort is completed. (Redrawn from data courtesy Dr. Glen Auble, Ord, Nebraska.)

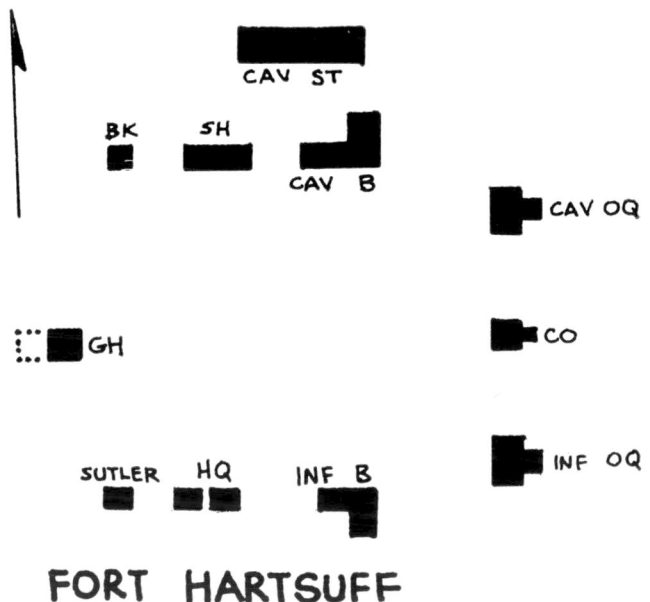

COMMANDING OFFICER would have hard time cleaning up his living room. Trees, heavy brush fill its hollow, double-story shell.

(Courtesy Dr. Glen Auble, Ord, Nebraska.)

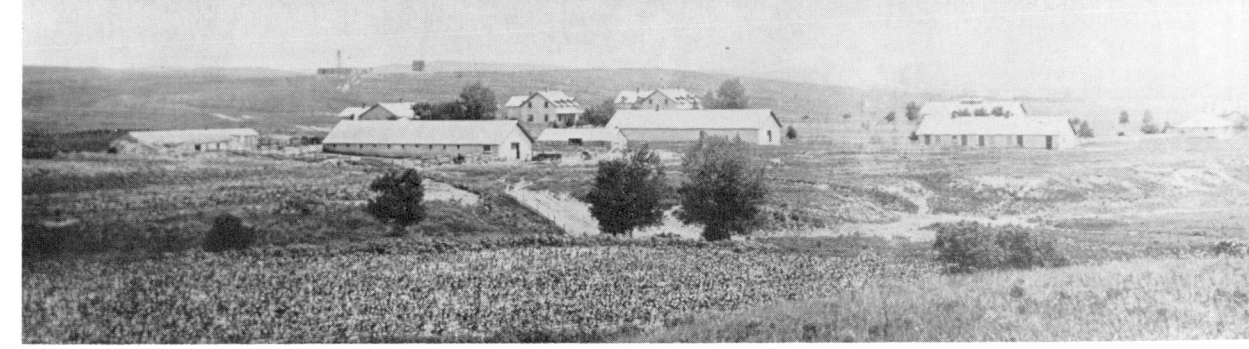

FORT HARTSUFF in 1881. Commanding officer's quarters were large double-story residence in center of picture. Cavalry stables are in foreground. Spring and stockade are on hill to rear.

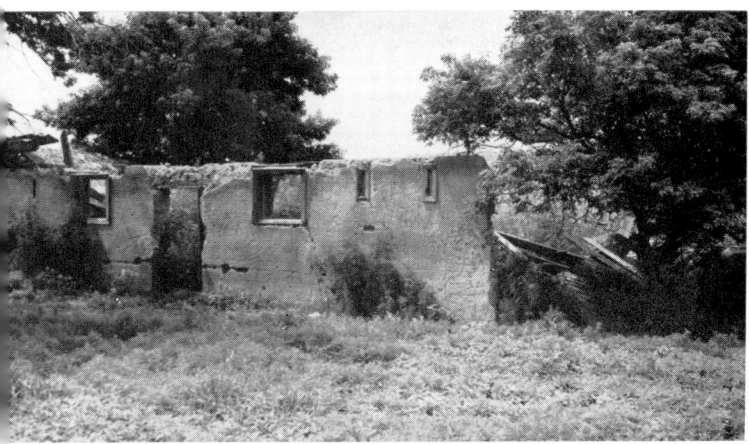

SLITS FROM WHICH TO SHOOT Indians never were used in Fort Hartsuff guard house.

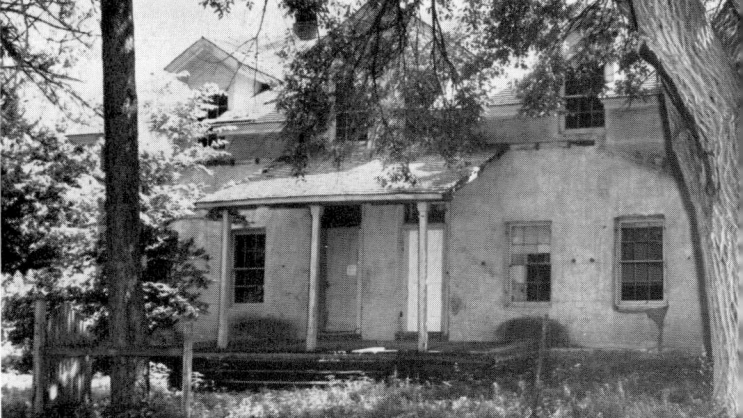

OFFICERS' QUARTERS were converted to single 17-room house in recent years, although infantry officers used it as duplex. Tunnel to water supply led from this house.

ACROSS PARADE GROUND from cavalry barracks. Headquarters building is at left, guard house at right.

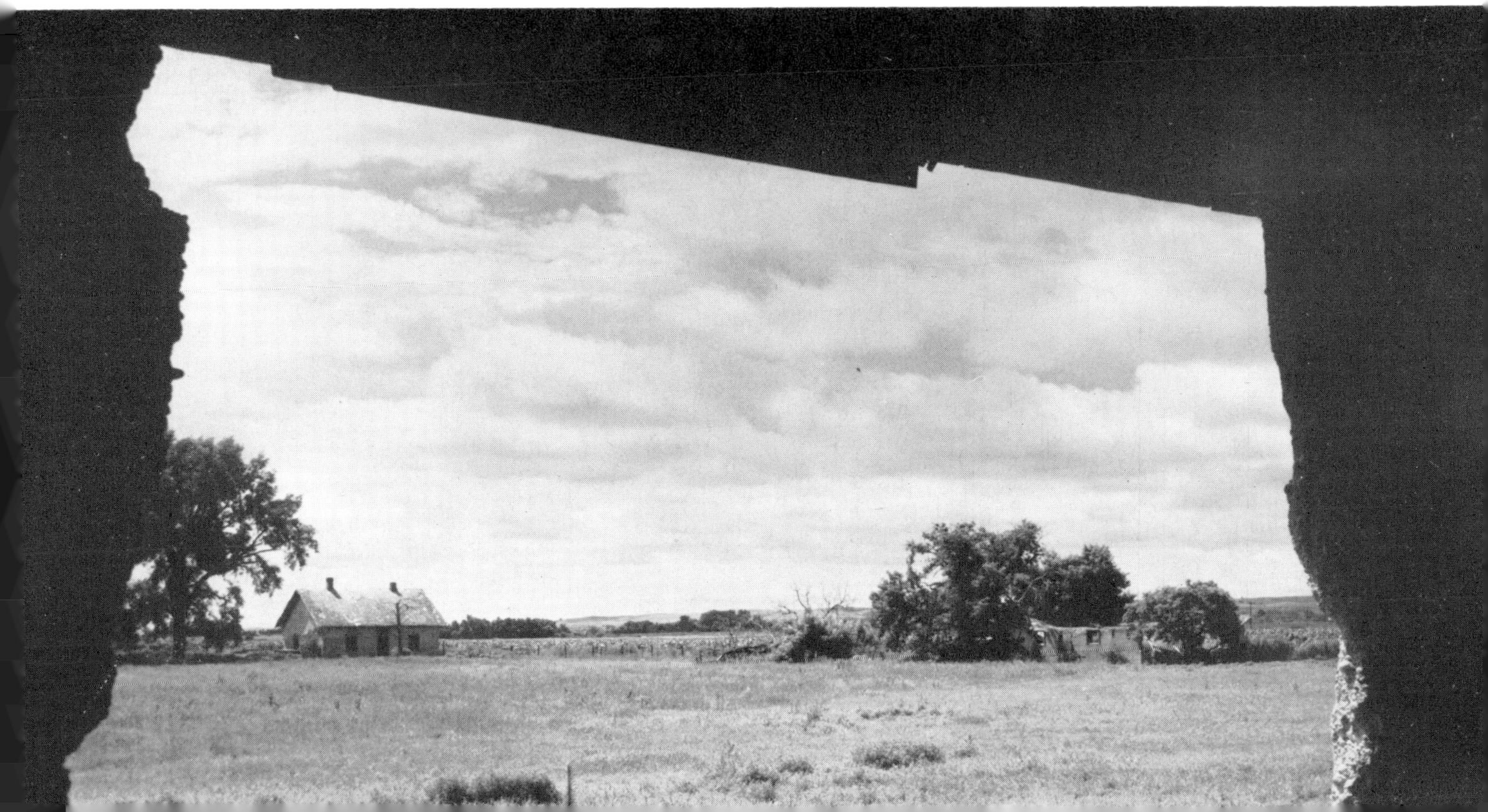

Camp Lyon, Idaho

The soldiers who established Camp Lyon, Idaho, had just about as many helpers as they had opponents, and it was a question on which side some people happened to be.

The camp was spread across a valley floor in southwestern Idaho but right on the Oregon line. To the east were the Owyhee mountains, to the west were the Steens mountains of Oregon.

General Order 36, Department of the Pacific, May 6, 1865, that gave birth to this camp, didn't sound too encouraging: "The force established at these posts will be considered in the field, no purchase of lumber or other building material will be allowed."

No sooner had the troops arrived, than they were greeted with a crisis.

The Owyhee Mine stage route was actually two roads: the "Overland" way through Oregon up from California by way of Fort Bidwell, and the "Humboldt" route up from Nevada by way of Camp Winfield Scott. In June, 1865, a traveler reported that all stations on the Humboldt route had been abandoned and he "had been compelled to run the gauntlet of about 200 miles of hostile savages."

To complicate things, nine months later the local settlers gathered in the Challenge saloon, Silver City, for what they called a "War Meeting." They established a company to go "Indian Hunting," and offered these bounties: "That for every buck scalp be paid $100, and every squaw scalp $50, and $25 for everything in the shape of an Indian under ten years of age." To make certain these legal murders were not fraudulent, they specified that "each scalp shall have the curl of the head, and each man shall make oath that the said scalp was taken by the company."

In May, 1866, 49 of 50 Chinese enroute to Idaho City were waylaid and killed, their mining picks run through the bodies. A week later, a company of soldiers engaged 500 Indians south of Camp Lyon, near where Camp Three Forks was to be established four months later. The Army lost one man and a howitzer, sunk in the Owyhee river when a boat capsized.

On April 13, 1869, Camp Lyon was abandoned. Ultimately, its timbers found their way into a rancher's pole corral, manger and barn. Others were used to build a summer shack that is now a silent sentinel on a barren hill overlooking the site.

TO GET THERE: *From Boise, Idaho, take U.S. 30 west 36 miles to junction with U.S. 95, west of Marsing. Go south on U.S. 95 for 37 miles to northern edge of Sheaville, Oregon. Turn left on dirt road, follow it about 2 miles to east, bearing right at dead end. At cluster of old town buildings, now ranch, turn left, go up hill. Idaho border signs are quarter of mile further. At this point, Camp Lyon site is directly to north; single log cabin is evident on bare hill. Sign was placed in fall 1962, indicating site.*

SOLDIERS BUILT Camp Lyon using local timber. All buildings were of logs, with pole and dirt roofs. Road between Ruby City and Owyhee Crossing passed through post. (Drawn from SHS research.)

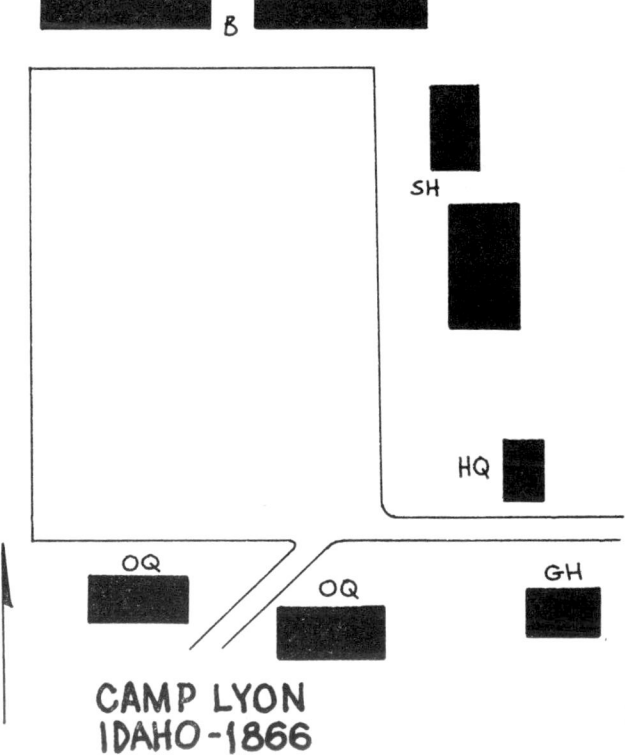

CAMP LYON
IDAHO-1866

JORDAN CREEK is dominated by hills to north and south; old cabin stands alone overlooking fort site from north.

CAMP LYON timbers are supposed to be in this cabin which stands on hill above fort site. Soldiers built all Camp Lyon buildings, but weren't always treated with greatest respect by citizens. Due to their eastern origin, they were termed "New York Wharf Rats" by some, especially after several raided a farmhouse and walked "off with anything movable." Rancher suggested, "New York sent them out of here to get rid of them, and placed them in a weak territory where we need help instead of a den of thieves."

OREGON-IDAHO BORDER signs are beside road in foreground. Camp Lyon site was in field and along north fork of Jordan Creek, middle of picture.

Fort Bidwell, California

The corner where California, Nevada and Oregon intersect isn't usually publicized as a resort area, but it was once considered choice to be stationed near here at Fort Bidwell.

Appropriately enough, Bidwell was located in Surprise Valley, a 60-mile stretch of greenery broken only by three alkaline lakes. The emigrants of the nineteenth century named it after leaving the sun and sagebrush of Nevada.

What with Indians and other bushwackers, this wasn't the most peaceful place around. For the same reason, it wasn't the most popular for settlers. It wasn't until 1865 that 140 citizens could be gathered to petition for troops. They reasoned that someone had to go, either themselves or the marauders. The presence of the Army might even up the odds a little.

THIS WAS SECOND site of fort. Original location was to north. Officers' quarters and barracks were double-storied, resembled many built later during both World Wars. Some of the enlisted quarters, one officer's set, school, and a cavalry stables remain at locations shown here. (Redrawn from California Division of Beaches & Parks data.)

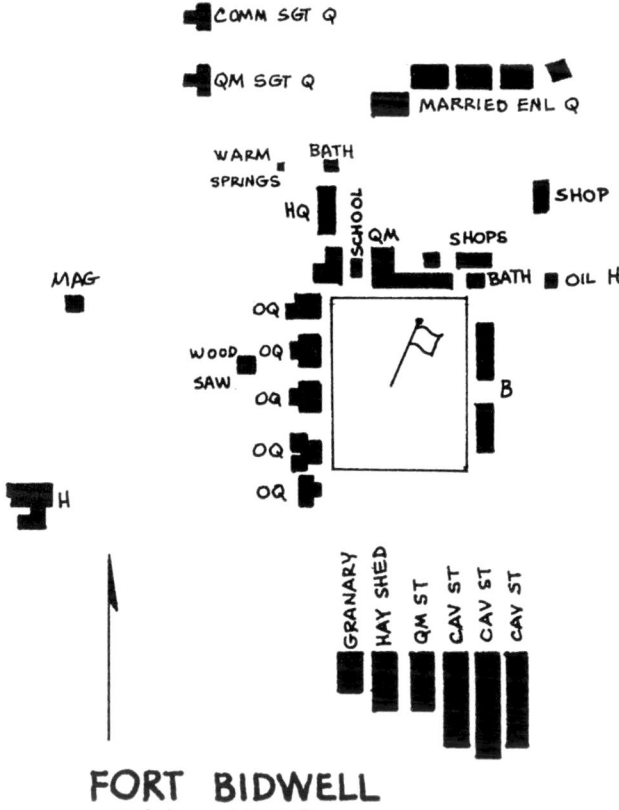

FORT BIDWELL
CAL - 1889

The first Fort Bidwell wasn't but a few months old when its troops joined with a citizen detachment to fight Indians in Guano Valley, Nevada. They attacked the Indian camp, killing 81 braves and 15 squaws and papooses: "it being impossible to distinguish one sex from the other."

This first fort, called "Camp Bidwell" from 1866 to 1879, was just north of the final location. It consisted of pine log single story buildings with high ceilings that complicated the winter heating problems.

By 1870, it became obvious that the place was going to be around for awhile, so plans were made for a more permanent post. Through the location of its corrals, theatre and other buildings, it had begun to spread to the south, so that was the area to which the rest of the post went.

A town grew beside the fort and took to itself the name of the fort. The two Fort Bidwells challenged each other on many matters, from target practice to, it can be deduced, occasional more realistic marksmanship endeavors.

Bidwell was an active combat post throughout most of its existence. Half of its horses were stolen before the camp was built. Its troops fought in the Battle of Infernal Caverns in 1867 with General George Crook, the Modoc War of 1872–73, and the Bannock and Nez Perce campaigns.

As time passed, more of Bidwell's efforts were expended on noncombatant activities when no one seemed to want a fight. Major Andrew S. Burt was the post commandant from 1882 to 1886, bringing with him a fine combat record, and credits as the author of two professional stage plays and miscellaneous other works.

This influenced the life of both the post and the town. Amateur theatricals vied with rifle marksmanship to pass the time . . . and the records show Major Burt was the leading sharpshooter of the U.S. Army in 1885.

TO GET THERE: *Town of Fort Bidwell in Surprise Valley, California, can be reached by U.S. 299 from the west. U.S. 395 is the north-south junction with U.S. 299 west of the valley 24 miles. In center of Fort Bidwell town, turn left at Lowell's store, go west 300 yards to fort site, now part of Indian agency.*

(Courtesy of California Division of Beaches and Parks.)

FORT BIDWELL, 1885, looked like this from northeastern edge of parade ground. Officers' row is in background. One item was pride of Fort Bidwell: water piped into houses from hot springs in valley.

FIRST FORT BIDWELL stood here. Barracks row ran downhill, left side of picture Buildings visible at left are the sergeants' quarters shown on plat. Later fort site is at right side of picture.

(Courtesy Colonel F. B. Rogers.)

SCHOOLHOUSE is now Indian residence, but stands at same location shown on plat. Trees hide television antenna.

Fort Harney, Oregon

In 1867 fifty Chinese were ambushed enroute to their mines at Silver City, Idaho. One lived to tell the tale and settlers demanded that the Army do something about protecting them.

The answer was the rapid expansion of brand new Camp Steele to a full-fledged post. Ultimately renamed Camp Harney and later designated Fort Harney, it was located at the northern tip of Harney Lake Valley in southeastern Oregon, an arid region at first inhabited more by bears, coyotes and wild geese than by people.

Actually it underwent four name changes, starting first as Camp on Rattlesnake Creek, then Camp Steele, the Camp Crook, finally Camp Harney. The Crook name lasted only a short time, apparently in deference to the general in command of the area.

In 1868 Crook negotiated a peace with the Piutes on the camp's parade ground. In typical Crook fashion, he stated his terms: go back to the reservation and report troubles to the Army, rather than trying to fight them out with the whites.

The peace lasted almost ten years until it erupted in the Bannock War. This fracas started in Idaho over a land decision, spreading westward until Harney became the Army's base in settling it. Settlers flocked to the fort and some volunteers accompanied patrols.

Fire and bloodshed ran through the land until the Bannock chief, Egan, was killed by other Indians. His head was brought to the Army in a sack as proof of his death. The Bannock War lost momentum after that.

Harney next was the gathering point of the formerly hostile Indians and 543 of them were under guard by the start of 1879. Old uniforms were distributed to the half-clad men and so much food was passed out that some tribesmen suffered from overeating.

In January, 1879, these Indians were ordered 350 miles north to the Yakima Reservation and Fort Simcoe, Washington. It required a freezing wagon march through snowstorms to get there.

With the transfer of the Indians, and their later refusal to locate on the reservation north of Harney, the fort's use was outlived. On June 13, 1880, it was abandoned and squatters moved in soon afterward.

RATTLESNAKE CANYON was 300 yards wide where Fort Harney was located, and all space was used. Stage road ran through post and gave business to hotel, upper right. Barracks were 100 feet long, 30 wide. (Redrawn from NA data.)

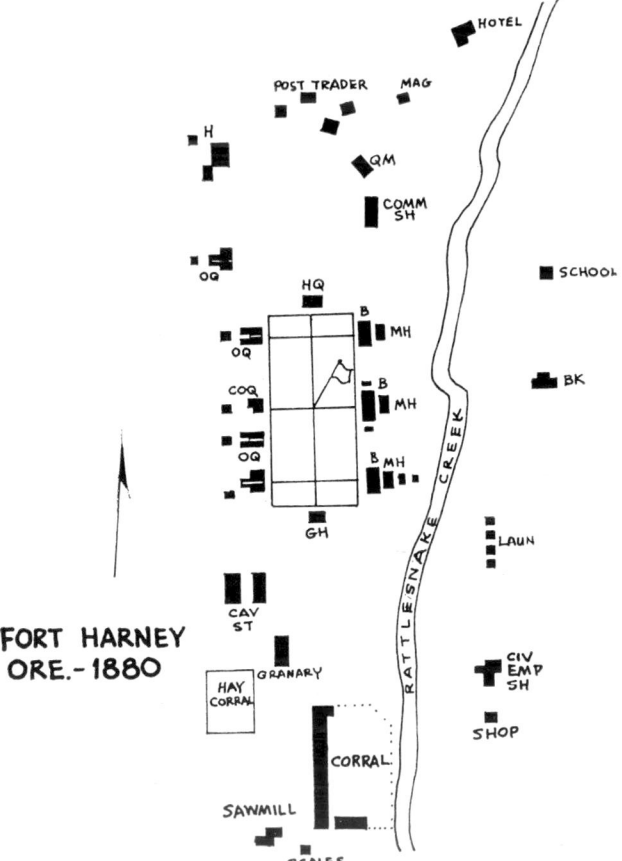

FORT HARNEY ORE.-1880

TO GET THERE: *From Burns, Oregon, take U.S. 20 east 12 miles. Turn left at gravel road. Harney City remains are at left, two miles, fort site is past Catterson Ranch, two miles further up valley road.*

FORT CEMETERY contains two civilian graves, is only reminder that site had military uses. This enclosure is on Jack Catterson ranch in southeastern corner of fort location.

FORT HARNEY IN 1872 matched plat almost perfectly. Officers' log and frame quarters ran along left side of parade ground, hospital stood on knoll 50 yards to northwest, headquarters building and guard house were at opposite ends of parade ground.

ELECTION IN 1890 determined county seat would not be at Harney City by 512-415 vote. Amid fraud charges courts decided vote was legal and citizens of Burns, new county seat, rode to Harney City after dark, moved records away under armed guard. City continued to boom, but by 1938 was down to three residents, though counters and showcases remained in general store. Now these ruins mark west edge of town. Fort Harney was through canyon mouth in background.

GHOST TOWN of Harney City was booming town after fort closed. Army buildings were moved, or lumber used, to mouth of Rattlesnake canyon, and town soon had general store, hotel, two blacksmiths, sawmill, lawyer, newspaper, doctor, school, and of course, saloon. Single family now owns it, plants crops across its main street. Harney City name is retained on small sign balanced in deer antlers on fence post.

Fort McDermit, Nevada

Protecting whites from the Indians, and Indians from the whites might have been missions common to many Army posts. Some had a third dimension to this: protecting Indians from Indians.

That was the case at least once in April, 1872, at Camp McDermit, Nevada, when an Indian admitted shooting a squaw.

He claimed he did it to revenge a fatal beating the woman had given his wife a month before. McDermit's commander checked the story.

"I immediately visited the Indian camp," he reported, "and found his statement regarding the death of his wife to be untrue, who, although not in good health, did not appear to be dangerously ill."

The culprit did not stay long in the guard house at the fort. He escaped the next day, dodged bullets fired at him by the sergeant of the guard and a sentinel, and eluded a five-man patrol that tried to follow him.

Camp McDermit was established in August, 1865, both to protect the 2,000 Paiute Indians living in the area, and to watch over the road north into Oregon. Its troops participated in the Bannock Indian Wars, in which it played a major role, and in minor "keep the peace" engagements between 1865 and 1889.

In 1872 when its cavalry troop was moved to Fort Lapwai, Idaho, the commanding officer left at McDermit asked that the excess horses be left with him. He wanted the 10–15 extra horses so he "would be supplied with the means of showing a well-armed mounted party of at least 20 men occasionally to hold in check the unruly."

Trouble from a different direction seems to have come to McDermit, as it did to many frontier posts: John Barleycorn. In 1872 the post trader was ordered "not to sell more than two drinks of any kind of liquor daily to any one enlisted man of this command, and those only between the hours of 10 a.m. and 12 noon and 4 p.m. and 6 p.m., and not more than one drink at either the times stated."

Whether this order had the desired effect is answered by the reissuance of a stronger version of it eight months later. The two drinks a day ration remained but the one-per-period restriction was left off. Instead, the post trader was warned:

"And should these instructions be not fully complied with, he (commanding officer) will withdraw the privilege of your selling or having any liquor in this reservation. Please acknowledge receipt of this letter."

TO GET THERE: *From Winnemucca, Nevada, take U.S. 95 north 96 miles. A mile south of state border, turn right at Indian Agency sign. Fort site is at end of this road, about two miles.*

McDERMIT was designated a fort in 1879, bordered parade ground 660 by 225 feet. Most buildings were stone, one officers' quarters was adobe. Indian Bureau acquired fort in 1889. (Redrawn from Division of the Pacific report, 1877.)

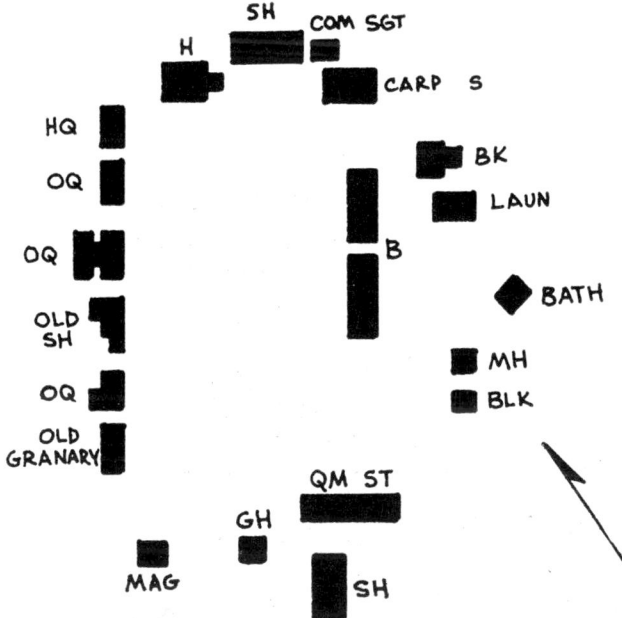

CAMP MCDERMIT
NEV. -1877

(Courtesy Fred Buckingham, Paradise Valley, Nev.)

IN 1887, Lieutenant Holley took this picture of Fort McDermit. Most of buildings shown on plat remain, though new construction is evident, especially new hospital (top right corner). Flagpole stands in front two buildings remaining today. Picture looks directly north.

INDIANS OCCASIONALLY use left officers' quarters for weddings, community parties. It was once agency school. Other officers' quarters is occupied by family of tribal secretary. During its peak, McDermit was center of military patrols straddling Oregon-Nevada border, usually had sub-posts at most vulnerable ranches.

TWO OFFICERS' QUARTERS remain, are used by Indians. These show on plat as top two quarters, left side of parade ground. McDermit's commander in 1878 suggested that if camp were abandoned "no trouble would ensue between whites and Indians unless originated by the whites—and I am also of the opinion that the whites would endeavor to cause trouble in order to secure the retention of this post."

SANTA ROSA MOUNTAINS look down on Fort McDermit site. This is northern end of parade ground. Former Indian agency jail stands near site of bakery; house was built after date of plat.

Camp Winfield Scott, Nevada

To hear the commanding officer of Camp Winfield Scott, tell it, he was all but surrounded by racketeers, profiteers and ne'er do wells.

In January, 1867, only a month after post was established he had caustic comments to make about the residents of Dun Glen, 60 miles southwest. With their tiny Army post of 1865 abandoned, they had petitioned for soldiers.

"The petitioners are of two classes," he told departmental headquarters. "One, quite large in numbers, is composed of gamblers . . . I saw enough of this class in Dun Glen to exterminate all the Indians in Nevada. Class number 2 is made up of merchants—respectable, I doubt not, and patriotically disposed to assist the government by contracting to deliver hay, grain, and other supplies—for a consideration.

"Many live in the village and, generally, own no stock and have no more to fear from Indians that an industious dry goods dealer. With them, 'protection' means 'patronage' and they naturally regard with envy their more fortunate neighbors of Paradise Valley who have been so liberally protected."

If he seemed unduly harsh in his opinions, it may have been because of the distractions of building the new camp. At the time, mid-winter, he had his whole company squeezed into an uncompleted barracks designed for half a company and lacking both windows and doors. His officers were living in buildings built as laundresses'

quarters, and the hospital occupied the blacksmith shop. All buildings were of adobe with sod roofs.

A year later and a new commanding officer found the opinion of local attitude unchanged. First Lieutenant Joseph Karge had led a patrol through the snows of December, 1867, to recover six yoke of oxen stolen by Indians from a Paradise Valley rancher.

In telling of his 10-day, 380-mile, below zero patrol, Karge concluded his report: "As far as to the citizens of Paradise Valley, I respectfully beg leave to add, that had they one tenth of the time which they spend in whiskey mills and gambling halls devoted in guarding their property, this never would have occurred."

The attraction of liquor wasn't confined to the Nevadans, though. The problem became so bad at the camp that the commanding officer marked Christmas Eve, 1870, by prohibiting the sale of liquor on the post and closing the sutler's store. He noted that not only was the camp the daily victim of drunkedness, but that the trader's whiskey was "vile" and soldiers had run up a $700 debt for it in a little more than three months.

The soldiers of Winfield Scott had more than their share of Indian fighting, despite the other problems besetting them. Being located in barren range country at the foot of the Santa Rosa mountains, it was easy for Indians to approach close to the camp.

Three Indians did so on August 1, 1867, catching James A. Banks, a civilian guest of the commanding officer, who was fishing alone. They shot him fatally, then stripped and disembowled him.

A five-man patrol was sent to capture the In-

TINY CAMP IN NORTHERN NEVADA'S PARADISE VALLEY lasted from 1866 to 1871. Bottom two officers' quarters and bottom barracks remain. Top barracks and officers' house were planned, probably never built. (Redrawn from NA data.)

SHEEP LIVE in old barracks. Remains of fireplace, chimney, doorways are obvious, though not usable any more.

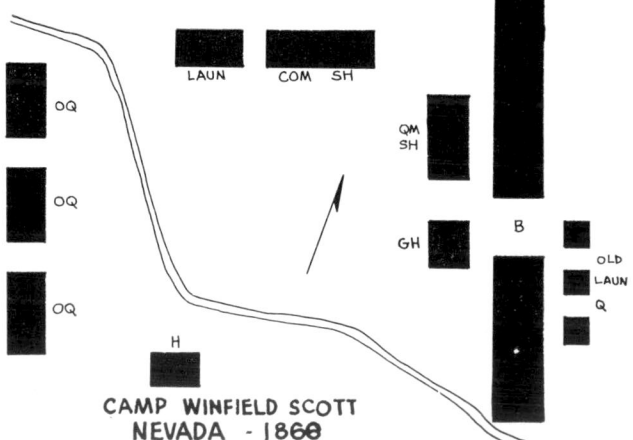

CAMP WINFIELD SCOTT
NEVADA - 1868

dians. It deserted after touring the saloons of Rebel Creek Station, reducing Camp Winfield Scott's strength to two officers and 28 enlisted men.

A bloody encounter with the Indians occurred on April 29, 1863, when a four-man patrol was ambushed in a canyon eight miles northeast of the post.

One soldier was killed and two wounded, including the lieutenant in command. The patrol holed up in a cave and the unwounded man kept up steady carbine fire from its mouth.

A rescue patrol was mustered at the camp by taking all of the combat soldiers. The paymaster happened to be passing through and he took charge of the post.

TO GET THERE: *From Winnemucca, Nevada, take U.S. 95 north 22 miles, bear right onto state road 8B. Go 18 miles to Paradise Valley. At eastern end of main street, turn right, then take next left past collapsed building. Four miles further is Buckingham ranch, privately owned, site of fort.*

OFFICERS' QUARTERS were duplexes, are still occupied. This is ranch house, other building is bunk house. Behind this residence is sunken stone cellar with barred window that suggests past use as magazine or guard house.

CAMP WINFIELD SCOTT TODAY is ranch of Fred E. Buckingham. Two officers' quarters and single barracks can be seen, almost in shadows of eastern slopes of Santa Rosa mountains.

PARADE GROUND from barracks shows both officer's quarters.

ADOBE NEARLY 100 years old makes up walls of former barracks, now barn and stables. When built in 1867, it measured 120 by 30 feet.

Fort Logan, Montana

Nature, not Indians, presented the greatest problem for the troops at Fort Logan, a post that went under its first name, Camp Baker, for most of its existence.

In the Smith River valley of mid-western Montana, Logan—or Baker, as it was first known—started as a sub-post of Fort Ellis. Its name was in honor of Colonel Eugene M. Baker, the Ellis commanding officer.

This region of Montana wasn't renowned for its temperate climate, and the troops at the new post found out why. On April 14, 1877, the post surgeon's official report stated, "The National colors hoisted and flown all day, the first time in over a year." The drainage ditches at the post still were frozen, then, though. It wasn't until June 19 that he could report, "The ditches open, the first time this season."

Climate wasn't the only natural problem. Grasshoppers did their share in the pre-DDT days.

The surgeon kept careful records of the swarms in 1877. They arrived in March, he reported, but "the cold stormy weather succeeding will probably annihilate millions of these pests."

Millions annihilated or not, they reappeared "full grown" on July 21, disappeared on July 29. On August 1 a gray cloud of them flew over the post for three hours at an altitude of about a half mile. Following days many of them lighted on the buildings and grounds of Logan, and then suddenly disappeared on August 9.

But the garrison had more to occupy it than grasshoppers. In its first year its main concern was building a fort, a task complicated by a 10-mile move during the summer of 1870. In November, 1869, the post had started near the junction of Smiths river and Camas creek, then shifted to a point where the valley was less than three miles wide. The Bell mountains came to within 500 yards of the fort and Indian graves were found bleaching in the crevices nearby.

The area was so lively that the two nearest towns were deserted during most of the winter. These were Diamond City, 18 miles west, and Thompson Gulch, 13. Supposedly, their safety was the main reason for locating the fort.

Indians were not widespread, but occasional reports of horse thefts were blamed on them. While the fort was being built, only 16 of the 44 men were available for non-construction duties. The commander was prompted to request additional troops because "there is a possibility of depredations being committed in the Musselshell and Judith Basin during the coming winter and summer." Undoubtedly he hoped his reinforcements would include a few carpenters and stone masons for other than anti-depredation duty.

Camp Baker's location made it available to reinforce various Indian-fighting actions in Western Montana. When one of its officers, Captain William Logan, was killed in the Battle of the Big Hole, the post took his name in 1878.

TRACES OF ALMOST ALL of these buildings remain today, although some have been relocated. Barracks was log building 100 feet by 29, planned for one company. Canvas partition was used when second company was crowded in later. (Redrawn from Division of Missouri Report, 1876.)

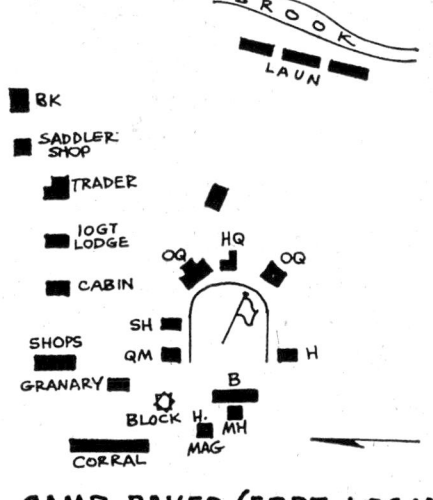

BLOCK HOUSE SAW much action, but most of it disciplinary. It served as guard house, prisoners were kept on second floor, guard stayed on first. It was moved in 1962 to center of old parade ground where trees, saplings in 1878, have matured. Plaque on side was placed by Daughters of the American Revolution in 1924.

CAMP BAKER (FORT LOGAN) MONT. – 1876

FORT LOGAN ladies rode side-saddle across parade ground in seventies. Block house appeared in this picture to east of officers' circle, although official plat of 1876 located it to west of parade ground. Its roof can be seen behind left building in this picture. Today it stands on flagpole site.

Fort Logan didn't last long under its new name. As early as 1873, its commander had reported "the country perfectly safe for small parties for a hundred miles in every direction." By 1880, headquarters decided there was no further reason for a fort in Smith's River valley, and Logan was abandoned.

It is assumed that abandonment of the fort didn't mean loss to the Army of the books in its library. A book order in the seventies indicates that $12 was spent on an unabridged dictionary, but that some of the other publications desired by the soldiers included "Agatha's Husband," "Two Marriages," "A Life for a Life," "Queen of Hearts," and a particular prize, "Thirty Years in a Harem."

TO GET THERE: *From White Sulphur Springs, Montana, take asphalt road past post office west of town. In about one mile, turn right on gravel road. Take 19 miles to ranch of Mrs. Nancy Bird. This privately owned ranch occupies old fort buildings. Blockhouse is on old parade ground, right of road.*

TIME HAS DISCOLORED wood used in building officers' quarters. This is porch of right hand residence in old picture. It was a duplex, occupied in 1875 by surgeon who complained it had only fireplace heat, was extremely cold in winter. Present occupant, owner of ranch Mrs. Nancy Bird, agrees. She uses it as summer home, spends winters in White Sulphur Springs, or where it is warmer: Milwaukee, Wisconsin.

ADOBE STORE HOUSE is rapidly deteriorating. This probably was quartermaster storehouse.

INTERIOR of storehouse shows plaster was placed directly over adobe bricks.

OFFICER'S QUARTERS are virtually unchanged since 1878, except for television antenna. Fort Logan was named for captain killed in Nez Perce War's Battle of the Big Hole.

The Protectors

"You will never have a worse enemy than the whiskey sellers and the bad whites who intrude upon you and your families . . . It is very sad to find that the discovery of gold and the consequent rush of miners to this country should have brought such a mass of the very worse white men in contact with you, and thus impeded your improvement."

—General Alvord to the Nez Perce chiefs, Lapwai Agency, October 24, 1862.

ONCE THE Indians had consented to reservation life, voluntarily or otherwise, the Army had to be more concerned with protecting them than fighting them.

Usually it was a matter of policing the whites who coveted the Indian lands. On occasion, the Army role was the protection of the Indian Agency. Other times, it supervised the distribution of the annuities to the tribes.

The ups and downs of the Indian problem was of vital concern to the Army. Sometimes post commanders rebelled against the dishonesty and double dealing of some agents. The politicians were summarily removed from the post, and an Army officer assigned temporarily.

The introduction of farming was a slow, spoon-fed program complicated by Indian disinterest and governmental indecision.

Time and progress solved what the Army and Indian Bureau could only attempt. The first Americans no longer are wards of the government and dependent upon Congressional handouts. They are full fledged citizens of the United States, the country that now occupies the hunting grounds of their ancestors.

Fort Simcoe, Washington

Fort Simcoe was a place of sorrow for its first commanding officer.

A former Commandant of Cadets at West Point, Major Robert S. Garnett built this post at the "Mool Mool," the Indian name for a bubbling spring.

A gathering place for the tribes, the Mool Mool was not far from the site of the two-day battle where the Yakimas bested a 100-soldier force in 1855. The fort was intended to command the central Washington trails and place the Army at the Indian tribes' rear.

Garnett began to build the fort in 1856, bringing materials by wagon from Fort Dalles, 65 miles away. The architect must have come, too, as the buildings at Simcoe bear a striking resemblance to the lone remainder at Fort Dalles.

Since the Yakimas still were active, block houses took first priority. Garnett was confident, though, and outfitted them with large windows and doors so that other uses could be made of them. Soon they became shops for the blacksmith and carpenter and quarters for the laundresses.

It was a cold first winter at Simcoe, and work was pushed on two company barracks, two officers' quarters and a guard house. In the spring Garnett went east to be married to the former Marianna Nelson. Her arrival in the Yakima country generated considerable social activity.

The Commandant's House took on the appearance of a mansion. The lower floor and two bedrooms on the second floor were occupied by himself and his bride, although records are not certain as to when the second story actually was completed. His office also was on the second floor.

In 1858 a son was born to the Garnetts. At the same time, the Indian hostilities of 1858 demanded the major's presence in the field, especially after the Battle of Steptoe Butte in May.

Miners pressured to enter the Indian lands, and notice that the government was considered running a railroad from Missouri to the Columbia, stirred up the Indians.

Garnett left Simcoe on August 10 for a 44-day, 700-mile expedition. Some Indians were rounded up, 10 accused of murdering miners were executed, but the patrol fought no major engagements. A Lieutenant George Crook commanded a company in this affair, though much of the time his unit was a 20-canoe "navy" exploring the Columbia river.

Garnett was camped 15 miles from the fort when a messenger reached him with the news his wife and baby son had died of a fever. For Garnett, that was the end of his days at Fort Simcoe. He applied for leave and took the bodies of his family to the east for burial. Three years later, he was to be killed as a Confederate brigadier general at Carricks Ford, Virginia.

Not long after Garnett left, the Indian policy changed. General Harney opened the area to settlement and the need for Fort Simcoe ceased. In 1859, the troops were moved north to Fort Colville, Washington, and the Indian Service took over Garnett's elaborate layout.

After two agents were dismissed for graft, an Episcopalian priest, the Rev. James H. Wilbur, was placed in charge. His theory was that the Indians could become self-supporting and soon Simcoe became the model Indian agency of the Northwest. Father Wilbur even was able to turn back appropriations to Congress!

TO GET THERE: *From Yakima, Washington, take U.S. 97 to Toppenish, 15 miles. Turn right to state 3B, go 20 miles to White Swan. Follow signs 8 miles to end of road and Fort Simcoe State Park.*

MOOL MOOL, bubbling spring of the Indians, provides water for horses stabled near old fort. Spring rises in a number of spots in valley.

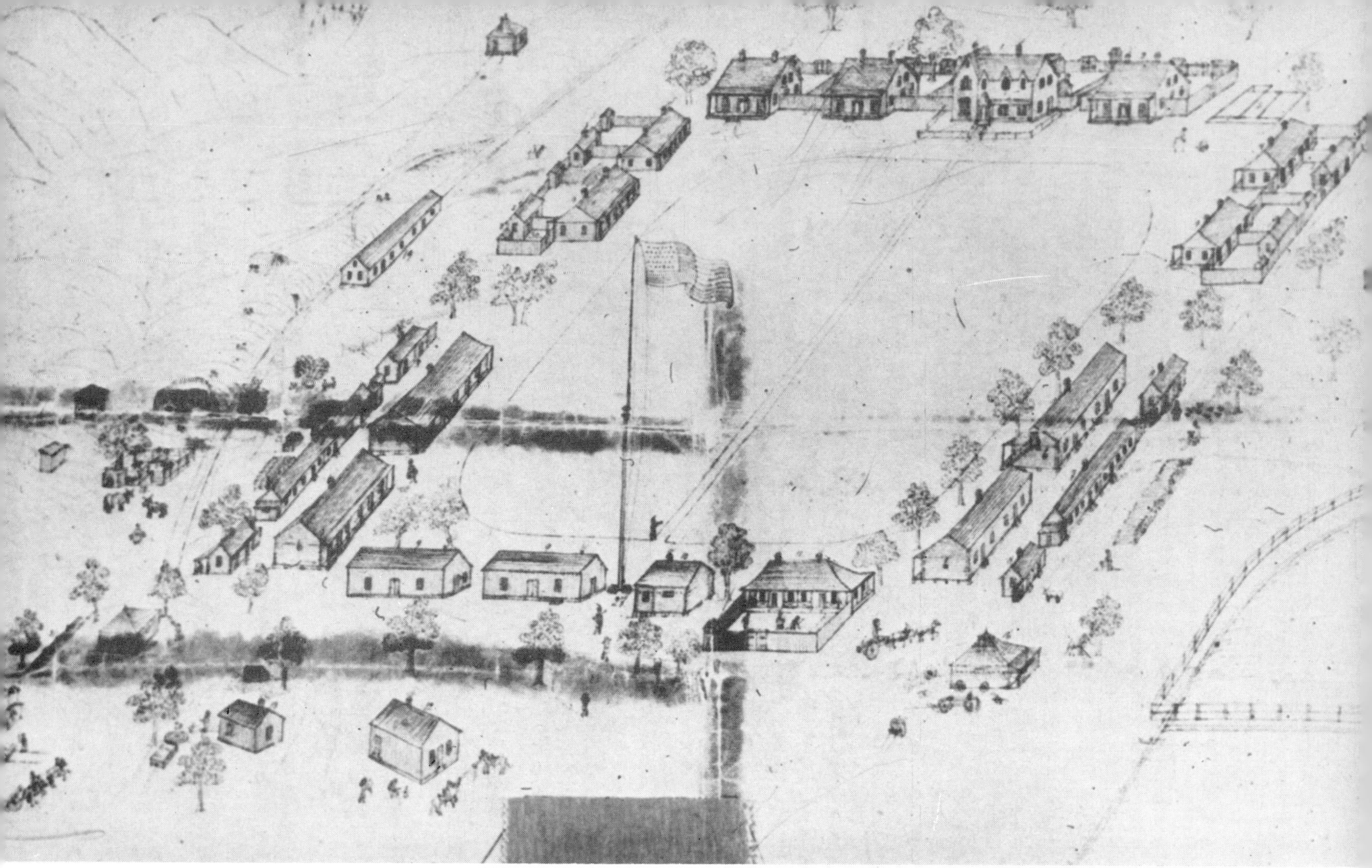

(Courtesy of University of Washington Library.)

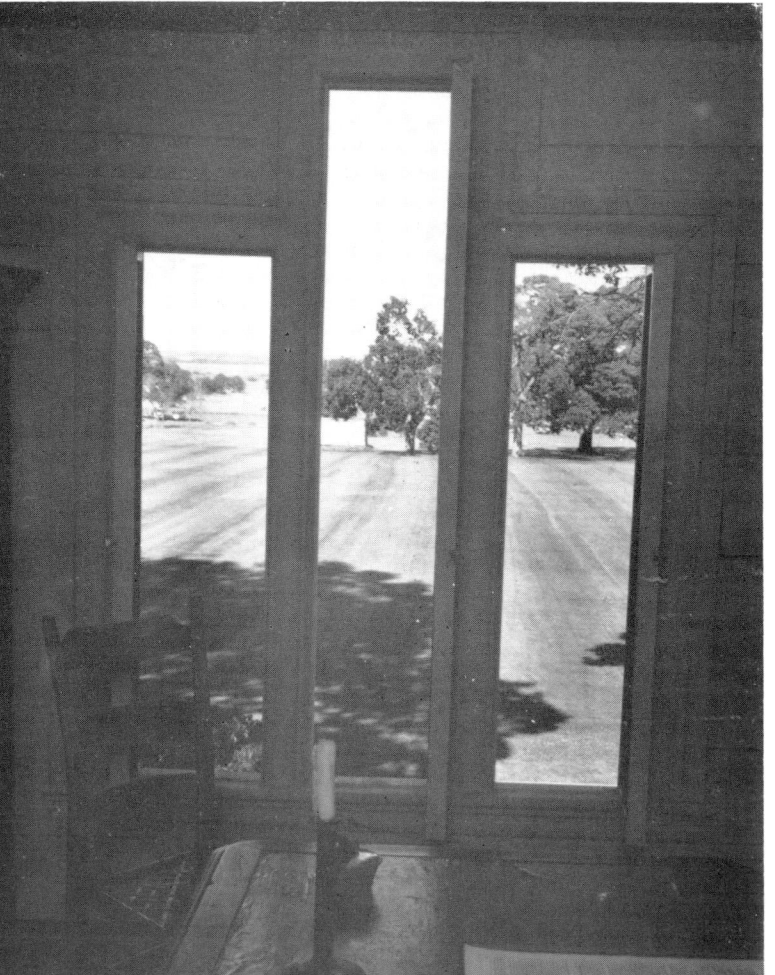

FORT SIMCOE IN 1858, sketch by Private C. M. Schultz, was found mixed with other papers by University of Washington Reference Librarian Ronald Todd. Barracks flanked 420-foot square parade ground. Commandant's House is at far end, center, with other officers' quarters on each side. Guard house is at right of flag pole. Three of the four block houses appear at fort's corners; the one at top left is the southwestern bastion that still exists.

COMMANDANT'S OFFICE overlooked parade ground. They were conveniently located for him on second floor of his house. Indian Agency used building until 1923. Restoration started in 1953 under joint sponsorship of federal, state, and Yakima Nation governments.

COMMANDANT'S HOUSE was place of sorrow for first occupant, but of success for Father Wilbur's experiments in Indian Agency management. Building is restored, furnished to 1860 era.

KITCHEN WING behind commandant's house has been restored, equipped with period cooking utensils.

ORIGINAL BLOCK HOUSE was one of first buildings at Fort Simcoe. It was built of pine logs before winter of 1856, and still remains on hill southwest of fort.

Camp Lincoln, California

When the gold fever ran high, off to the "get rich quick" fields went some men of Northern California in 1862, creating a tempting situation for the Indians. Farms and families were left unprotected at the same time the Indians were being re-settled in the Smith's River Valley. This brewed a situation that bubbled and near-exploded many times.

Petitions for troops to protect the families, were not readily appreciated by the Army, already stretched thin in keeping open the stage lines.

General Wright, commanding the Department of the Pacific, considered "a very poor argument" that the men "have gone to the mines and left the women and children to the mercy of the Indians."

His feelings were definite: "There is either no danger from Indians or the men who will thus abandon their wives and little ones for the gold fields deserve death," he concluded.

In the long run, though, the settlers won out. Fort Terwaw, four miles from Klamath, California, was wiped out by a flood in 1862, and its troops moved to a temporary Camp Lincoln at the Agency headquarters near Crescent City.

Major James F. Curtis arrived at Camp Lincoln on August 21 and almost immediately announced that it was to be moved six miles north of Crescent City at 1 p.m. on September 11, 1862.

This would put the troops between the whites and Indians and "will prevent any molestation on the part of the whites and yet be a good position from which to act against these tribes should they commence hostilities," he said.

"The camp is upon dry, sloping ground, an opening in a redwood forest, and upon the main road between Crescent City and the Indian reservation." Curtis reported. "Good water, wood, and grazing in abundance . . . The name Camp Lincoln is retained and the postoffice address not changed."

While Curtis was in the process of building a small post of two barracks and a like number of officers' quarters, most of his attention was distracted by the aggravations in white-Indian relations. Settlers felt the government should either buy the Smith's River Valley, or get the Indians out. With the government not indicating steps to do the former, the civilians took the latter in hand. The fact that many of the settlers had seccessionist leanings did not help matters.

Indian crops were burned and stock run off. The Indians were told to get out or be killed. The 400 to 500 members of Con Cow and Hat Creek bands decided that the reservation existed no longer and left. The 1,500 who stayed did so only because of Curtis' troops.

One of his two companies pursued the Indians, but the redwood forests swallowed them up.

It took martial law and companies of militia to bring an unsettled peace across the valley temporarily. Indians and whites persisted in mutual harrassment, and the Army had a continual task to keep the combatants separated.

June 11, 1869, Camp Lincoln was deserted and in May, 1870, it was officially closed. The final peace had not yet come, but the postwar Army could not afford the luxury of many small posts inadequately manned, and Lincoln was one of those to feel the axe.

TO GET THERE: *From Crescent City, California, take U.S. 199 northeast about six miles. Turn left at Smith's River Valley road (marked). This road almost parallels highway. Fort site is about two miles north, flanking road. Marker is on right hand side. Former officers' duplex, privately owned, is next to road, left side.*

POST WAS BUILT on gentle slope and even parade ground was on slight grade. Because it was not flat, parade ground drilling involved both up-hill and down-hill marching. Camp flagpole was in front of guard house. Diary of private at camp tells of Indian maidens being tied to flagstaff by sergeant of guard, but doesn't say why. (Redrawn from NA data.)

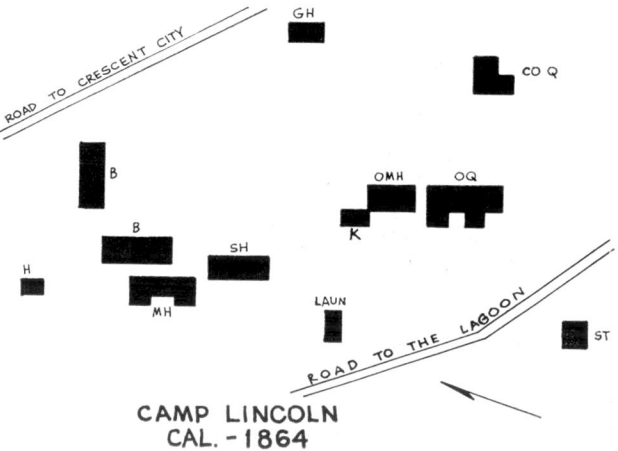

CAMP LINCOLN
CAL. -1864

CAMP LINCOLN IN 1862 was sketched by Private George B. Young. Guard house is on slight knoll in foreground. Officers' quarters, still existing, is at left, their mess hall and kitchen next door. Barracks are at right. Sketch and plat agree basically, though tents used temporarily show in sketch.

TWO OFFICER's FAMILIES lived in this residence. It was a duplex, had four rooms, two fireplaces. Now remodeled, it is a farm house but early location and appearance have not changed. This building appears as right hand building, middle row, in plat.

COMMANDING OFFICER'S residence has been re-built, but stands on original site, resembles former self. Marker was placed in spring, 1962.

145

Fort Robinson, Nebraska

One Indian agent had been killed, another brought before an Indian "kangaroo court," and an attempt to erect a flagpole at the agency had ended when the Sioux chopped it down. In northwestern Nebraska in 1873, things were in an uproar and the Army at Fort Robinson knew it.

Soldiers had been rushed to this place when the hot-headed Sioux appeared close to taking over the Red Cloud Agency. Almost 1,000 cavalrymen and infantrymen were divided between protecting that agency and the one at Spotted Tail, 40 miles to the northeast. Four companies of infantry and a gatling gun were left at each post, that at Red Cloud being named Camp Robinson, the other, Camp Sheridan.

In May, 1874, the Army realized that its daily presence generated friction with the Indians. They moved a mile and a half west where Soldier Creek met the White River.

It wasn't long before the Army showed the Sioux it meant business. An escaped convict had been caught in the Indian camp, and was put in the Robinson guard house. When the Sioux tried to free him in a midnight attack on the post, the soldiers formed a skirmish line and advanced

IN 1874, fort had two adobe officers' quarters (right of commanding officer's house), three barracks, adjutant's office, left guard house, some of the store houses. Second guard house, other buildings, were added between 1875 and 1884. Crazy Horse was wounded in 1874 guard house. After Fort Laramie's importance lessened, Fort Robinson was enlarged and new post built immediately to the north, but flagpole remained here until 1890. (Redrawn from SHS data.)

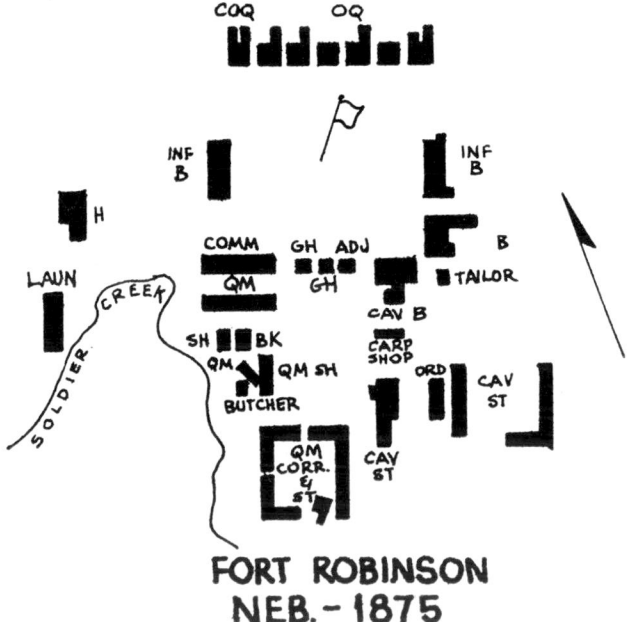

FORT ROBINSON NEB.- 1875

into the flashing guns of the Sioux. The Indians fell back.

The Custer Expedition into the Black Hills of Dakota passed through Robinson and the aftermath required regular patrols from the post to clear illegal miners from the Indian territory. General Crook's Rosebud campaigns of 1876 also used Robinson.

Robinson's troops were involved in the great Indian roundup after the Custer defeat. Crazy Horse, said to have been a leader of the battle, was brought to a camp near the post. When he left it to take his ailing wife to a doctor, rumors were that he planned to flee to Canada. He was invited into Robinson to talk to the commanding officer.

When he saw that the parley was to be behind the guard house bars, he pulled a knife out of the folds of his shirt. A soldier lunged with a bayonet. By midnight Crazy Horse had died in the adjutant's office next door, and with him, the hope of the Sioux nation.

On this spot on January 9, 1879, another nation's fate was sealed. The pitiful remnants of Dull Knife's Cheyenne warriors, friendly to the Army for sometime, had escaped from their Oklahoma reservation, after disease spread among them in the strange climate. They preferred to "die fighting than to perish of sickness," Dull Knife said.

After a parley in which Dull Knife announced, "Tell the Great Father if he tries to send us back we will butcher each other with our knives rather than go," the tribe was put under guard in a barracks.

On January 5, the Indian department telegraphed that the band was to be marched immediately to the south. Snow was deep on the ground, the weather below zero. Dull Knife refused to go, even when the Army said it would cut off fuel and food to the barracks.

Five nights later a shot from the barracks killed a sentry. Three more shots and two more sentries pitched forward into the snow. From the windows and doorways, Dull Knife's band poured, warriors, women, old people, children.

Clad only in their underwear, the soldiers rushed out of their barracks. A running fight followed across the fort grounds, Indian women and young boys taking the weapons as the warriors were killed. By the time they reached the foot of the bluffs behind the fort, the Indians

DULL KNIFE'S WARRIORS died against bluffs to rear of 1879 Fort Robinson. Old picture shows the six single-story officers' quarters, double-story commander's residence, barracks and flagpole. New fort was begun in 1880 between this post and bluffs.

were lead by the "Princess," Dull Knife's daughter. A charge by Army cavalry, now clothed and formed, scattered their rear guard, but the rest had time to climb the cliff.

Thirty-seven Cheyennes died, 52 were recaptured by nightfall that day. On January 21, 1879, the remainder were located at Hat Creek Bluffs, 41 miles away. With 22 dead and nine critically wounded, the three remaining Cheyennes fired their weapons the last time, then charged the 300 rifles of the Army. True to their word, they died rather than submit.

TO GET THERE: *From Scottsbluff, Nebraska, take state 87 north 48 miles to junction with state 2. Turn left, go north on 2 for 26 miles to Crawford. State museum, hotel, cabins, all former fort buildings, flank highway a mile west of Crawford on U.S. 20.*

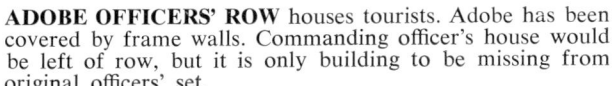

NEW FORT ROBINSON dates to 1880's. Officers' quarters in background were built in 1887 of adobe covered by wood. More than 100 buildings were added when post became regimental headquarters. Its troops were at Wounded Knee affair, 1890. In later years fort was cavalry remount station, prisoner of war camp, training center for K-9 corps war dogs. Army abandoned it in 1947, state and federal agencies now use it.

CRAZY HORSE DIED HERE. Stone marker is on site of first guard house, other signs identify landmarks of first fort. Buildings behind trees date from 1904. This is original parade ground, 160 yards square.

ADOBE OFFICERS' ROW houses tourists. Adobe has been covered by frame walls. Commanding officer's house would be left of row, but it is only building to be missing from original officers' set.

Fort Yates, North Dakota

The Messiah War which was to climax with the Massacre, or Battle, of Wounded Knee, began at Fort Yates and the Standing Rock Indian Agency, North Dakota.

Sitting Bull had kept the peace since his surrender at Fort Buford in 1881. Since 1883 he had lived at the Standing Rock agency immediately north of Fort Yates.

But during his stay at Standing Rock, things hadn't gone well. The agent took an instant dislike to him, terming him "crafty, avaricious, mendacious and ambitious," although some other observers have gone so far as to regard him the "George Washington of the Sioux nation."

In the late 1880's, the Messiah Craze appeared in Nevada and spread throughout the Indian world. Sitting Bull was still a prominent figure in this world, having successfully fought agency attempts to strip him of his tribal authority.

Although records are not clear as to the extent of Bull's role in the craze, it appears that he left the reservation when Kicking Bear, the medicine man who brought the Craze to Standing Rock, was ordered away from it.

A detachment of Indian Police went to get Sitting Bull at his tribal home in Grand River, South Dakota. Soldiers from Fort Yates followed them.

The ensuing melee resulted in the death of Sitting Bull and seven Hunkpapa warriors, as well as seven policemen.

Word of Sitting Bull's death spread like the wind. Two fights occurred on the Cheyenne river. The remnants of Sitting Bull's band joined Big Foot and fled to the Dakota Bad Lands.

Three thousand troops closed in. On December 28, the 7th Cavalry surrounded the Indians at the village of Wounded Knee in the southwestern part of the state. The Indians agreed to surrender, were herded into a group and surrounded by 500 troops. Four Hotchkiss guns were trained on them.

While the soldies were searching the Sioux for weapons, a shot rang out. Before anyone could explain the shot, the soldiers began to fire. The 7th Cavalry was avenging the Battle of the Little Big Horn with a savagery that all but wiped out the tribe. Twenty-nine whites were killed and 33 wounded. Conservative estimates place the Indian losses at more than 200.

Running down the remaining hostiles occupied 8,000 soldiers for the next month. General Miles led what was the largest force ever assembled in one place to fight Indians.

Minor skirmishes continued until the end of January, 1891. The cooler heads among the Sioux saw the futility of the fight. The Indian Wars of the Northwest were over.

BOTH NEW AND OLD forts existed in 1879. The log barracks and officers' quarters facing them (at top of plat) were built when Fort Yates was founded in 1874, torn down after 1870. Fort had 60 men in 1874, 458 in 1877 after Custer massacre. Indian troubles worsened at that time and fort commander replaced Indian agent with an Army officer. (Redrawn from NA data.)

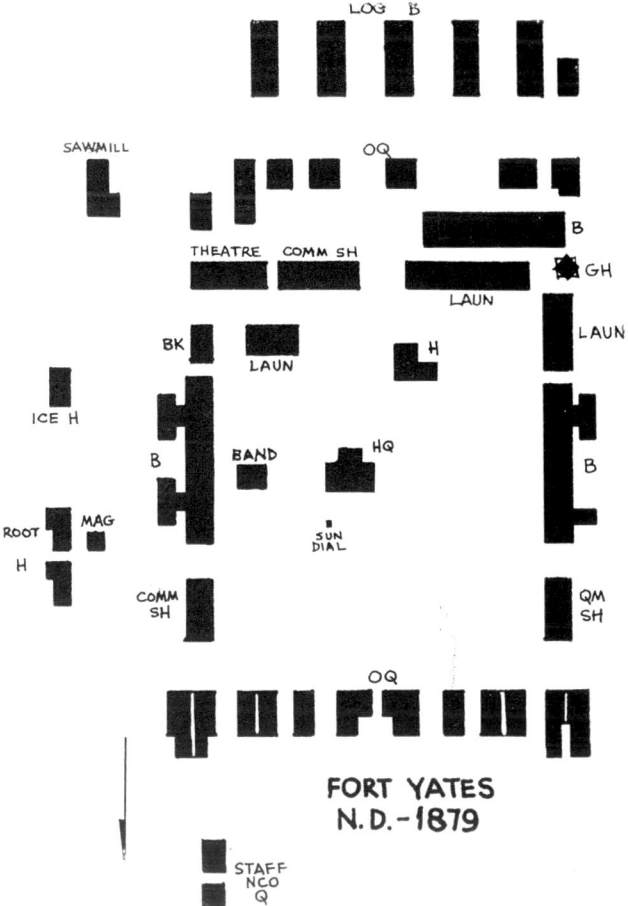

FORT YATES
N.D.—1879

TO GET THERE: *From Mobridge, South Dakota, take U.S. 12 across the Missouri 34 miles northwest to McLaughlin. Go straight on state 63 for nine miles to Dakota line; this road becomes North Dakota 6. Six miles north of line, turn right on state 24 and take this gravel road to its end. This is Standing Rock Indian Agency and town of Fort Yates. The "Standing Rock" is on bluff above river at north end of town.*

STANDING ROCK AGENCY, foreground, and Fort Yates, background, in 1880's presented trim but bare appearance. Block house that served as fort's guard house is in row of fort buildings right background. Fort lies between it and Missouri river, left background. Agency buildings are in foreground.

MODERN FORT YATES and agency are no longer barren. Few period buildings are left. Fort was abandoned in 1903 but agency remains. Across river, left, nothing remains of fort's "hog ranch," town of Winona. Its "expansive bars and amiable hostesses" attracted Indians and soldiers alike. They could cross frozen river to visit its "six or eight blind pigs, or properly speaking, liquor saloons, running wide open."

SACRED STANDING ROCK stands on bluff above Missouri. Legend claims it is Indian mother and baby who turned to stone when husband abandoned her in favor of a second wife. Stone was venerated by Teton Sioux who placed it in center of each village in which they lived.

INDIAN POLICE KILLED in Sitting Bull's capture are buried in Catholic cemetery at Fort Yates. Sitting Bull once was buried here, at another time in town, now lies near Mobridge, S. D. Police killed at his death are listed on other side of their marker: Lieutenant Bull Head, Sergeants Shave Head and Little Eagle, Privates Warriors Fear Him, Broken Arm, and Hawk Man.

Fort Lapwai, Idaho

Troops were rushed to Idaho in the fall of 1862 when the Nez Perce reported that 10,000 to 15,000 whites had moved into their reservation. A company of cavalry was sent. It was joined by a second in November after the tribe requested that a fort be built to protect them against the white invasion.

They showed their willingness to cooperate by turning over to the Army the Indians accused of killing two white men. The Nez Perce were proud of their boast that no member of the tribe had taken the life of a white man for fifty years, something the white race couldn't say about their relations with the Nez Perce.

THIS WAS FORT LAPWAI at the start of the Nez Perce war. Two barracks on east side of parade ground were 112 by 30 feet and 91 by 30 feet respectively. (Redrawn from Division of Pacific Report, 1877.)

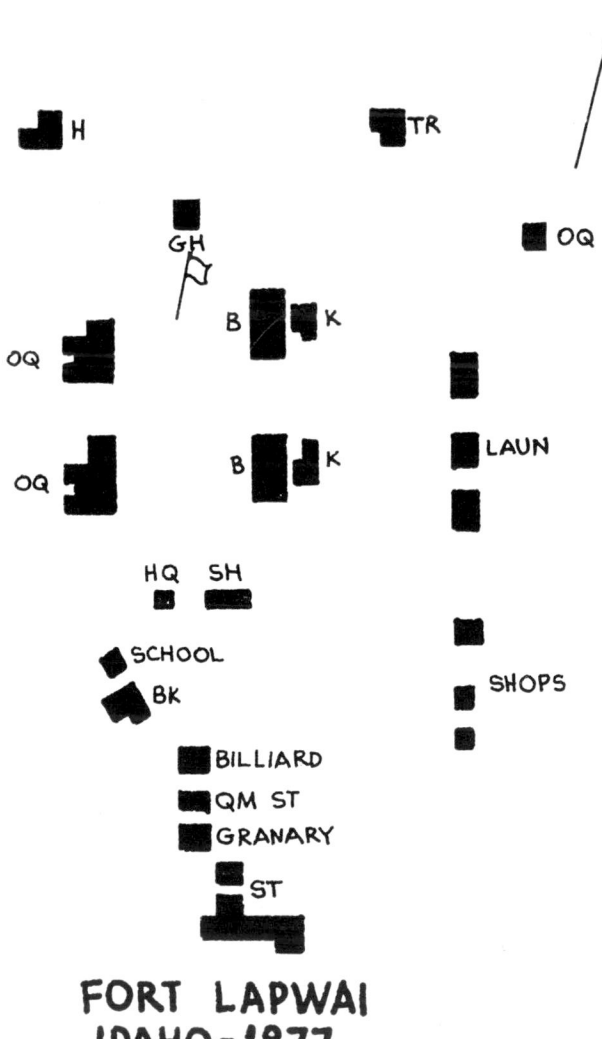

FORT LAPWAI
IDAHO-1877

The Army's post, Fort Lapwai, was in Lapwai valley, twelve miles southeast of Lewiston and 96 miles northwest of Fort Walla Walla. In 1877, the government announced that all of the Nez Perce would have to move to the Lapwai reservation. This meant that the Southern Nez Perce would have to abandon its traditional home in southeastern Washington.

Young Joseph, chief of the southern tribe, attended the council at Fort Lapwai upon the insistence of General Howard. In a day-long conference, Joseph could not be swayed. The land still belonged to the Indians, he said, and they should not be made to move.

"If we ever owned the land," he declared, "we own it still, for we never sold it."

Howard's patience was at an end. He argued with one of the Indian priests and he had him arrested. The council broke up in protest.

Five days later Joseph decided to move so his friend could be freed, but by then the Nez Perce had taken action in their own hands. Blood ran in northern Idaho as the Nez Perce remembered every wrongdoing of the past and took revenge against the whites who had mistreated them.

For an unwilling Joseph, as leader he had no choice. He had to fight.

A massacre in Salmon Valley was reported and Howard sent two cavalry troops to punish the Indians. In White Bird Canyon, the Army blundered right into an ambush of 200 Nez Perce, placed by Joseph who showed a tactical genius from the start. This was his first fight, but 37 soldiers were dead.

From safety across the Salmon river, Joseph watched as Howard moved 300 men up to the banks and camped, unable to cross. A day later he saw two troops of cavalry leave. After dark, Joseph abandoned his camp, and swooped down on the cavalry detachment. The Army force threw up hasty defenses in the Cottonwood, but this did not protect two scouting forces that Joseph's Indians met, killing 11 men and Lieutenant Rains, their commander.

On July 10, Howard had followed Joseph to the banks of the Clearwater river, far south of the reservation. The wily Indian selected his ground, erected breastworks, and commanded the river banks and the only spring in the area. Both forces assaulted the others' position, and Joseph tried to envelop the Army defenses. Then the artillery and gatling guns arrived.

LAPWAI AT TURN OF CENTURY was an Indian agency, after Army abandoned post in 1884. New barracks was located at northeastern end of parade ground, new administration placed amidst old barracks row. Few of these buildings remain today. Stables in foreground and officers' quarters (left, top floor shows beyond closest hill) still flank parade ground.

The Army tried to hit Joseph from the rear. He lead a determined charge and routed the attack. He attacked Howard again, but as a delaying action while the bulk of his tribe retreated.

After the Battle of the Clearwater, the losses were 13 soldiers dead, 27 wounded; 23 Indians dead, 46 wounded, mainly because of the artillery.

Joseph then began his dramatic retreat over most of the northwest. Before he surrendered, he took his tribe 2,000 miles, fought the Battle of the Big Hole, Wyoming, and the Battle of Bear Paw, Montana. He faced the combined forces of Howard and Miles, and finally gave up, defeated only because his time had run out. He had lead the Army on a chase that won him the grudging admiration of its generals, and he had displayed a tactical skill the envy of the Army's experts.

His surrender speech is still a classic:

"Tell General Howard I know his heart," he said, referring to the friendship that Howard felt toward the Indians. "What he told me before—I have it in my heart. I am tired of fighting. Our chiefs are killed . . . It is cold and we have no blankets. The little children are freezing to death. My people—some of them have run away into the hills, and have no blankets, no food . . .

"Hear me, my chiefs, my heart is sick and sad. From where the sun now stands, I will fight no more, forever!"

TO GET THERE: *From Lewiston, Idaho, take U.S. 95 east to town of Lapwai, about 25 miles. One mile south of town is Lapwai Agency headquarters, right hand side, site of old Fort Lapwai.*

FORMER HEADQUARTERS or guard house faces middle of parade ground of old fort, now is residence of officer of Nez Perce tribal council staff.

THIS OFFICERS' QUARTERS serves same use today for agency staff at Lapwai Indian Reservation. Basically unchanged except for face-lifting, building stands at southwest corner of parade ground. Half-mile further south is old fort cemetery, metal number stakes showing where graves once were.

151

Fort Washakie, Wyoming

"A little jewel of a post beside a rushing stream" is how the wife of Lieutenant Colonel Andrew S. Burt described Fort Washakie when her husband became its commander in spring, 1889.

Washakie was not only a little jewel of a post, but also one of the few named after a living Indian. That Indian, Chief Washakie of the Shoshones and a friend of the whites, was the only full-blooded Indian to be buried with full military honors of a captain when he died in 1900.

The story of Fort Washakie is really the story of its namesake, for 60 years the despot of the Shoshone. He refused to fight the white man, regardless of provocation. He kept the Shoshone at peace throughout the Indian wars, sometimes siding with the Army and rendering valuable service in the Battles of the Rosebud and Dull Knife.

Washakie served with the Army as a scout, and periodically reenlisted until his death. The government conveniently overlooked physical examinations and age limits. When he died, he died a Christian after being Baptized in 1897. His tombstone bears the dates 1804–1900, but there is general agreement the first date should read 1798, with his age 102 years upon death.

The first fort of Washakie was 17 miles from the agency and originally named Camp Augur, then Camp Brown. In 1870 it was moved next to the Shoshone Agency in the Wind River Indian Reservation. This place had been given to Washakie during the Civil War, and by shrewd maneuvering later he was able to retain it.

When part of the original reservation was requested by the government, Washakie agreed to sell for a price and the promise of protection.

The chief had an understanding uncommon to the Indians . . . he was one of the few who realized the old days were dead. He figured that he would never be able to keep all of the old reservation, so he gave part of it up in return for conditions that he felt would guarantee ownership of the remainder.

He was right. One of the conditions was that a fort be built to protect his tribe—against both Indian and white foes alike—and the Army set aside a one-mile reservation and built a new Camp Brown.

The Shoshone united with the Crow to help the Army fight the Sioux, Cheyenne, and Arapaho. The end result was that the Shoshone later were required to share their reservation with the Arapaho. By 1962, the Arapahoes outnumbered the Shoshone, 2,373 to 1,816, but contacts between the two are traditionally strained.

On December 30, 1878, the post was renamed Fort Washakie. Three years before the post surgeon's report had described this man, and the conditions at the post.

"Their chief, Wash-a-kie," he wrote with some extra hyphenation, "has a benevolent and kindly expression of countence, is well made, strictly honest, and possesses superior intelligence and influence; he is a half-breed Snake and Flathead, brave to a fault, and long the fast friend of the white man.

PARADE GROUND of Fort Washakie was 181 by 141 feet, two adobe barracks measured 75 feet by 30. (Redrawn from NA data.)

FORT WASHAKIE
WYO.-1879

![Photograph]

(Courtesy National Archives.)

TWO WASHAKIE'S ARE IN THIS PICTURE, a man and a fort. Chief Washakie, pointing, left, is talking to a group of Shoshones before Fort Washakie flag staff. A store house is at left, guard house and corral in rear. Taken in 1892, picture indicates changes fort underwent after plat of 1879.

"At present 1,400 rations per diem are issued to them, and they also receive annually large quantities of clothing, etc. A great deal of clothing and more valuable articles soon become the property of the agency employees and neighboring ranch-men."

The government wanted to abandon Fort Washakie in 1899, but sly Washakie told of visions he had: Sioux descending on the reservation, scalping his warriors, stealing his women and children. His strenuous objections, and active imagination, delayed the abandonment of the fort.

He died a year later, but the Army took no chances with the spirit of the fabled chief. They waited nine more years before abandoning the fort, turning the site and buildings back to the tribes.

TO GET THERE: *From Lander, Wyoming, take U.S. 287 north 17 miles to town of Fort Washakie. Wind River Indian Agency is site of old fort. Chief Washakie is buried in former military cemetery, about four miles south.*

OLD GUARD HOUSE shows signs of adobe finally giving way to march of time. This is not same guard house identified in 1892 picture.

OLD BARRACKS had little use after Army left Fort Washakie in 1909.

(Courtesy of Ray H. Mattison, National Park Service.)

A Home for General Custer

"Use your own judgement, and do what you think best if
you strike the trail; and whatever you do, Custer, hold on
to your wounds."

—Final orders of General Terry's to General Custer, June 22, 1876, at the camp on the Rosebud before the
Battle of the Little Big Horn, according to General Miles' debatable version of the story.

Lieutenant Colonel Brevet Major General George Armstrong Custer is today more a
myth than a man.

That he was vain and colorful, historians agree. That he and five troops of the 7th cavalry died on July 25, 1876, on a hill overlooking the Little Big Horn river of Montana, historians agree.

On just about every other facet of Custer and the so-called "Custer Massacre," historians have argued interminably, as many supporting a theory as debunking it.

Several western forts are woven into the thread of Custer, but none more than those
at Bismarck, North Dakota. Here the 7th cavalry had its headquarters, and from here it left
on May 17, 1876 as part of a three-pronged expedition to suppress the hostile Sioux.

General Crook was to advance from the south and Fort Fetterman, Colonel Gibbon was
to come from Montana. With General Terry in overall command, Custer's 7th Cavalry was
to move from the east. The plan called for the Sioux to be caught in a nutcracker.

What went wrong has been debated so that now the only definite fact is that Custer
and his entire force of 200-some men were killed two months later. The Battle of the Little
Big Horn was the high water mark for the Sioux nation, but it was also their death knell.

The spotlight of publicity mustered the undivided attention of the American Congress
and public on the Indian problem. The Army finally was permitted to wage aggressive, well-
supported war against the red man, and brought peace to the Northwest.

Fort McKeen, North Dakota

On the bluffs 270 feet above Fort Abraham Lincoln was located both its father and its son: Fort McKeen, the infantry post that came before but was absorbed by the larger cavalry installation.

Stockaded in the earlier tradition of the frontier forts, McKeen still compromised with those who preferred the open fort. The palisades only protected the two sites that faced the plain. The sharp drop to the river was considered sufficient protection to the east.

Work on Fort McKeen began in June, 1872, by six officers and 84 enlisted men. Frequent Indian attacks came, some directed at McKeen, more shared with Abraham Lincoln when it was built in 1873.

McKeen was not as elaborate as its younger sister fort.

"This little post," wrote Elizabeth Custer, "had been built before the railroad was completed, and the houses were put together with as few materials as possible. There was no plastering, but the ceilings and partitions were of thick paper made for the purpose."

TO GET THERE: *From Fort Abraham Lincoln, take road that climbs bluffs immediately north. McKeen block houses can be seen from Abraham Lincoln.*

THREE BLOCK HOUSES looked over western plains from Fort McKeen. Bluff line protected open sides. Stockade was reconstructed in thirties by CCC, but has disappeared. Sites of buildings are marked. (Redrawn from data courtesy Del Skjod, Mandan, N. D.)

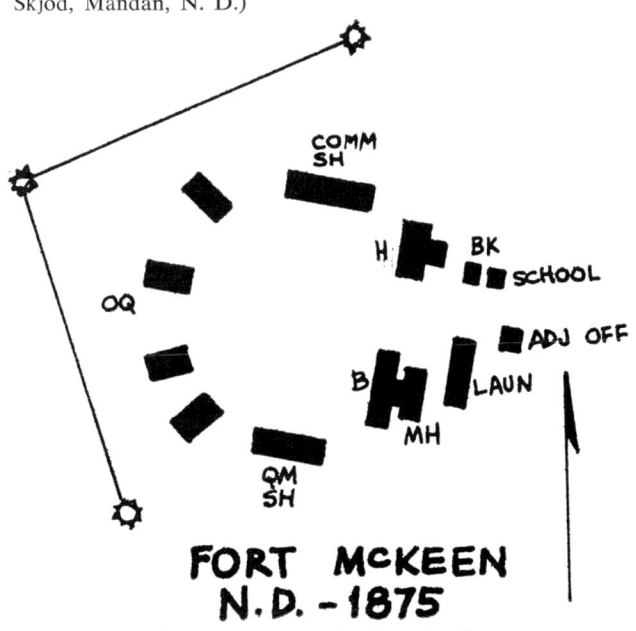

FORT McKEEN
N. D. – 1875

FORT McKEEN TODAY from northern block house. Commissary store stood where brush is in foreground, officers' quarters were in half-circle, vaguely marked by mounds of brush and rubble.

SOUTHERN BLOCK HOUSE is immediately above Fort Abraham Lincoln. Missouri river is in left background.

Camp Hancock, North Dakota

At the rail head in Bismarck, a sub-post of Fort Abraham Lincoln greeted the Northern Pacific cars that carried supplies for Custer's post and others in the district.

It was built in 1872, soon after Fort McKeen was established six miles to the south. Originally called Camp Greeley, it was first designed to protect the railroad crews, then became a supply post after the rail head was completed to what was then called "the crossing."

The next year the town next to the camp tried to induce German capital to invest in the railroad's intercontinental expansion. Bismarck was adopted as its name, honoring the German chancellor. Camp Hancock quickly was outgrown by the booming new city.

In 1875 it consisted of a single log barracks, 100 by 20 feet, two officer's quarters, two married soldier's quarters, a 20 by 20 foot guard house and a store house. Three tents served as a hospital, and the stables took care of seven horses.

By 1877, Camp Hancock had outlived its usefulness and it was absorbed by Fort Abraham Lincoln.

TO GET THERE: *Camp Hancock site is at 117 Main avenue in downtown Bismarck, N.D. From the capitol building, go south on Sixth street to Main avenue (U.S. 10 and U.S. 83 East). Turn right 4 blocks to Camp Hancock building on south side of street. Museum is open June 1 through September 30, closed Sundays.*

(Courtesy State Historical Society of North Dakota.)

CAMP HANCOCK was not the most impressive of Army posts by any means. As a supply depot, its mission was confined to storing and forwarding supplies landed at Bismarck by railroad and steamboat.

MODERN CAMP HANCOCK consists of this single restored and remodeled building housing museum of relics from Dakota pioneers and Indian tribes.

Fort Abraham Lincoln, North Dakota

"In the dim light I could see the great post of Fort Lincoln," wrote Elizabeth Custer telling of her arrival there in 1873. "Our quarters were lighted, and as we approached, the regimental band played 'Home, Sweet Home,' followed by the general's favorite 'Garryowen.'"

To Elizabeth Custer, and to half of the 7th Cavalry, Fort Abraham Lincoln was to home until the Battle of the Little Big Horn three years later.

In its earliest weeks, in the fall of 1872, the new fort was harassed by Indians even before it was finished. Apparently the end of construction and arrival of several hundred men did not dissuade the Indians from further attacks as there were three in 1873. The fort herd was driven off by Indians in 1874. While Custer was at Little Big Horn in 1876, the pickets and outer guards were attacked in broad daylight.

The presence of the railroad at Bismarck, and the steamboats from the Missouri, brought elements of the east to Abraham Lincoln, however. The Custer House was always open and entertaining seemed to rank for priority with Indian fighting. A new residence was built in 1874 after a fire, and was described by the post surgeon's report as "a commodious and elegant building."

The soldiers found their own diversions, especially in the winter. A frozen river offered easy access to the "Point" on its eastern bank, the usual collection of saloons and sporting houses. Liquor smuggled off steamboats also enlivened the dull days in the new barracks.

Elizabeth Custer wrote considerably of Fort Abraham Lincoln. In "Boots and Saddles," she describes it:

"Fort Lincoln was built with quarters for six companies. The barracks for the soldiers were on the side of the parade-ground nearest the river, while seven detached houses for officers faced the river opposite. An the left of the parade-ground was the long granary and the little military prison, called the 'guard house.'

"Still farther beyond were the quarters for the laundresses, easily traced by the swinging clothes-lines in front, and dubbed for this reason 'Suds Row.' Some distance on from there were the log-huts of the Indian scouts and their families, while on the same side also was the level plain used for parades and drill. On the left of the post was the sutler's store, with a billard room attached. Soon after the general arrived he permitted a citizen to put up a barber-shop, and afterwards another built a little cabin of cottonwood, with canvas roof for a photographer's establishment."

None of this remains today except signs and stones marking the corners of the buildings. The fort was abandoned in 1891 after completion of the Northern Pacific railroad made it unnecessary.

The "commodious and elegant" Custer House, and all but three other fort buildings, literally disappeared when 100 settlers descended upon the deserted post the night of December 1, 1894. Buildings were dismantled and hauled away by 60 teams. When the guilty parties were tried, their punishment of 30 days in the county jail was more than worth the lumber, staircases, windows and building parts that even today make up many houses in the Bismarck area.

CONSIDERED FINEST ARMY fort of its day, Abraham Lincoln was on flat plain below Fort McKeen, to the northwest. Its stables had room for 600 cavalry horses. Custer's house is large officers' quarters left of flagpole. (Redrawn from data courtesy Ike Smith, Fort Lincoln State Park.)

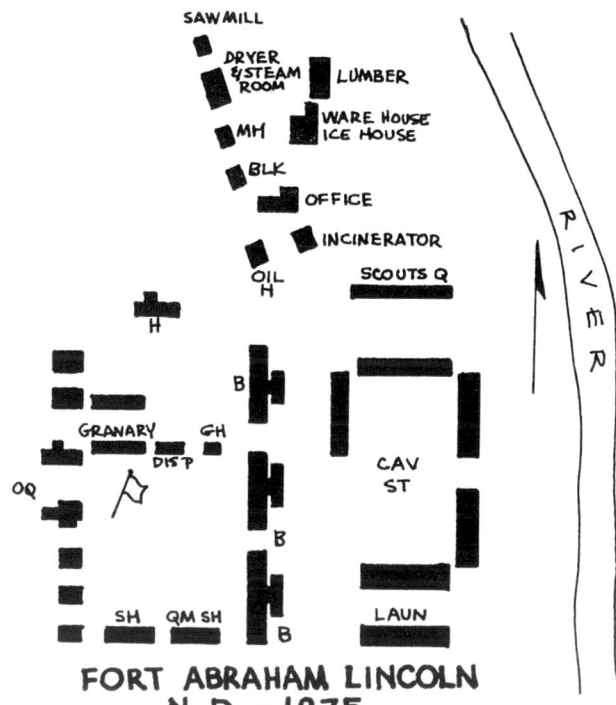

FORT ABRAHAM LINCOLN
N. D. -1875

TO GET THERE: *From Bismarck, N.D., take Main avenue (U.S. 10) across Missouri river Memorial Bridge to Mandan, four miles. Turn south at Sixth avenue, go five miles to Fort Abraham Lincoln State Park. Museum is on left side of road, main part of old fort is on right. "Trail West," pageant of Custer story, is presented here nightly throughout July and August.*

ORIGINAL FLAGPOLE stands in front of "Custer House" marker. Only foundation corners remain of this 10-room mansion that included eight closets, pantry, kitchen, cellar. Of a story-and-a-half it served for parties and receptions. It was a church whenever minister visited post.

UP RAVINE TO RIGHT Custer marched to Little Big Horn. His wife wrote that the 7th Cavalry officer's wives gathered on June 25, 1876, trying to bolster their courage by singing hymns. "Indescribable yearning for the absent, and untold terror for their safety, engrossed each heart . . . At that very hours the fears that our tortured minds had portrayed in imagination were realities, and the souls of those we thought upon were ascending to meet their maker." Wounded 7th Cavalry soldiers not in main fight returned to Fort Abraham Lincoln aboard steamboat Far West at 1 a.m., July 6, 1876.

(Courtesy State Historical Society of North Dakota.)

FORT ABRAHAM LINCOLN in the 1880's. "Custer House" is to right of flagpole.

FORT ABRAHAM LINCOLN TODAY. Only flagpole remains. Officers' row ran along left of picture paralleling thin line of trees. Foundations of store houses are in foreground. Fort McKeen's southern block house is on horizon, center of picture.

Twilight

"We surrender. We would have done it before, if we had
known where to find you."

—Words of Big Foot, Sioux chief, at Wounded Knee, S.D., December 28, 1890.

THE INDIAN had fought the good fight and lost. The frontier had pushed itself to the Pacific and railroads criss-crossed the plains. The days of the "Old West" were at a close. The need for protection decreased to the point that the Army had to resort to training maneuvers to keep itself tactically sound.

Over the years, the western frontier had given to the United States the finest trained and blooded Army in the world. It had a cavalry arm without peer. Its other combat units had refined their skills in the postgraduate courses of the Indian Wars.

The tiny military posts could be justified no longer. Several were combined into a single large post. Within a decade or so, the justification for these central posts also could not be found.

Some were retained by the Army or its sister services as training and headquarters camps. None were kept with the thought that a battle would be found at the stockade or on the other side of the ridge.

The Spanish-American War closed the chapter on the Western Army. Troopers went to the Phillipines, Cuba, and points west, east, and south, never to return to the frontier service of the "old days" that were no more.

Camp Sturgis and Fort Meade, South Dakota

Two military posts of the seventies were almost in the shadows of Bear Butte, a craggy, cone-shaped hill in southwestern South Dakota. Both Camp Sturgis and Fort Meade were there in 1878, although the former came first.

Sturgis was little more than a row of tents in the buffalo grass beside the Spring creek. Troops arrived in June, 1878, from Forts Sully, Laramie, and Abraham Lincoln for a summer camp and to protect the Black Hills settlements. They were also to locate a site for a permanent post.

It was natural that the base of Bear Butte would be their starting point. It had served a like function for many earlier expeditions, including Custer's 1874 Black Hills trip.

Eight cavalry troops and six infantry companies pitched their tents at Bear Butte. By late summer part of the command was on the march against Dull Knife's Cheyennes who had escaped from their Oklahoma reservation. Sturgis' soldiers cornered the Cheyenne late in the fall in northwestern Nebraska and took them without a fight to Fort Robinson.

When this expedition returned, half-frozen in its summer uniforms, they found Camp Sturgis was no more. The site of a permanent post had been located five miles away in August, and Sturgis was abandoned in November.

Legend has it that General Phil Sheridan personally selected the new location, although he originally intended a site in the Spearfish valley. Speculators put such a high price on the Spearfish land that Sheridan took his fort elsewhere.

Legend adds that he rode over the new fort's grounds and pointed out the locations of buildings with his sword.

When Camp Sturgis moved, its less savory neighbor did likewise. Known as "Scooptown" or "Scoop,"—because the soldiers said they were likely to be cleaned or scooped out whenever they visited it—it was a Hog Ranch near the post run by Jim Fredericks. It offered the various entertainments of frontier hog ranches, and moved to the present site of Sturgis, South Dakota, as soon as its customers did.

Although soldier and civilian graves also were shifted to the new post, it's said that those of three of Jim Fredericks' ladies were left on a hill above the camp.

The new post first was named Camp Ruhlen, but was renamed Fort Meade on December 15, 1878. It was built around an octagonal parade ground, 1,025 feet long by 2,000. Five barracks were on the northern edge, 15 officers' quarters on the southern.

When the post was being built, a supposed mixup of plans gave Fort Meade one of the most elaborate Army residences in the west. The story is that the blueprints for the commander's house at Fort D. A. Russell, Wyoming, were erroneously sent to Fort Meade, and the plans for a small commander's house at Meade, were sent to Russell. The difference was considerable, as Russell was a much larger garrison than Meade.

This is supposed to be the reason that Fort Meade's commanding officer wound up with a 30-room house.

Aside from the peace keeping duties, Fort Meade's troops were involved in the Wounded Knee Battle and its aftermath in 1890–91, and much of the campaign was directed by a headquarters established at the post.

Not only was Fort Meade the last Dakota post of the Indian Wars, but it was the longest lived. It continued in operation as a cavalry post and a 1935 report termed it "one of the best cavalry posts in the Army from a professional point of view." In 1944 it was turned over to the Veterans Administration and is now a Psychiatric Hospital.

CAMP STURGIS IN 1878 was in shadow of Bear Butte, "a straight row of a dozen 'A' tents, flanked by the canvas headquarters of the commandant and his commissioned aide, a large corral of supply wagons, and a good number of hoofs," according to a contemporary newspaper description. Although this picture is sometimes said to be Custer's 1874 camp, local historians have checked landmarks, insist it is Camp Sturgis.

(Courtesy Richard B. Williams. Sturgis, S.D.)

FORT MEADE IN 1888 shows barracks on far side of parade ground, officers' quarters on near side. In 1892, Meade was first Army post to play Star Spangled Banner at retreat ceremony, later a custom adopted by all posts long before it became national anthem in 1931. Colonel Caleb Carlton, its commander, directed that during ceremony "visitors must remove their headdress and show proper respect for the flag."

TO GET THERE: *From Sturgis, S.D., take state 34 east 2 miles to right turn into Fort Meade Veterans Administration Hospital. For Camp Sturgis site, return to highway, continue east 2 miles to state 79, left turn. Bear Butte is three miles north, right side of road; Sturgis site is left side. Parking area and marker are next to road.*

FORT MEADE TODAY, taken from approximate location of 1888 picture. Early buildings were replaced after turn of century and Veterans Hospital has added more modern construction. Officers' quarters are basically unchanged from 1888, although trees now virtually hide them.

CAMP STURGIS TODAY is marked by slight indentations along Spring creek where huts were dug under canvas tops. Volcanic butte is 4,570 feet above sea level, appears higher because it rises abruptly 1,200 feet from surrounding plain.

MILITARY CEMETERY of Fort Meade, on hill overlooking post, contains special section for children, also graves of 23 members of 7th Cavalry. One tombstone marks burial place of two men killed by wood alcohol smuggled into post, a scandal that killed three and hospitalized ten more in late nineteenth century.

STABLES AT FORT MEADE commemorate Army's most famous horse, Comanche, only living survivor of Custer Massacre. It is said Comanche was ridden to top of Bear Butte by Captain Myles Keogh in 1874. Keogh died with Custer, but Comanche returned to Bear Butte area when 7th Cavalry made up Fort Meade garrison from 1879 to 1887.

Fort McKinney, Wyoming

The forerunner of armored cavalry was introduced in northern Wyoming, and this time traditional cavalry came out the winner. The fact that not a shot was fired indicates diplomacy played a larger role than firepower, though.

It was in 1892 in Johnson County, Wyoming, near Fort McKinney. For years cattlemen and farmers—nesters, as the ranchers called them—had fought over the barbed wire that was creeping across the once unlimited range land. By the late 1880's the settlers had teamed up with the cattle rustlers to present a united front against the cattlemen.

The cattlemen, in turn, organized a pesudomilitary outfit known as the Regulators, hired gunmen from Texas, Idaho, and Colorado, and put a former Army officer in command. They headed north to show the nesters they meant business.

In Buffalo, storekeepers donated guns, ammunition and tobacco to a newly organized Home Defenders Corps. When the Johnson County men heard that the Regulators had holed up at the TA ranch, 14 miles south, they headed that way. The Regulators were so anxious to get behind hastily dug breastworks that the Home Defense Corps captured their supply wagons.

At dark, the 400 Home Defenders dug rifle pits within gunshot range of the Regulators, and built a portable fort for 40 men on top of the captured wagons. They intended to push this early day tank into the cattlemen's barricade and throw dynamite from it.

Traditional cavalry put an end to the business before any blood could be spilled. Three troops from Fort McKinney appeared, took the cattlemen into "protective custody," and told the Home Defenders to go home. The Regulators were kept in the county jail in Cheyenne at Johnson County's expense, until the money ran out and the case dismissed. Fort McKinney men were stationed in Buffalo until tempers cooled.

The fort was 14 years old when this so-called War took place. It had originated at Cantonment Reno, 50 miles away along the Powder river, moving in 1878 to a site on Clear Creek next to Buffalo.

The first fall two sets of barracks and a trader's store were completed. It wasn't until General Phil Sheridan stated that the fort was to be a permanent one that Congress allocated $40,000 to complete construction. The hospital, officer's quarters, headquarters, and non-commissioned officer's were built from this appropriation.

TO GET THERE: *From Buffalo, Wyoming, take U.S. 16 west 3 miles. Fort McKinney, now Wyoming Soldiers and Sailors Home, is set back from left (south) side of highway.*

FORT McKINNEY'S reservation markers are part of flagpole, bear inscription: "U. S. MIL. RES'N." Plaques are for wars in which members of Soldiers and Sailors Home fought: Cival War, Indian Wars, Spanish-American and Cuban Wars, and World War I.

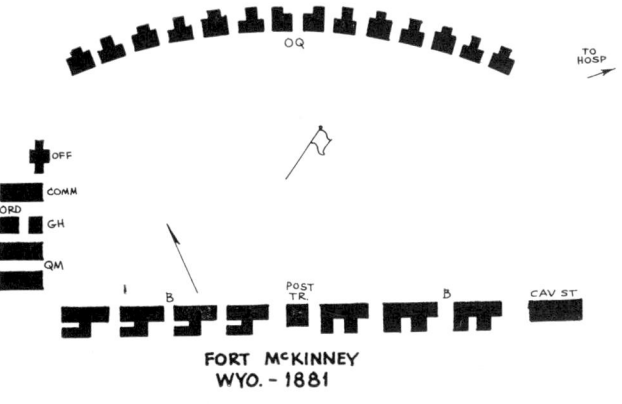

OFFICERS' QUARTERS at Fort McKinney alternated in size, while post commander and another senior officer occupied two single-family residences in center of row. By the time post was completed, barracks were double-storied buildings. Headquarters, indicated by "OFF" for offices, is at far end of parade ground. (Redrawn from NA data.)

FORT McKINNEY
WYO. - 1881

(Courtesy of Thelma G. Condit, Buffalo, Wyoming.)

FORT McKINNEY in the eighties shows officers' quarters at right, single-storied barracks, left, headquarters at end of parade ground. Big Horn mountains are in distance.

FORT McKINNEY TODAY shows Big Horn mountains overlooking bare plain. Some cellar ruins exist along fence line and in clumps of brush.

FORMER HOSPITAL now is visitors house for Wyoming Soldiers and Sailors Home, use made of fort after Army left it in 1894. Hospital was west of original fort and this wing was moved after fort was abandoned. Memorials to former military days are next to flagpole.

OLD MULE STABLES remain from military days southwest of cavalry stables, also remaining but now used as a garage. McKinney's last combat action was to help General Miles after Wounded Knee action in 1891.

Fort Custer, Montana

The barn door was closed, but a bit too late, when the government followed up the Battle of the Little Big Horn with a fort 15 miles away.

Appropriately enough, the new fort was named Fort Custer on November 8, 1877, although it had been called Big Horn Post when building first started in May, 1877.

And with the barn door closed and the horses (and Indians) all gone—to the reservation, in this case—there was little for the cavalrymen at Custer to do. Nothing of a military nature occupied them in the immediate area of the post, though detachments were sent to most of the wars of the eighties in the northwest, especially those with the Bannocks and Nez Perce.

In company with the other permanent-type posts of its era, Fort Custer was an elaborate installation, on a bluff overlooking the junction of the Big Horn and Little Big Horn rivers.

It did have one Indian incident, however. It was one fit to warm the heart of any movie producer.

It seems that in 1880, a theatrical troupe was presenting a play, "Captain John Smith," at the post. Local Crow Indians were playing members of Pocahontas' band. Suddenly the announcement was made that non-theatrical Indians were stealing the Crows' horses.

Soldiers, actors, Indians and all mounted the remaining horses and took after the thieving Indians . . . truly a matter of not knowing the players without a program!

The railroad arrived at Custer in 1895. By 1897 things were so quiet that even the Indians had moved, and no excuse remained for keeping Fort Custer active. It was abandoned, its buildings sold and used as the nucleus for what is now thriving Hardin, Montana, two miles northeast of the fort site.

The site itself became a golf club, though now that, too, has been abandoned. Only scattered cellars and a marker from the Daughters of the American Revolution remain to indicate where once more than a thousand soldiers were stationed.

TO GET THERE: *From Hardin, Montana, take U.S. 87 south about two miles. After crossing Big Horn river, turn right on dirt road that climbs to top of bluffs. Abandoned golf clubhouse is on site of Fort Custer; marker is near road.*

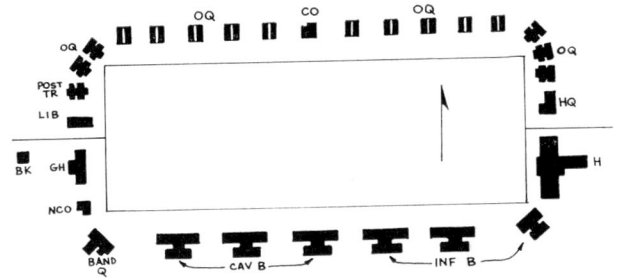

BIG HORN RIVER flowed to rear of officers' quarters at Fort Custer. Stables were west of post. Not all buildings were completed by 1877, but this was plan at the time. (Redrawn from NA data.)

FORT CUSTER
MONT.—1877

CAVALRY KEPT IN TRAINING at Fort Custer with formation like this. Officers' row is in background. Commanding officer's house was third from left, band stand in front of it. Not even trace of trees remains today.

(Courtesy National Archives.)

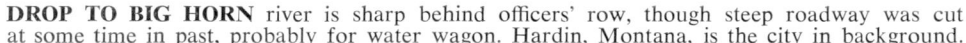

BARRACKS ARE depression in ground today, flanking Daughters of the American Revolution marker. View is to west; guard house, library, stable area were located in background.

DROP TO BIG HORN river is sharp behind officers' row, though steep roadway was cut at some time in past, probably for water wagon. Hardin, Montana, is the city in background.

Fort Missoula, Montana

What John Mullen had built and nature and time had put asunder, it fell to the lot of the new garrison of Fort Missoula, Montana, to restore.

So it was in the summer of 1879 that the Third Infantry was taken from its task of building a new fort next to Missoula, Montana, in order to restore the Mullan Road toward Coeur D'Alene, Idaho.

They had only been at the fort a year, spending most of that time building shelter after a first winter in tents.

As that winter ended, it became necessary to warn the countryside of the possibility of Indian troubles. The Battle of the Big Hole had been fought nearby in 1877 and troops temporarily at the site of the new fort were involved. The Indian captives were brought to the new fort after the battle.

Hostile Indians renewed their harassments the next summer until a detachment form Missoula surprised and captured the largest band on July 21. This ended the Nez Perce threat. It was also the only Indian engagement involving troops permanently stationed at Fort Missoula.

The next summer their road restoration project began. Trunks of trees had fallen across Mullan's old trail, and bridges and timberland burned. Packers for mining supplies were blamed—this had been their way to stop any competition from stage coaches on the road.

At some places the logs were piled 10 feet high. At other places, the road was washed out. On the St. Regis Borgia river, 40 substantial bridges had to be repaired or replaced. With the obstacles out of the way, then long stretches of road had to be corduroyed.

One item can't be ignored when talking of Fort Missoula: its "Infantry Bicycle Corps," the brain child of Lieutenant James A. Moss, later a retired brigadier. In 1896 a squad from this "corps" followed the lieutenant on an 800 mile tour of Yellowstone Park. In 1897, Moss lead a 23-man detail 1,900 miles to Saint Louis, Missouri, a 40-day trip marked by an exceptionally wet period of weather.

Moss hoped to prove that bicycles could replace the horse. The trip was a success, but something called the gasoline buggy proved to be an even better horse replacement.

TO GET THERE: *From Missoula, Montana, take U.S. 93 southwest to edge of city. Road to fort branches off to right at city limits. Modern buildings are occupied by reserve units, various government agencies.*

INTERIOR OF SERGEANTS' quarters shows that logs even were used in partition that separated two parts of duplex. Kitchens were to rear, stoves are still in place.

THIS WAS THE PLAN of Fort Missoula as of 1879, but only a few of the buildings had been built by then. Store house in center of parade ground was only temporary. Remaining today are the magazine, sergeants' quarters, and the northern laundresses' quarters. All other buildings have disappeared and main area of modern post is east of hospital. (Redrawn from NA data.)

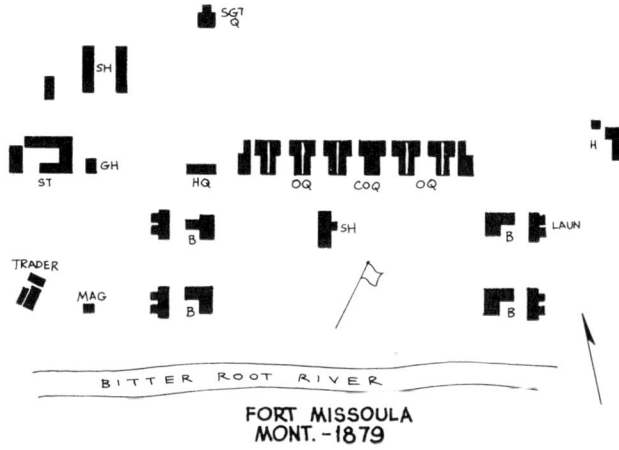

FORT MISSOULA
MONT. - 1879

OFFICERS' ROW looked like this in the eighties, but no longer exists. Service at Missoula was considered choice in the Army. As recent as 1935, an officer reported excellent fishing and hunting at the fort and "the richest man in the country cannot buy better facilities for pleasure than are enjoyed by the soldiers at Fort Missoula."

ORDNANCE AND COMMISSARY sergeants' families occupied this building after it was built in 1878. In later years it was covered with boards and matched other buildings in a row built more recently. When row was being torn down in 1961, logs were revealed, and its early date established. Plans to turn it into a museum are being considered.

MAGAZINE COST $485 when built in 1878, and still is in use.

RECREATION BUILDING is oldest structure at Fort. Built in 1877 for $450, it housed officers temporarily, then was laundresses' quarters. It is now a semi-officer's club for the reserve activities at the fort. Flagpole, right, is modern addition to scene.

NEZ PERCE CAMPAIGN, Fort Missoula's only major Indian engagement, is commemorated on fort's entrance plaque. Fort Missoula was occupied by military 1877-1918; 1921-41; 1944-46.

Fort Sherman, Idaho

Although General Howard personally selected the site for Fort Sherman in 1877, by 1883 the medical officer was to comment officially, "The selection of this site for a post reflects little credit on its projectors."

He felt that important matters of drainage and flood control were ignored by the founders who were moved "more apparently by sentimental views."

This is understandable. The fort stood a half mile wide and more than a mile deep on the northern shore of Lake Coeur d'Alene in northern Idaho, at the point where the lake emptied into the Spokane river. It was in a clearing in the timber, with the "primeval forest still remaining seeming to ward off something of the harshness of the lake winds and perhaps to modify somewhat the raw grandeur with the medicinal balm of pine."

Sherman's location presented problems, though. It was only five feet above a lake that periodically put the parade ground under water. The post's water supply was a problem from the beginning, reported the surgeon, "due to a well known difficulty of trying to make water run uphill," and $7,000 had to be spent on a pumping and pipe system.

Established on April 16, 1878 as Fort Coeur d'Alene, by troops who had been at Spokane Falls since August, 1877, the post had three missions. It was supposed to keep the peace in northern Idaho, watch the Canadian border, and protect railroad and telegraph crews. It was busy at the first and third tasks, but somehow the Canadians never really needed much watching, although American Indians skipping back and forth across the border posed a mutual diplomatic embarrassment.

Alcohol was a problem at the fort, blamed by the surgeon on the close proximity of the town of Coeur d'Alene. This had sprung up simultaneously with the fort, and was incorporated in 1877 with a population of 36. A mining boom in 1882 didn't help.

Earlier, Sherman's commander had to direct the owners of the "Bonanza Ranche," three miles from the post, to stop delivery of their goods on the reservation. Not only was this a violation of the charter granted by the government to the post trader, but the Bonanza didn't have the rosiest reputation. It was, according to a report, "an intolerable nuisance that liquor is sold to soldiers at 'Bonanza Ranche' by the drink and by the bottle, that many of the men resort there without authority, induced by the prospect of gaming, and plentiful supply of liquor, etc., and that good soldiers are becoming demoralized and frequently subjected to the disgrace of courtmartial."

On the post, the whiskey was easier to control. The post trader was told to place a slate or blackboard above the bar on which he was to keep a "Black List," the names of those men deemed by their company commanders to "have forfeited the privilege of purchasing or otherwise obtaining liquor, spirits, or malt."

TO GET THERE: *From Spokane, Washington, take U.S. 10 east 20 miles to western edge of Coeur d'Alene, Idaho. Upon entering city, turn right toward city park. Fort marker is at western corner of park. Four blocks further west is site of fort.*

LAKE COEUR D'ALENE closed one end of Fort Sherman parade ground, barracks, two others. Barracks, 132 by 23 feet, were built in 1870's, a fifth, 135 by 24 feet joined them in 1885. Each had porch across front, eight rooms on first floor, single dormitory room on second. Today two of the officers' quarters and the chapel remain. Former are apartments next to Coeur d'Alene Junior college. (Redrawn from NA data.)

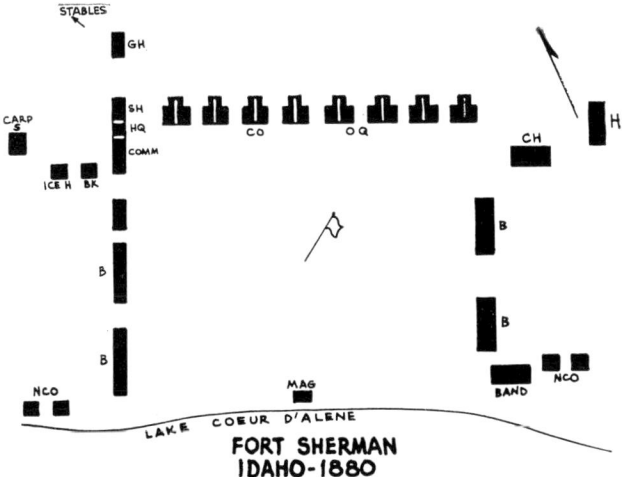

FORT SHERMAN
IDAHO-1880

FORT SHERMAN IN the eighties was almost crowded into lake by forest. Officers' row can be seen at left, hospital offset from far end. Next to hospital is chapel, the two barracks. Headquarters buildings and barracks are obvious on next row. Fort tried to run a steamboat on lake in 1880, but had trouble getting more than five miles an hour on a full head of steam.

CHAPEL FROM FORT SHERMAN still serves as church on original site. Painted a bright red, it still faces fort's parade ground, though railroad spur line and gas storage tanks mar appearance of site. Fort was abandoned in 1900 and much of its old area has been used since 1933 by junior college.

REAR OF OFFICERS' QUARTERS, now apartments, show that duplexes were good-sized. Right building has been renovated only slightly from early appearance; garage is modern addition. Left building has seen major remodeling, but still retains lines of former quarters.

Fort Spokane, Washington

Fort Spokane might not have done much fighting, but it was a fine place to be stationed, if the 1893 post surgeon's report was any indication.

"I think," wrote Major V. B. Hubbard, "the manifest contentment and even cheerfulness of the men here is due in great measure to a cause of which they are almost not entirely unconscious: viz. the great beauty of the natural scenery and the healthfulness and salubrity of the climate."

Located in northwestern Washington, it was selected by General Howard to replace Fort Colville, to the north, and Camp Chelan to the west. The site of the latter had been selected in 1880 and announced as the most ideal; within months it was abandoned and the site proclaimed as extremely undesirable.

Howard selected Spokane's site 56 miles northwest of the city of the same name, and on the south bank of the Spokane river, a mile above its junction with the Columbia. Construction of elaborate quarters, barracks, and storehouse began in 1882, two years after Howard's visit, and lasted three years.

Originally named Camp Spokane on October 21, 1880, it was renamed a fort on January 12, 1882 when six companies of infantry and cavalry were located there. It was supposed to serve as a control point in keeping the peace between the whites and Indians, and as a guardian along the Canadian border, but it saw little more than occasional police activity. By the time it was built, the Indians, Americans, and Canadians all got along quite well together, and Spokane's troopers had little to do but enjoy the climate.

When war came, it spelled the end of the fort. The Spanish-American war drained the post of its garrison, and it was officially abandoned on August 26, 1899. It was used as an Indian school until 1914, and as an Indian hospital until 1929.

TO GET THERE: *From Spokane, Washington, take U.S. 2 west to Davenport, 32 miles. Turn right on state 22. Take it 23 miles north to town of Miles, right of road. On left side is site of old fort. Beyond, half mile, is recreational area on river and Franklin D. Roosevelt Lake. Picnicking, camping, swimming, boating facilities available.*

GUARD HOUSE, seen from stable loft, is to become museum and headquarters for Fort Spokane recreational area. Cell block area is obviously on the left side of building; small windows opened into individual cells.

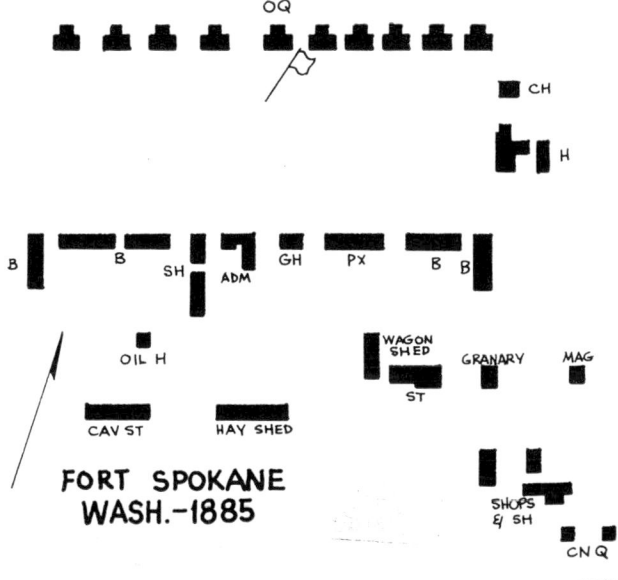

OFFICERS' ROW was half mile from bank of Spokane river. Most buildings were frame except brick guard house, magazine, and granary. Along with quartermaster stables, these are only buildings left today. (Redrawn from NA and National Park Service data.)

FORT SPOKANE WASH.–1885

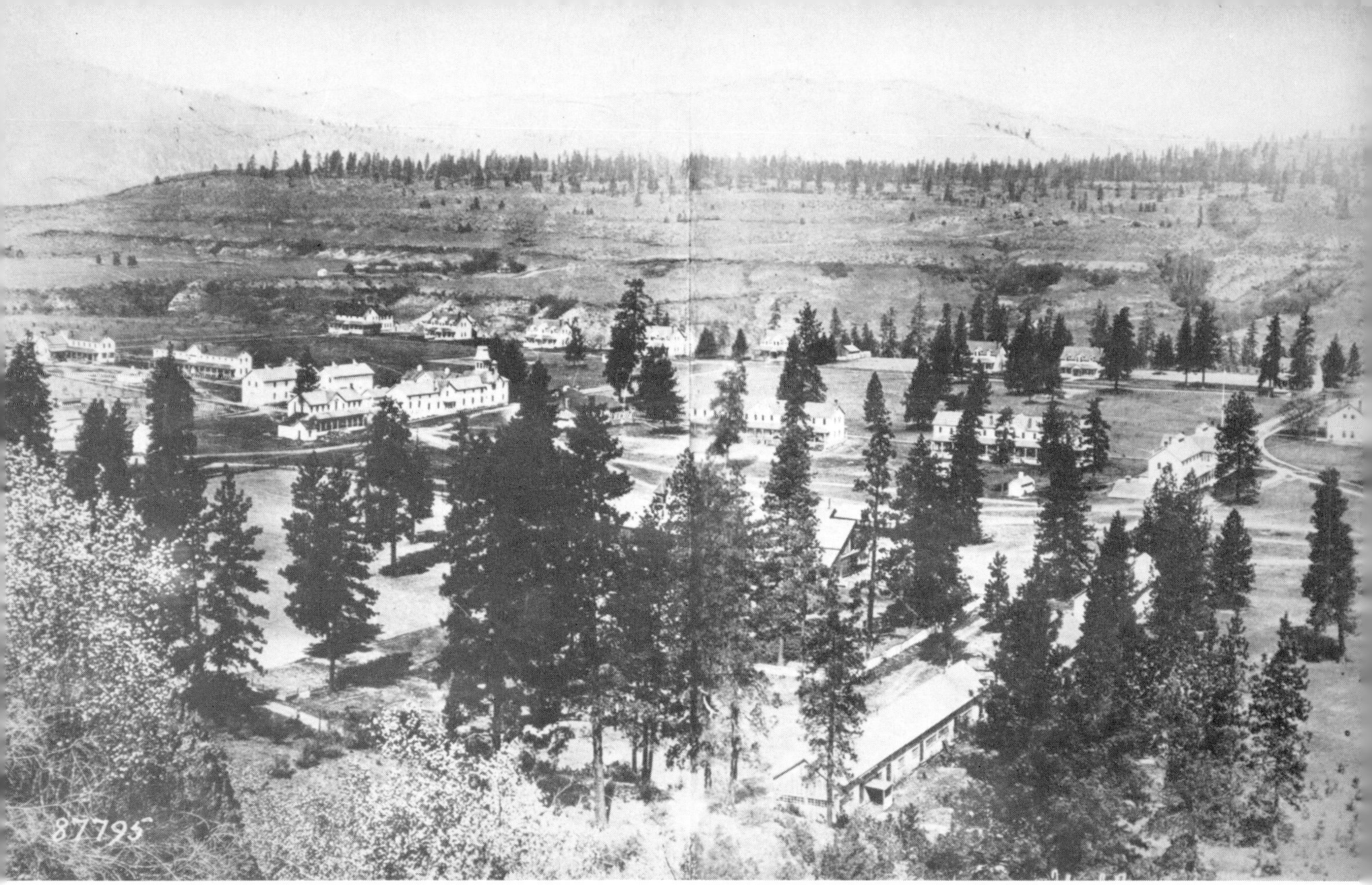

(Courtesy National Archives and National Park Service.)

FORT SPOKANE in 1890 all but hides the few buildings that remain today. Guard house and stable are behind trees in center of picture; cupola of stable is left of the break in picture.

FORT SPOKANE TODAY shows guard house, stable, and, at right corner, granary. Now a National Park Service recreational area as part of Grand Coulee Dam, building sites are marked and background data provided to visitors.

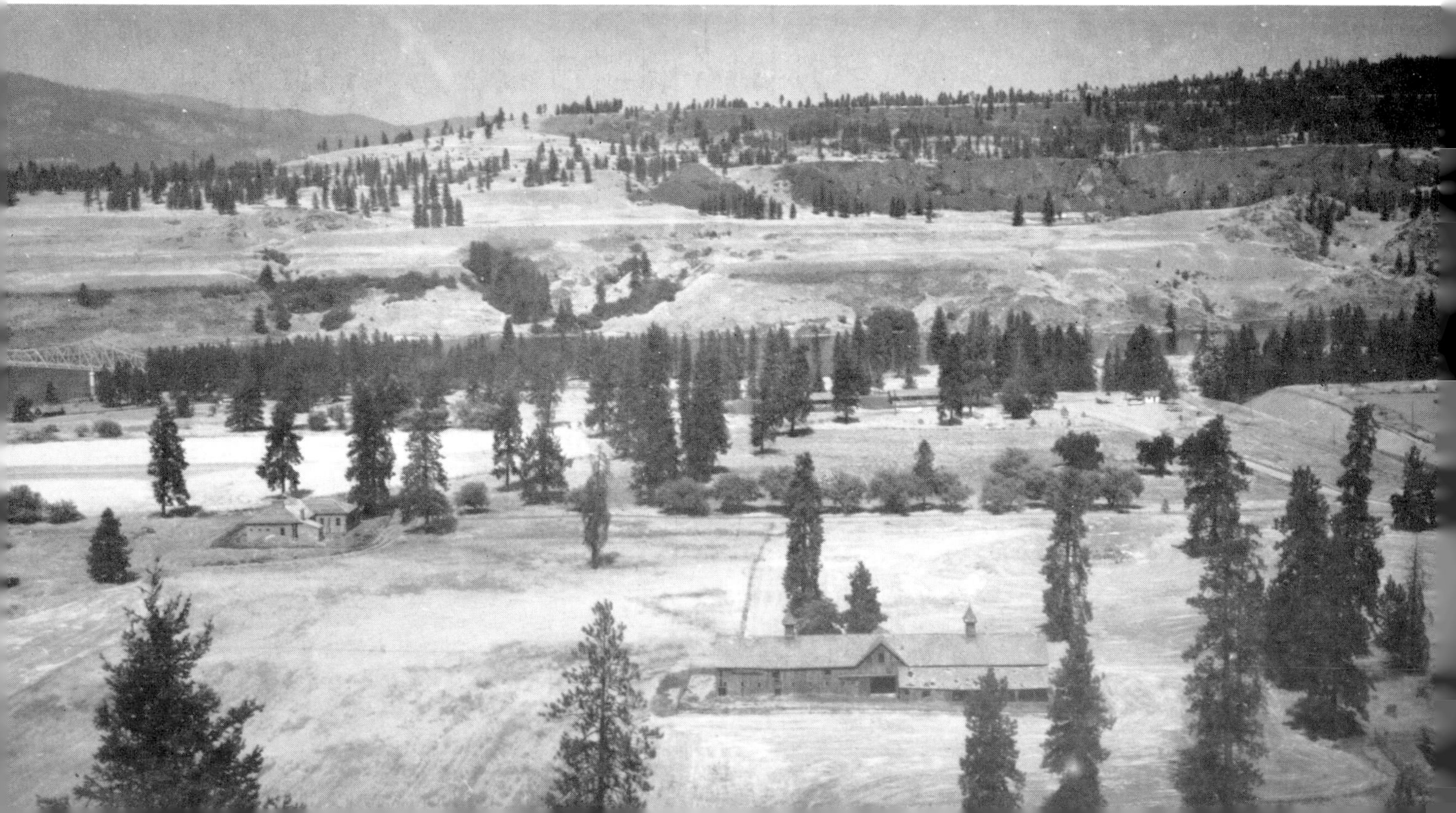

Fort Maginnis, Montana

Fort Maginnis was planned with good intentions, but its actual operations were a disappointment. Not only did it come too late to protect the central Montana wagon roads, but the fort had its own ideas about what it was supposed to do.

The reason it didn't do much toward wagon road protecting was obvious: by 1880 no one was interested in attacking the road. The reason the Army ran the show its own way was equally obvious: every group of citizens had their own problems and solutions, and personal gain lay at the root of most.

Maginnis started in late 1880 as a series of log buildings along Forge creek, 10 miles north of Gilt Edge. This was a 19-saloon gold camp that sometimes drew more gold from soldier pockets than the surrounding Judith mountains, especially after liquor was banned from the fort.

Two hundred civilians built the post in the spring of 1881. After the Army arrived and looked around for something to do, all they could find were a few anti-rustler expeditions.

By civilian standards, they were less than successful in this mission. When Indian rustlers were cornered, the Army had to return both rustler and loot to the reservation even though the owner of the stock was present. Once back at the agency, the culprits could wait for things to quiet down, and disappear, booty and all. On one such occasion, the owner settled matters himself. At the point of a Winchester, he relieved the Army of its responsibility for his stolen cattle, an incident quietly forgotten by the soldiers.

Rustlers were both red and white. Vigilantes were more effective than the military against the latter, though they operated close to the fort.

Known as the "Stranglers," they had no qualms about hanging one rustler in Forge Creek below the post. The soldiers profited in the long run. They found three gold pieces hidden in his moccasins.

TO GET THERE: *From Lewiston, Montana, take U.S. 87 east 14 miles to gravel road leading to ghost town of Gilt Edge. Turn left, go north about 7 miles. About one mile short of Gilt Edge (buildings appear in distance), turn right and follow winding road about 9 miles to site of fort. Small markers appear at road junctions. Fort is across Forge Creek, left side of road. Although maps indicate site can be reached from north across Judith mountains, roads are now closed and only access is from south.*

THIS IS BARRACKS row today, marked by one of few signs remaining on foundations. Fort site belongs to various owners whose fences criss-cross foundations of old buildings.

ONLY FOUNDATION STONES remain to mark sites of elaborate Fort Maginnis buildings. Signs have been placed at some, but most foundations are unmarked but obvious. When fort was abandoned in 1889, buildings were sold. Some were moved on rollers, others torn down and lumber used in houses throughout county. (Redrawn from SHS data.)

RUINS OF STABLES run in long line from foreground. Judith mountains are in background.

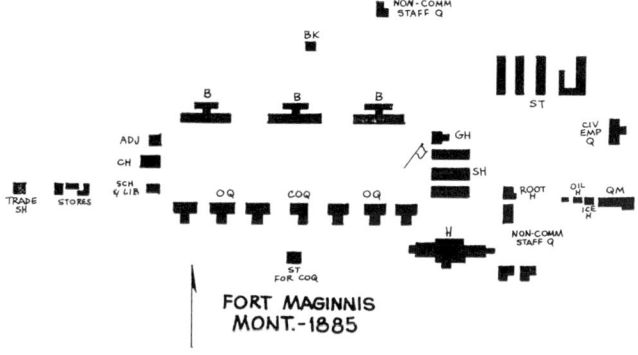

FORT MAGINNIS
MONT.-1885

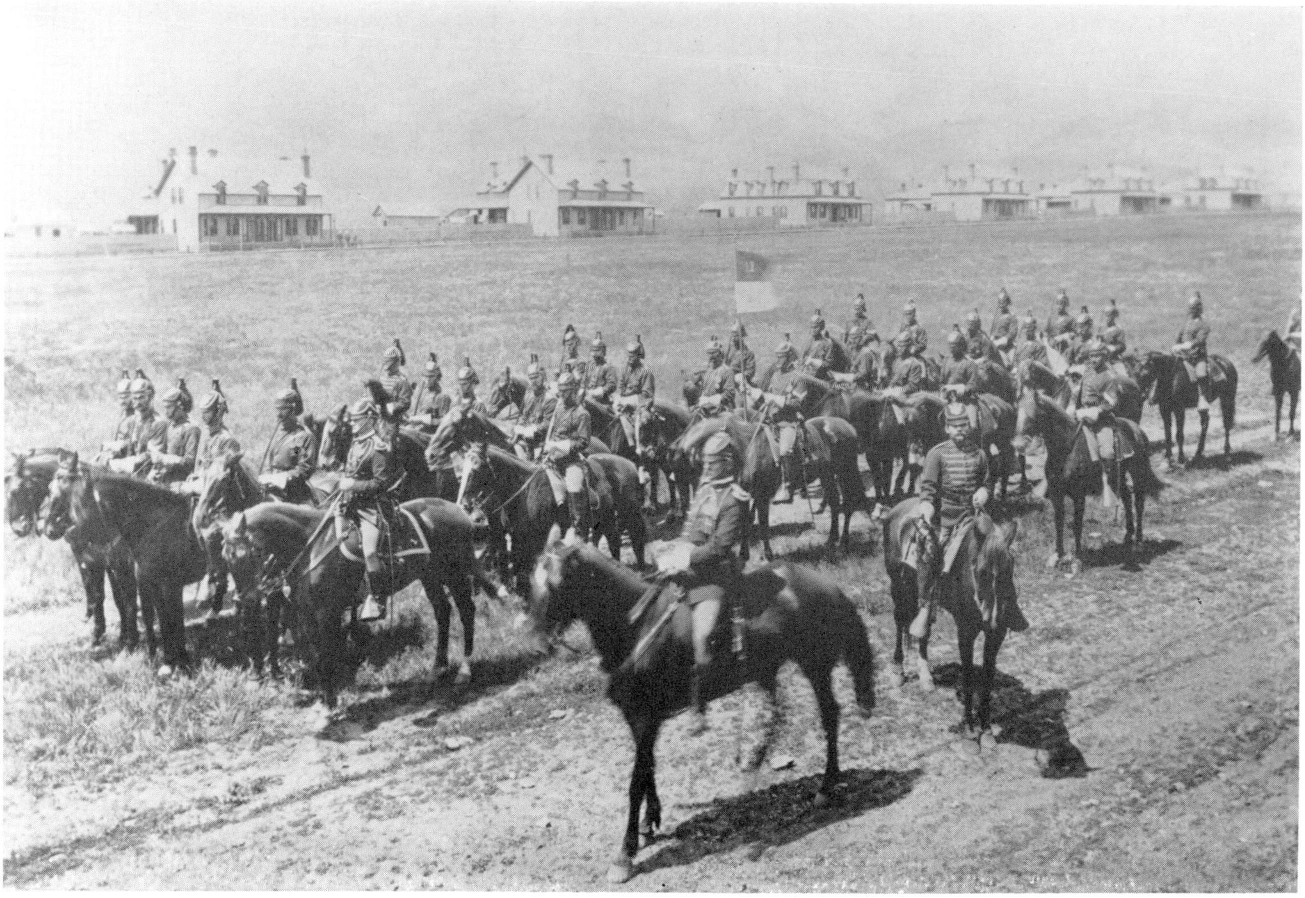

(Courtesy of Montana Historical Society.)

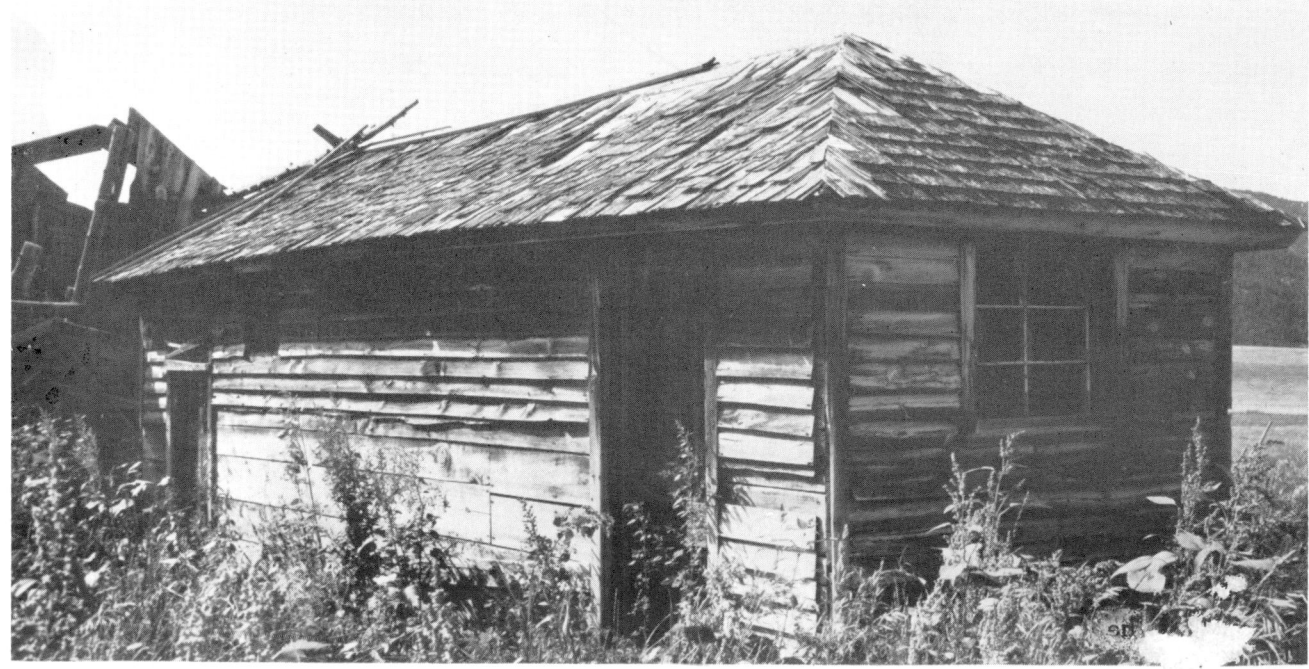

OFFICERS' QUARTERS were large duplexes at Fort Maginnis in the eighties, just about as grand as the dress uniforms of its soldiers. Commanding officer's residence was third house from left.

MOVED ON ROLLERS from fort, this building now has out-lived its second career, work shop on ranch near Gilt Edge, 9 miles away. Its appearance probably has changed little since Army days.

Fort Assinniboine, Montana

When Sitting Bull and company crossed into Canada after the Custer battle, his nearness didn't contribute to the peace of mind of northern Montanans.

They were so upset, in fact, that in 1878 Congress appropriated $100,000 to build a fort that would calm their nerves. That was why Fort Assinniboine was built. Its construction was pushed so vigorously on the plains near Havre, Montana, that Indian onlookers announced it must have risen out of the ground.

With Sitting Bull sitting fast in Canada, the Army wasted no time getting ready for him. Bricks were made in new kilns near the post, other materials shipped up the Missouri. Soon Fort Assinniboine was the largest military post ever constructed in Montana.

It was a fort in the grand style. Long rows of brick buildings faced an immense parade ground. To add to the effect, castle-like towers were built on the end buildings of each row. Their design made it obvious they were for decorative rather than tactical purposes.

Bad water and powerful mosquitos plagued the first summer of the fort. A later attempt to dam Beaver Creek, the fort's water supply, involved many man-hours but was defeated by the first heavy rain.

Sitting Bull never did come to the Assinniboine area, but the post had more Indian incidents than many of its contemporaries. The Reil Rebellion of the Crees in Canada kept the garrison on the alert. Chief Little Poplar appeared near the post with his tribe, but he was killed by a half-breed before the Army could decide what to do with him.

During the winter of 1886–87, Assinniboine's commanding officer issued food to the Crees when he heard they were starving and eating their dogs. It was many months and mountains of red tape before this humane action was approved and the commander relieved of financial responsibility for what had been given out.

Through 1889 Indians camped near the fort. ̄ ̄ ̄ ̄ ̄esence made the whites more than a little ̄re̖ ̄ ̄ ̄ ̄ en the Messiah War started in the ̄ ̄ ̖ ̄ ̄nnibone's troops were rapidly deployed to Pine Ridge Agency and the post near Fort Peck, and the fast movements and shows of strength maintained the peace in northern Montana without firing a shot.

TO GET THERE: *From Havre, Montana, take U.S. 87 south 7 miles to a gravel road. Turn left to U.S. Agricultural Experiment Station, one mile, now occupying buildings of old fort. Daughters of American Revolution marker is on parade ground.*

TAKEN FROM INDIAN for "Mountain Sioux," Assinniboine also referred to tribe in Northern Montana. Post was 38 miles from Canadian border. At the time of this plat, barracks and officers' quarters at eastern edge of parade had not been built. (Redrawn from NA data.)

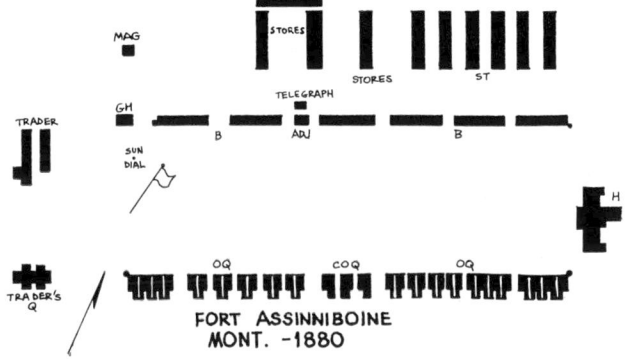

FORT ASSINNIBOINE
MONT. -1880

CASTLES OF NORTHERN MONTANA flanked Assinniboine's immense parade ground. Hospital was at far end, flag pole is 90 feet high. Today almost all of these buildings are gone except for single officers' apartment, right, and the duplex beyond it. State legislature appropriated funds to convert fort to a college, but ran out of money every year before reaching that allocation. A building at Northern Montana College was built of fort's bricks, is named Pershing Hall after junior officer who served at Assinniboine in nineties, later commanded in World War I.

GUARD HOUSE now serves another use, seed house for the Agriculture Experiment Station. Abandoned in 1911, post was turned over to Department of Agriculture in 1913, most of its buildings torn down in 1927.

SIX OFFICERS' FAMILIES lived in this multi-plex at southwestern edge of parade ground. It cost $21,600 to build, an economy due to local manufacture of bricks by soldiers enlisted especially because of their experience in brick production.

Dakota

Fort Keogh, Montana

Fort Keogh might be called General Nelson Miles' post. Not only did he build it, but he commanded it during most of its major Indian fighting.

Ultimately Fort Keogh became an extensive installation, but it started off as a shabby affair. Konwn as the Tongue River Cantonment, the New Post on the Yellowstone, and then Tongue River Barracks, its predecessor was at the mouth of the Tongue River at the south bank of the Yellowstone.

General Miles described its buildings as "rude shelters constructed in quite a primitive manner." They were wooden uprights with sod roofs arranged around a rectangular parade ground, but the soldiers did not have to stay in them very long.

In 1877, only a year after the arrival at the site of the cantonment, Miles and his men moved to the west a few hundred yards to the "comparatively commodious quarters of Fort Keogh," Miles wrote later. The name change, almost coincident with the move, was in memory of one of Custer's officers at the Little Big Horn.

Things picked up with the move to the large post. "The social circle was enlarged by the arrival of officers' families," Miles wrote. "The upper story of a large storehouse was turned into a hall for entertainments, pianos and comfortable

furniture appeared, the valuable library of the Fifth Infantry was unpacked, and the fine band of the same regiment contributed to make of the post an oasis of civilization."

Amateur theatricals and horsemanship divided the off duty hours of the post, but it also had its share of soldiering. Even before moving from the cantonment, in 1876, Miles troops met and defeated Sitting Bull, Crazy Horse, Lame Deer, and Chief Joseph, each one in a separate engagement.

The expedition against Lame Deer's band was highlighted by a display of typical Miles strategy. His force moved into Indian country, past the probable location of the Indian camp, and then doubled back after dark. A dawn attack on Lame Deer's camp was successful, though Miles narrowly escaped death when the chief fired a rifle at him from 10 feet. The general's horse balked and the shot missed, but killed the soldier next to him.

In 1881 a modern invention helped bring on the Sioux surrender when Sitting Bull sent an advance detail from Canada to ask about terms. Miles suitably impressed the Indians with a demonstration of the white man's mastery of electricity and, especially, the telephone.

Miles divided the Indians into two groups. Talking to each other over the new instruments,

THIS WAS THE ARRANGEMENT of the original Fort Keogh two years after it was abandoned. Mounds of dirt, rubble remain today. (Redrawn from NA data.)

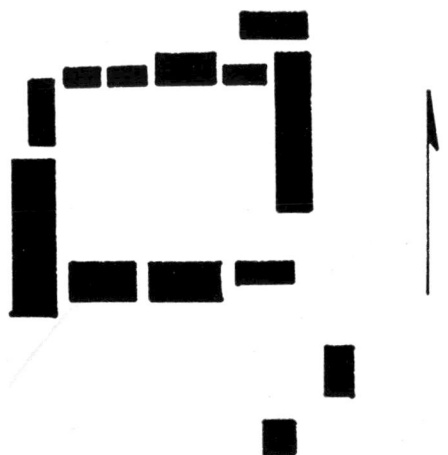

TONGUE RIVER CANTONMENT MONTANA - 1879

DIAMOND-SHAPED PARADE GROUND was unusual in western posts. General Miles' residence was at western point of diamond. Remaining today are southwestern row of officers' quarters, southeastern barracks, some of the non-commissioned officers' quarters. Army left Fort Keogh in 1908. (Redrawn from NA data.)

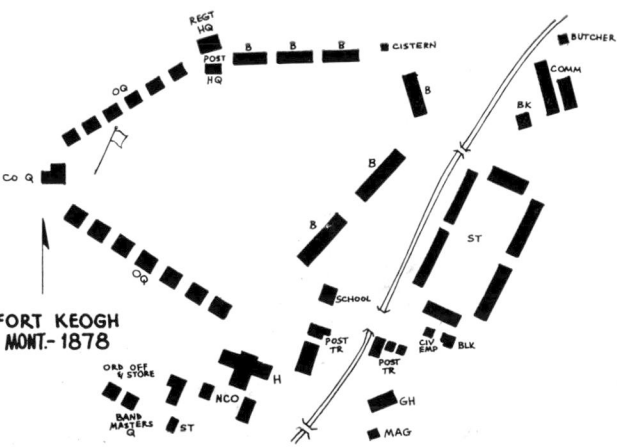

FORT KEOGH MONT.- 1878

(Courtesy National Archives.)

SIOUX CAMPAIGN from Fort Keogh included Captain Adams and Lieutenant Casey's Indian scouts. Adams is in the foreground; the scouts to the rear. Officers row is in the background. Road and traces of sidewalk remain today, the trees are full grown.

TONGUE RIVER CANTONMENT today. Only old well is at its original location. Cantonment was spread from this point to trees. Post was next to present-day Miles City, once lively neighbor of Fort Keogh. Its main street was segregagted, "bad" element on south side, "decent" on north. "Decent" were bankers, buffalo buyers, pawnshop operators.

"their hands shook visibly, their bodies trembled with emotion, and great drops of perspiration rolled down their bronzed faces."

Whether this had anything to do with it, Miles said "they carefully laid the instrument back upon the table and wished to go immediately away," and it wasn't long before 2,000 Sioux and allied tribes were encamped around the fort. The "whispering spirit" was more than the Sioux could fathom.

TO GET THERE: *From Miles City, Montana, take Main street southwest to edge of town. On right is Range Riders Museum, graphic presentation of Montana's early cattle days. In field to south is site of Tongue River Cantonment. Further west a mile is U.S. Range Livestock Experimental Station, site of Fort Keogh.*

180

GENERAL MILES' HOUSE is now used by superintendent of Range Livestock Experimental Station. After defeat of Chief Joseph, wives were gathered at fort awaiting news when Miles' Indian scouts arrived, reported two officers and 20 men were dead. Women were in near panic by time civilian interpreter arrived much later and identified the dead.

WATER WAGON SHED was original Fort Keogh building, but horse at its right corner is from later era.

A Directory of Military Forts of the Northwest 1850-1890

Many names meant a fort, and a fort meant many things in the Old Northwest. Generally speaking, a "fort" was a relatively permanent installation, though this term was used loosely to describe many non-military defended stockades, trading posts, or blockhouses. "Cantonment" meant a more temporary place, many times the ancestor of a fort. "Post" was a short-term installation, usually for the defense of a certain thing, such as a railroad junction, telegraph station, stage stop. "Camp" was a semi-permanent fort, or even an overnight stop, though the ups and downs of Army policy and Congressional budgets sometimes shifted forts to camps and vice versa. A Barracks usually was just that, a barracks from which troops were deployed for action elsewhere.

These are the military installations listed here. Some militia and volunteer forts are included, usually after due regard to whether they were garrisoned by uniformed military personnel. Fur posts are included only if they were military garrisons at some time, and then the dates indicate only the period of military use.

Many temporary or "end of track" camps have been left out, usually because definite data was lacking. Some are included and then only after a studied guess as to the location and dates. The locations given are in terms of modern towns which may not have existed at the same time as the fort.

The dates and locations are approximate, based on the best data available. No attempt is made to show changes as "fort" or "camp," and the most common designation has been used for the garrison. Other names by which it was known are noted under the most common or most official designation. Trading posts and fort-type places in a state are listed in a paragraph after each state section.

Major sources of this directory are described in detail in the Bibliography. They are National Archives record groups 94 and 98, all of the publications of the United States government listed, and the works of Hamersly, Heitman, Hunt, Mattison, Schmitt, Utley, and Whiting.

CALIFORNIA (NORTHERN)
Above 40th Parallel Only.

Anderson, Ft	Northeast of Arcata	1862–66
Baker, Ft	Northeast of Bridgeville	1863–66
Bidwell, Ft.	At Fort Bidwell	1865–85
Capell, Ft	Above Ft Terwaw	1856
Crescent City, Cp at	Crescent City	1856
Crook, Ft	At Glenburn	1857–69
Curtis, Cp	At Fortuna	1862–65
Gaston, Ft	At Hoopa	1858–92
Gilmore, Cp	At Trinidad	1863
Grant, Cp	Near Scotia	1863–65
Humboldt, Ft	At Eureka	1853–66
Iaqua, Cp	At Blue Lake	1863–66
Jones, Ft	At Fort Jones	1852–58
Lincoln, Old Cp	Near Crescent City	1862
Lincoln, New Cp	6 miles north Crescent City	1862–69

(Lincoln's Fort, Ft Lincoln, Cp Long, Long's Fort)

Lippitt, Ft	Near Ft Humboldt	1862
Lyon, Ft	20 miles east of Arcata	1862
Reading, Ft	At Redding	1852–67
Seward, Ft	65 miles southeast Ft Humboldt	1862–63
Steele, Cp	Mercer River	1852
Taylor, Cp	8 miles southeast Ft Crook	1859
Terwaw, Ft	East of Crescent City	1857–62
Wool, Ft (Cp Strowbridge)	140 miles above mouth Klamath River	1855

Ft Dick, Ft Cass, Ft Goff, Ft Hooper, Lockhart's Fort, Ft Shasta.

COLORADO (NORTHERN)
Above 40th Parallel Only.

Collins, Ft	At Fort Collins	1862–67
Latham, Ft	6 miles south of Kersey	Unknown
Lupton, Ft (Ft Lancaster)	At Fort Lupton	1864
Morgan, Ft	At Fort Morgan	1864–68

(Post of Junction Station, Ft Wardwell)

Sedgwick, Ft	Near Julesburg	1864–71

(Cp Rankin, Post at Julesburg Station)

Vasquez, Ft	Near Platteville	Unknown

Ft St. Vrains, Cp Union.

IDAHO

Boise, Ft (Boise Bks)	Boise	1863–1913
Buford, Cp	Northwest of Bruneau	1866
Connor, Cp	At Soda Springs	1863–65
Hall, Ft	At Fort Hall	1870–83
Howard, Cp	2 miles from Mount Idaho	1877
Lander, Cp	North of Fort Hall	1865–66
Lapwai, Ft	At Lapwai	1862–65; 66–84
Loring, Cant	Near Fort Hall	1849–50
Lyon, Cp	East of Sheaville, Oregon	1865–69
Owyhee River, Cp	Opposite Old Ft Boise (Fur)	1860
Polk, Cp	Unknown	1865–68
Salmon Falls, Cp	North of Buhl	1862
Sherman, Ft (Cp Coeur d'Alene)	At Coeur d'Alene	1878–1900
Soldier, Cant	At Fairfield	Unknown
Supply, Cp	At Camp Supply	Unknown
Three Forks, Cp	Southeast corner of Idaho	1866–71

Cp Colfax, Cp Defiance, Ft Henry, Ft Koolante, Ft Lemhi, Ft Malade, Cp Phoenix, Ft Russell, Cp Stevenson, Cp Wallace, Cp Wardner.

MINNESOTA

Bacon, Cp	At Walker	1856–1900
(Cp J. M. Bacon)		
Belle Plain, Cp	Yellow Medicine Agency	1857
Edwards, Cp	Near Lake Preston	1859
Lake View, Cp	At Lake City	Unknown
Livingstone, Cp	West of Yellow Medicine	1860
Release, Cp	Near mouth of Chippewa River	1860
Ridgely, Ft	Near New Ulm	1853–67
Ripley, Ft	At Ripley	1849–Present
(Ft Gaines)		
Sanborn, Ft	At Georgetown	1862
Snelling, Ft	South Minneapolis	1819–1946
(Cant New Hope, Cp Coldwater, Ft St Anthony)		
Yellow Medicine, Cp	Upper Sioux Agency	1860

Ft Beaukarnois, Ft LaSeur, Cp at Leech Lake, Cp Lincoln, Ft L'Huilher, Ft Perrot (Ft Bon Secours), Ft Pike, Pike's Stockade, Cp Ramsey, Ft Rush, Ft William.

MONTANA

Assinniboine, Ft	Near Havre	1879–1911
Benton, Ft	At Fort Benton	1869–81
(Ft Lewis)		
Bridger Pass, Cp	At Bridger Pass	1867
Browning, Ft	West of Dodson	1868–72
C. F. Smith, Ft	Near Yellowtail Dam	1866–68
Cooke, Cp	Northeast of Lewistown	1866–70
Cummings, Cp	At Virginia City	1867
Custer, Ft	South of Hardin	1877–98
(Big Horn Post)		
Elizabeth Meagher, Ft	8 miles from Bozeman	1867
Ellis, Ft	At Bozeman	1867–86
Helena Barracks	Helena Fairgrounds	1877–78
Keogh, Ft	Near Miles City	1876–1908
(Cant on Tongue River, New Post on the Yellowstone, Tongue River Barracks)		
Lewis, Cp	Near Lewiston	1874
Logan, Ft (Cp Baker)	West of White Sulphur Springs	1869–80
Maginnis, Ft	East of Lewistown	1880–90
Merritt, Cp	Tongue River Agency	Unknown
Missoula, Ft	At Missoula	1877–1946
Pease, Ft	On Yellowstone River	1876
Poplar River, Cp	Near Fort Peck	1880–93
Porter, Cp	Yellowstone River & Glendive Creek	1880–81
Reeve, Cp	Mouth of Musselshell River	1868
Rocky Point, Cant	Near Ft Maginnis	1881
Shaw, Ft	At Fort Shaw	1867–91
(Cp Reynolds)		
Stevens, Cant	Vicinity Hamilton	1859

Ft Ashley and Henry, Ft Alexander, Ft Assinniboine (fur), Ft Belknap, Ft Benton (on Yellowstone), Ft Cass, Ft Chadron, Ft Charles, Ft Clagget, Ft Cotta, Ft Flathead, Ft Galpin, Ft Hawley, Ft Henry, Indian Fort, Ft Jackson, Ft Kipp, Ft Musselshell, Ft McKenzie, Ft Kootenaie, Manuel's Fort, Ft Owen, Ft Parker, Ft Peck, Ft Piegan, Ft Sarpy, Cp Stewart, Ft Van Buren.

NEBRASKA

(Small posts for protection of stage-telegraph stations arc included in some cases.)

Alkali, Post	2 miles southwest of Paxton	1864–66
Alvin Saunders, Cp	At Lincoln	Unknown
Atkinson, Ft	At Fort Calhoun	1819–27
(Cant Missouri, Cp Missouri)		
Beauvais Station, Post at	Near Brule	1864–66

NEBRASKA (Continued)

Canfield, Cant	Ponca Creek & Missouri River	1855
Columbus, Post at	At Columbus	1864–69
Croghan, Ft	Near Omaha	?–1843
Crook, Ft	Now Offutt Air Force Base	1891–1948
Engineer's Cant	3 miles below Ft Atkinson	1819
Fallons Bluff, Post	Southwest of Sutherland	1864–66
Gilman's Station, Post at	In Lincoln County	1864–66
Grattan, Ft	South of Lewellen	1855
Hartsuff, Ft	Near Ord	1874–81
(Post on North Fork of the Loup River)		
Junction Station, Post	Southwest Cottonwood Springs	1864–66
Kearny, Old Ft	At Nebraska City	1846–48
Kearny, New Ft	Southeast of Kearney	1848–71
(Ft Childs)		
Little Blue River, Post	Near Oak Grove	1864–66
Millillas, Post	Near Gothenberg	1864–66
Mitchell, Ft	Near Scottsbluff	1864–67
(Cp Shuman)		
McPherson, Ft	South of Maxwell	1863–80
(Cant McKean, Post at Cottonwood Springs, Ft Cottonwood)		
Niobrara, Ft	East of Valentine	1880–1906
North Platte Station, Post	At North Platte	1867–81
(Cp Sergeant, Cp Sargent)		
Omaha, Post	At Omaha	1863–1947
(Post at Omaha, Omaha Barracks)		
Pawnee Agency, Cp at	Pawnee Agency	Unknown
Pawnee Ranche, Post at	West of Post Little Blue River	1864–66
Plum Creek, Post	Southeast of Lexington	1864–66
Poncas Island, Cp	Missouri River & Poncas River	1856
Red Willow, Cp	Near McCook	1872
Robinson, Ft	West of Crawford	1874–1948
(Post at Red Cloud Agency)		
Ruggles, Cp	2 miles from Ft Hartsuff	1874
Seclusion, Cp	Near mouth Little Missouri River	1855
Sheridan, Cp	North of Rushville	1874–81
(Cp Near Spotted Tail Agency)		
Sidney, Ft	At Sidney	1867–74
(Sidney Barracks)		
Vincent, Cp	Vicinity Omaha	1872

Bellevue Post, Big Sioux Post, Cabannet's Post, Ft Calhoun, Ft Charles, Ft Grove, Lisa's Post, Cp Meiklejohn, Ft Mitchell, Ponca Post, Sarpy's Post.

NEVADA (NORTHERN)

Above 40th Parallel Only.

Dun Glen, Cp	10 miles northwest Mill City	1865–66
Halleck, Ft	South of Halleck	1867–86
McDermit, Ft	South of McDermit	1865–89
McGarry, Cp	Near Summit Lake	1865–68
McKee, Cp	On Granite Creek	1866
Ruby, Cp	In Ruby Valley	1862–69
Winfield Scott, Cp	East of Paradise Valley	1866–71

NORTH DAKOTA

Abercrombie, Ft	At Abercrombie	1857–77
Abraham Lincoln, Ft	South of Bismarck	1872–91
Atcheson, Cp	At Devil's Lake	1863
Badlands, Cant	West bank Little Missouri & Railroad	1879–83

NORTH DAKOTA (Continued)

Berthold, Ft (Ft Atkinson)	West of Garrison	1864–67
Buford, Ft	At Buford	1866–85
Hancock, Cp (Cp Greeley)	At Bismarck	1872–77
Houston, Cp	Near Dickinson	1880
Mandan, Ft	Near Bismarck	1804–05
McKeen, Ft	Sub-post of Ft Abraham Lincoln	1872–91
Pembina, Ft (Ft George H. Thomas)	At Pembina	1870–95
Ransom, Ft	West of Fort Ransom	1867–72
Rice, Ft	Southeast of Fort Rice	1864–78
Seward, Ft (Ft Cross)	At Jamestown	1872–77
Stevenson, Ft	Southwest of Garrison	1867–83
Sykes, Cp	James River and Railroad	1872
Totten, Ft	Devil's Lake	1867–90
Union, Ft	West of Buford	1864–65
Yates, Ft	At Fort Yates	1874–1903

(Post at Standing Rock Agency)

Cp Ambler, Cp Arnold, Ft Ashley and Henry, Cp Atchison, Cp Austin, Cp Banks, Cp Barton, Cp Braden, Cp Briggs, Cp Buel, Cp Burt, Cp Carter, Ft Clark, Cp Corning, Cp Cox, Cp Defender, Ft Dilts, Cp Edgerton, Ft Floyd, Cp Forbes, Cp Gilfallen, Cp Grant, Cp Hall, Cp Hayes, Cp Johnson, Cp Kennedy, Cp Kimball, Kipp's Post, Cp Libby, Ft Manual Lisa, Ft Mandan, Cp Monroe, Ft Mortimer, Cp Olin, Cp Parker, Cp Pfaender, Cp Sheardown, Cp Shoeneman, Cp Sibley, Cp Slaughter, Cp Smith, Cp Stees, Cp Stevens, Tilton's Post, Ft Vanderburgh, Cp Weiser, Cp Wharton, Cp Whitney, Ft William, Cp Williston.

OREGON

Alvord, Ft	Near Andrews	1865–66
Baker, Ft	Near Jacksonville	1861–Unknown
Big Bend, Cp at	On Rogue River	1856–57
C. F. Smith, Cp	Near Denio	1866–69
Cheteo River, Cp on	At mouth of Cheteo River	1856
Clatsop, Ft	Near Portland	1805–06
Curry, Cp	Vicinity Canyon City	1865–66
Dalles, Ft (Cp Drum, Ft Lee)	At The Dalles	1850–68
Harney, Ft	East of Burns	1867–80

(Cp on Rattlesnake Creek, Cp Steele, Cp Crook)

Henrietta, Ft	At Echo	Unknown
Hoskins, Old Ft	6 miles north of Corvallis	1856–?
Hoskins, New Ft	30 miles west of Corvallis	?–1866
Jones, Ft	Wilamette Valley	1852
Klamath, Ft	Klamath Lake	1863–90
Lafayette, Ft	Post at Grand Ronde Agency	1863
Lane, Ft	North of Medford	1853–56
Logan, Cp	North of Canyon City	1865–69
Medill, Cp	At Grove Creek	1858
Orford, Ft	At Point Orford	1851–56
Randolph, Cp	Near Ft Dalles	1859
Rogue River, Cp	Mouth of Rogue River	1856
Russell, Cp	Near Salem	1864
Siletz, Blockhouse	At Siletz	1855–66
Stevens, Ft	At Fort Stevens	1865–1948
Stuart, Cp	Vicinity of Medford	1851–53
Table Rock, Ft	Rogue River & Stewarts Creek	Unknown
Umpqua, Ft	At Reedsport	1856–62
Warner, Cp	Near Lakeview	1866–74
Watson, Cp	Near Mitchell	1864–69
Wright, Cp	At Wright's Point	1865
Yamhill, Ft	Vicinity Dayton City	1856–66

Ft Cowlitz, Ft Clatsop, Cp Dahlgren, Ft Defiance, Ft Disappointment, Ft George, Ft Hall, Haskin's Fort, Ft Lamerick, Ft Leland, Cp Murray, Ft Rains, Ft Rocks.

SOUTH DAKOTA

Bennett, Ft (Post at Cheyenne Agency)	35 miles from Pierre	1870–91
Brule, Ft	Near Brule	Unknown
Cedar, Ft	28 miles north of Pierre	1856
Collier, Cp	North of Edgemont	1876
Crook, Cp	At Camp Crook	1870s
Dakota, Ft (Ft Brookings)	At Sioux Falls	1865–70
Grand River Agency, Post at	Near Mobridge	1870–75
Hale, Ft (Post at Lower Brule Agency)	Vicinity Ft Lookout	1870–84
Hutchinson, Ft	East of Yankton	Unknown
James, Ft (Ft Laroche)	Southeast of Mitchell	1865–73
Keya Paha, Cp	28 miles west of Ft Randall	1879
Lookout, Ft	Northwest of Chamberlain	1856–57
Meade, Ft (Cp Ruhlen)	Near Sturgis	1878–1944
Oakwood, Cant	At Oakwood Lakes	1857, 1864–65
Pierre, Ft	At Fort Pierre	1855–57
Ponca, Ft	At Ponca Agency	1865–66
Rains, Old Cp	3 miles west of Beaver Creek	1874
Rains, New Cp	6 miles above mouth Niobrara River	1877–79
Randall, Ft	West of Pickstown	1856–84
Sisseton, Ft (Ft Wadsworth)	Northwest of Eden	1864–90
Sturgis, Cp	East of Sturgis	1878
Sully, Old Ft (Ft Bartlett)	4 miles east of Pierre	1863–66
Sully, New Ft	North of Pierre	1866–94
Thompson, Ft (Post at Crow Creek Agency)	At Fort Thompson	1863–71
Whetstone Agency Post at	North of Bonesteel	1870–72
Whittelsey, Cp	At Larren's Fork	1867

Ft Aux Cedres, Ft Defiance, Dickson's Post, Ft Galpin, Ft George, Ft Kiowa, Fts Lookout #1 and #3, Ft La Framboise, Loisell's Post, Ft Manuel Lisa, Ft Mitchell, Ft Pierre, Ft Primeau, Ft Recovery (Cedar Ft, Pilcher's Post, Ft Brasseaux), Sublette and Campbell's Post, Ft Tecumseh, Ft Teton, Ft Vermillion.

UTAH (NORTHERN)

Above 40th Parallel Only.

Battlecreek Settlement, Cp	Near Salt Lake City	1859
Crittenden, Ft (Cp Floyd)	Fairfield	1857–61
Douglas, Ft	At Salt Lake City	1862–1948
Duchesne, Ft	At Fort Duchesne	1886–1912
Murray, Cp	43 miles from Salt Lake City	1885
Rawlins, Cp	2 miles from Provo	1870–71
Rush Valley, Cp	23 miles from Cp Floyd	1859
Shunk, Cp	25 miles southwest Cp Floyd	1858
Thornburgh, Old Ft	Duchesne & Graeves River	1881–82
Thornburgh, New Ft	On Ashley Creek	1882–83
Timpanagos, Cp	8 miles from Provo	1859

Ft Ashley, Ft Ephraim, Ft Garrison, Ft Hamilton, Ft Harriman, Ft Johnson, Cp Kingston, Ft Uintah, Ft Utah.

WASHINGTON

Alden, Ft (Ft Alder)	60 miles from mouth Snake River	1856
Bennett, Ft	Vicinity Ft Waters	1855–56
Bellingham, Ft	At Bellingham	1856–60

WASHINGTON (Continued)

Canby, Ft	Near Illwaco	1864–1950
(Ft Cape Disappointment)		
Cascades, Ft	Near Cascade City	1855–61
Chelalis, Ft	Lower Chelalis	1860–61
Chelan, Cp	Vicinity Chelan	1879–80
Colville, Ft	At Colville	1859–82
Cowlitz Landing, Ft at	Near Toledo	1856
Decatur, Ft	At Seattle	1853
(Seattle Blockhouse)		
Dent, Ft	Unknown	1855
Ebey, Ft	Near Everett	1855
Hays, Ft	Connell's Prairie	1856
Henderson, Ft	Vicinity Falls City	1856
Hicks, Ft (Ft Patterson)	South Prairie crossing & Puyallup River	1856
Lander, Ft	North of Seattle	1856
Lone Tree Point, Ft	Near Puget Sound	1856
Maloney, Ft	Near Puyallup	1856
Mason, Ft	23 miles from Ft Walla Walla	1856
McAllister, Ft	At South Prairie	1856
Miller, Ft	At Tenalquot Plains	1856
Na-chess, Ft	Near Naches River	1856
Taylor, Ft	60 miles from mouth Walla Walla River	1858
Thomas, Ft	On Green River	1857
San Juan Island, Cp	San Juan Island	1859–72
(Cp Reynolds, Cp Pickett, Cp Steele)		
Simcoe, Ft	West of Toppenish	1856–59
Slaughter, Ft	On Muckleshoot Prairie	1856
Spokane, Ft	Northwest of Spokane	1882–99
Steilacoom, Ft	At Fort Steilacoom	1849–68
Townsend, Ft	At Port Townsend	1856–93
Vancouver, Ft	At Vancouver	1849–Present
(Vancouver Bks, Columbia Bks)		
Walla Walla, Ft	At Walla Walla	1857–1911
Waters, Ft	Whitman Mission near Walla Walla	1848–?
White, Ft	At Puyallup Crossing	1856
Yakima Valley, Ft	Near Yakima Valley Gap	1856

Ft Arkansas, Ft Borst, Ft Colvile, Ft Discovery, Ft Duwamish, Ft Eaton, Cp Ephraim, Ft Henness, Ft Malikoff, Ft Mason, Ft Nesqually, Ft Nez Perce (Old Ft Walla Walla, Ft Wallah Wallah), Ft Nisqually, Cp Osoyees, Ft Okanagon, Ft Pike, Ft Posey, Ft Preston, Ft Raglan, Ft Riggs, Ft Rupert, Ft Smalley, Ft Skookum, Spanish Fort at Neah Bay, Ft Spokane, Ft Stevens, Ft Tilton.

WYOMING

Bitter Cottonwood, Cp	22 miles west Fort Laramie	1856
Bridger, Ft	At Fort Bridger	1858–90
Carlin, Cp	Near Warren Air Force Base	1867–1888
(Cheyenne Depot, Quartermaster Depot at Cheyenne)		
Caspar, Ft	At Casper	1865–67
(Platte Bridge Post)		
Crook Supply Camp	Near Sheridan	Unknown
D. A. Russell, Ft	Now Warren Air Force Base	1867–1948
(Ft Francis E. Warren, Post of Crow Creek)		
Devin, Old Cp	On Little Missouri River	1878
Devin, New Cp	Oak Creek south of Belle Fourche River	1878
Fetterman, Ft	West of Douglas	1867–82
Fred Steele, Ft	East of Sinclair	1868–86
Halleck, Ft	Near Elko Mountain	1862–66
Laramie, Ft	Near Fort Laramie	1849–90
Marshall, Cp	South of Douglas	1863
McGraw, Cp	At Lander	1857–58
McKinney, Ft	Near Buffalo	1877–94
(Cant Reno, New Ft Reno)		

WYOMING (Continued)

Medicine Butte, Cp	Near Evanston	1885–87
O. O. Howard, Cp	Vicinity Pine Bluffs	1885
Payne, Cp	North of Fort Laramie	1858
Pelouse River, Cp	Unknown	1858
Phil Kearney, Ft	North of Buffalo	1866–68
(New Ft Reno)		
Pilot Butte, Cp	At Rock Springs	1885–99
(Cp at Rock Springs)		
Platte River, Cp	120 miles above Fort Laramie	1856–59
(Cp Davis, Cp Clay)		
Reno, Cant	East of Kaycee	1876–77
(New Ft Reno, Reno Station)		
Reno, Ft	East of Kaycee	1866–68
(Ft Connor, Old Ft Reno)		
Sanders, Ft	South of Laramie	1866–82
(Ft John Buford)		
Scott, Cp	Sub-post of Ft Bridger	1857–58
Sheridan, Ft	Yellowstone National Park	1886–91
Snake Indian Reservation, Cp	At Wind River District	1869
Snake River, Cp	On Jackson	1879–83
Stambaugh, Ft	At Atlantic	1870–78
Walbach, Cp	Near Walbeck	1858–59
Washakie, Ft	At Fort Washakie	1869–1909
(Cp Augur, Cp Brown)		
Yellowstone, Ft	Yellowstone National Park	1866–1918

Ft Bernard, Ft Bonneville, Ft John, Ft Laclede, Ft McHenry, Ft Piney, Ft Platte, Ft Supply, Ft Thompson, Ft William.

Bibliography

"Old Forts of the Northwest" did not start as a definitive history of Western military posts, nor has it ended as such. But even to present it in its current form involved considerable research, far more than was first anticipated. The major publications consulted are listed here and all were of value, some more, some less.

Of equal importance, but not listed, were the many letters, personal interviews, and telephone conversations from local sources, most of whom are mentioned elsewhere. Also not listed are the valuable short pamphlets and folders published by the various Chambers of Commerce, historical societies, and the National Park Service.

Only publications used in preparation of this volume of the "Forts of the Old West" series are noted. Those used subsequently will be listed at that time.

UNITED STATES GOVERNMENT OFFICIAL PUBLICATIONS AND SOURCES

ADJUTANT GENERAL. *List of Military Posts, Etc., Established in the United States from Its Earliest Settlement to the Present Time.* War Department. Washington. 1902.

_____. *Records of the War Department, Outline Index of Military Forts and Stations.* Record Group 94 in the National Archives. 27 volumes.

INSPECTOR GENERAL. *Outline Descriptions of the Posts and Stations of Troops in the Geographical Divisions and Departments of the United States.* Major General R. B. Marcy, Inspector-General. Washington. 1872.

MISSOURI, MILITARY DIVISION OF THE. *Outline Descriptions of the Posts in the Military Division of the Missouri.* Major General Philip H. Sheridan, commanding. Chicago. 1876.

NATIONAL ARCHIVES. *Preliminary Inventory of Records of Army Posts 1813–1942.* War Division. Record Group 98: Records of United States Army Commands. 1949.

NATIONAL PARK SERVICE. *Historic Site Inventory Reports* of Military Forts in the Western, Southwestern, and Midwestern Regions. San Francisco, Omaha, Santa Fe. 1958–61.

PACIFIC, MILITARY DIVISION OF THE. *Outline Descriptions of Pacific Military Posts.* Major General Irvin McDowell, commanding. San Francisco. 1879.

QUARTERMASTER GENERAL. *Outline Descriptions of Forts and Stations in the Year 1871.* Quartermaster General M. C. Meigs. Washington. 1872.

_____. *Revised Outline Description of the Posts and Stations of Troops in the Military Division of the Pacific.* Lieutenant Colonel R. O. Tyler (ed). Washington. 1872.

SECRETARY OF WAR. *Annual Report.* Washington. 1866–90.

SURGEON GENERAL. *Report on Barracks and Hospitals with Descriptions of Military Posts.* Assistant Surgeon John S. Billings (ed). Circular No. 4. Washington. 1870.

_____. *Report on the Hygiene of the United States Army with Descriptions of Military Posts.* Assistant Surgeon John S. Billings (ed). Circular No. 8. Washington. 1875.

WAR DEPARTMENT. Official records in the National Archives of various Army posts. These include "Letters Sent," "Letters Received," "Medical History," etc. Many were scanned, but the following were searched in detail: Reno, Wyo.; Sherman, Idaho; Logan, Mont.; Cooke, Mont.; Shaw, Mont.; Sidney, Nebr.; Halleck, Nev.; Ruby, Nev.; McDermit, Nev.; Winfield Scott, Nev.; Ransom, N. D.; Meade, S. D.; Spokane, Wash.

_____. *War of the Rebellion: Official Records of the Union and Confederate Armies.* Volumes 1, 3, 8, 13, 22, 34, 41, 48, 50. Series I. Washington. 1880–1897. 128 volumes.

BOOKS AND OTHER SOURCES

Anonymous. *Fort Steilacoom History.* Fort Steilacoom, Wash. n.d.

_____. *History of Fort Douglas.* Ogden, Utah. 1954.

_____. *History of Fort Missoula, Montana.* Missoula. 1955.

_____. *Fort Sisseton in the Heart of the Dakota Lake Region.* Britton, S.D. 1959.

_____. *Word and Picture Story of Williston and Area.* Williston, N.D. 1962.

ALDRICH, Bess Streeter. *Lieutenant's Lady.* New York. 1942. (Fiction.)

AMERICAN ASSOCIATION OF UNIVERSITY WOMEN. *Historical Sheridan.* Sheridan, Wyo. n.d.

ATHEARN, Robert G. *William Tecumseh Sherman and the Settlement of the West.* Norman. 1956.

BANCROFT, H. H. *History of the Pacific States: Washington, Idaho, Montana.* (Volume 26 of his series.) San Francisco. 1890.

BASHIER, Mary. *The Story of Fort Hartsuff.* Nebraska History, Lincoln. June, 1961.

BEEBE, Lucius and CLEGG, Charles. *The American West.* New York. 1955.

BEERS, Henry. *Western Military Frontier.* Philadelphia. 1935.

BELL, W. S. *Old Fort Benton.* Helena. 1909.

BENSELL, R. A. *All Quiet on the Yamhill.* Eugene, Ore. 1959.

BERRY, Myrtle D. *Fort Sidney, Westward on the Union Pacific.* Nebraska On The March magazine, Lincoln. February, 1956.

BOATNER, Lt. Col. Mark M. III. *The Civil War Dictionary.* New York. 1959.

BRADY, Cyrus Townsend. *Indian Fights and Fighters.* New York. 1904.

BRANDES, Ray. *Frontier Military Posts of Arizona.* Globe, Ariz. 1960.

BRIMLOW, George F. *Harney County, Ore., and Its Range Land.* Portland. 1951.

BROWN, Dee. *Fort Phil Kearny: An American Saga.* New York. 1962.

BURDICK, Usher L. *Tales from Buffalo Land, the Story of Fort Buford.* Baltimore. 1940.

CALDWELL, McNUTT, SMITH. *Fort Randall Reservoir.* Corps of Engineers, Omaha. 1960.

CALLENDER, John M. *New Light on Old Fort Snelling.* St. Paul. 1959.

CARRINGTON, Mrs. Margaret I. *Ab-Sa-Ra-Ka, Home of the Crows.* Philadelphia. 1868.

CHAPPELL, Edith M. *A History of Old Fort McKinney*. Buffalo, Wyo. n.d.

CHITTENDEN, Brig. Gen. Hiram Martin. *The American Fur Trade of the Far West*. 1902. (Reprint of 1954, Stanford, Calif.)

CLEMMER, John S. *An Archeological Investigation of Fort Humboldt State Historical Monument*. California Division of Beaches and Parks. 1960.

COLORADO STATE HISTORICAL SOCIETY. *Forts and Camps in Colorado*. Denver. n.d.

CORVUSIER, William T. *Camp Sheridan, Nebraska*. Nebraska History, Lincoln. March, 1961.

COUES, Capt. Elliott. *Lewis & Clark Expedition. 1804–06*. Corps of Engineers, Omaha. 1952.

CULVERWELL, Albert. *Stronghold in the Yakima Country*. Yakima. 1956.

CUSTER, Elizabeth. *Boots and Saddles*. New York. 1885.

CUSTER, Gen. George A. *My Life on the Plains*. New York. 1962 edition.

DAHLQUIST, Laura. *Meet Jim Bridger*. Kemmerer, Wyo. 1948.

DANKER, Donald F. (ed). *Man of the Plains: Recollections of Luther North*. Lincoln. 1961.

DE TROBRIAND, Maj. Gen. Philippe R. D. de K., *Army Life in Dakota*. Chicago. 1941.

DOWNEY, Fairfax. *Indian-Fighting Army*. New York. 1941.

DUNN, J. P., Jr. *Massacres of the Mountains*. New York. 1886.

ELLISON, Robert S. *Fort Bridger—A Brief History*. Casper, Wyo. 1931.

ENCYCLOPAEDIA BRITANNICA. *World Atlas*. Chicago. 1959.

FEDERAL WRITERS PROJECT. *California, A Guide to the Golden State*. New York. 1939.

_____. *Colorado, A Guide to the Highest State*. New York. 1941.

_____. *Idaho, A Guide in Word and Pictures*. Caldwell. 1937.

_____. *Minnesota, A State Guide*. New York. 1938.

_____. *Montana, A State Guide Book*. New York. 1939.

_____. *Nebraska, A Guide to the Cornhusker State*. New York. 1939.

_____. *Nevada, A Guide to the Silver State*. Portland. 1940.

_____. *North Dakota, A Guide to the Northern Prairie State*. Fargo. 1938.

_____. *Oregon, End of the Trail*. Portland. 1940.

_____. *South Dakota Guide*. Pierre. 1938.

_____. *Utah, A Guide to the State*. New York. 1941.

_____. *Washington, A Guide to the Evergreen State*. Portland. 1941.

_____. *Wyoming, A Guide to Its History, Highways, and People*. New York. 1941.

FINERTY, John F. *War-Path and Bivouac*. Chicago. 1890.

FLETCHER, R. H. (Bob). *Montana Historical Markers*. Helena. n.d.

FLORIN, Lambert. *Western Ghost Towns*. Seattle. 1961.

_____. *Ghost Town Album*. Seattle. 1962.

FORSYTH, Bvt. Brig. Gen. George A. Forsyth. *The Story of The Soldier*. New York. 1900.

_____. *Thrilling Days in Army Life*. New York. 1900.

FORT ABERCROMBIE PARK BOARD. *The Historical Gateway to North Dakota 1857–1877*. Wahpeton, N. D. n.d.

GOETZMANN, William H. *Army Exploration in the American West 1803–63*. New Haven. 1959.

GOPLEN, Arnold O. *The Historical Significance of Fort Lincoln State Park*. North Dakota History, Bismarck. October, 1946.

GRAHAM, Col. W. A. *The Custer Myth*. Harrisburg. 1953.

GRANGE, Roger T. *Fort Robinson, Outpost on the Plains*. Nebraska History, Lincoln. September, 1958.

HAFEN, LeRoy R. (ed). *Far West and the Rockies Historical Series 1820–1875*. Glendale, Calif. 1954–62. 15 volumes.

HAILEY, John. *History of Idaho*. Boise. 1910.

HAMERSLY, T. H. S. (comp). *Complete Regular Army Register of the United States for One Hundred Years 1779–1879*. Washington, 1880.

HAMMOND, John M. *Quaint and Historic Forts*. Philadelphia. 1915.

HANSEN, Marcus L. *Old Fort Snelling*. Minneapolis. 1958.

HARRIS, Earl R. *Courthouse and Jail Rocks: Landmarks on the Oregon Trail*. Nebraska History, Lincoln. March, 1962.

_____. *Discovered: The Oregon Trail*. Gering, Nebr. 1962.

HEBARD, Grace R. and BRININSTOOL, Earl. *The Bozeman Trail*. Cleveland. 1922. 2 volumes.

HIEB, David L. *Fort Laramie National Monument*. Washington. 1954.

HEITMAN, Francis B. (comp). *Historical Register and Dictionary of the United States Army*. Washington. 1905. 2 volumes.

HORAN, James D. *The Great American West*. New York. 1959.

HOOVER and RENSCH. *Historic Spots in California*. Stanford. 1948.

HUNT, Aurora. *The Army of the Pacific (1860–66)*. Glendale. 1951.

_____. *The Far West Volunteer*. Montana, the Magazine of Western History. Helena. Spring, 1962.

_____. *Maj. Gen. James H. Carlton (1814–73)*. *Western Frontier Dragoon*. Glendale. 1958.

HURT, Wesley R. and LASS, William E. *Frontier Photographer*. Lincoln. 1956.

HUSSEY, John A. *Fort Vancouver*. Portland. 1957.

JEWELL, Donald P. and CLEMMER, John S. *The Archeological Findings of Fort Humboldt State Monument*. Central California Archeological Foundation. 1959.

JOHANNSEN, Robert W. *A Political Picture of the Pacific Northwest*. Montana, the Magazine of Western History, Helena. Spring, 1962.

JOHNSON, Roy P. *The Siege at Fort Abercrombie*. North Dakota History, Bismarck. January, 1957.

JOHNSON, Virginia W. *The Unregimented General*. Boston. 1962.

JOSEPHY, Alvin M., Jr. (ed). *American Heritage Book of Indians*. New York. 1961.

KENNY, Judith Keyes. *The Founding of Camp Watson*. Oregon Historical Quarterly, Portland. March, 1957.

KERR, Maj. Gen. John K. and WALLACE, Edward S. *The Story of the U. S. Cavalry*. Boston. 1953.

KIMMEL, Thelma. *The Fort Simcoe Story*. Toppenish, Wash. 1954.

LUCE, Edward S. and Evelyn S. *Custer Battlefield National Monument*. Washington. 1949.

MANTOR, Dr. Lyle E. *Brief History of Fort Kearny*. Kearny, Nebraska. n.d.

MARTINSON, Flora P. *Old Fort Ripley, Minnesota Frontier Post*. Gopher Historian, St. Paul. Winter, 1961–62.

MATTES, Merrill J. *Indians, Infants, and Infantry*. Denver. 1960.

_____. *Revival at Old Fort Randall*. The Military Engineer. March-April, 1952.

_____. *Scotts Bluff National Monument*. Washington. 1958.

MATTISON, Ray H. *The Army Post on the Northern Plains 1865–85.* Nebraska History, Lincoln. March, 1954.

_____. *Fort Rice—North Dakota's First Missouri River Military Post.* North Dakota History, Bismarck. April, 1953.

_____. *The Indian Frontier on the Upper Missouri to 1865.* Nebraska History, Lincoln. September, 1958.

_____. *The Military Frontier on the Upper Missouri.* Nebraska History, Lincoln. September, 1956.

_____. *Old Fort Stevenson—A Typical Missouri River Military Post.* North Dakota History, Bismarck. April, July, 1951.

_____. *Report on Historical Aspects of the Oahe Reservoir Area, Missouri River, South and North Dakota.* South Dakota Historical Collections, Pierre. Vol. XXVII, 1954.

_____. *Report on Historic Sites in the Garrison Reservoir Area, Missouri River.* North Dakota History, Bismarck. January-April, 1955.

_____. *The Upper Missouri Fur Trade: Its Methods of Operation.* Nebraska History, Lincoln. March, 1961.

McCRACKEN, Harold. *Frederic Remington, Artist of the Old West.* Philadelphia. 1947.

MILES, Gen. Nelson A. *Personal Recollections.* Chicago. 1896.

MOKLER, Alfred J. *Fort Caspar.* Casper. 1939.

MUMEY, Nolie. *Old Forts and Trading Posts of the West.* Denver. 1956.

MURBARGER, Nell. *Ghosts of the Glory Trail.* Palm Desert, Calif. 1956.

ODELL, Thomas E. *Mato Paha, the Story of Bear Butte.* Spearfish, S.D. 1942.

OVERHOLSER, Joel F. *A Souvenir History of Fort Benton, Montana.* Fort Benton. n.d.

PAULLIN, C. O. *Atlas of the Historical Geography of the United States.* Carnegie Institution of Washington, 1932.

PRUCHA, Rev. Francis P., S.J. *Broadax and Bayonet.* Madison, Wisc. 1953.

RAND–McNALLY, INC. *Road Maps of the United States.* Chicago. 1962.

RISTER, Carl Coke. *Border Command, General Phil Sheridan in the West.* Norman. 1944.

ROBERTS, Frank H. H. (ed). *River Basin Survey Papers.* Bureau of American Ethnology, Smithsonian Institution, Bulletin 176. Washington. 1960.

ROBINSON, Doane. *South Dakota Encyclopaedia.* Pierre. 1925.

RODENBOUGH, T. *The Army of the United States.* Washington. 1896.

ROGERS, Col. Fred B. *Early Military Posts of Del Norte County.* California Historical Society Quarterly, San Francisco. 1947.

_____. *Fort Bidwell, Modoc County, California.* California Division of Beaches and Parks. San Francisco. 1959.

RECRUITING NEWS. *Histories of Army Posts.* Governor's Island. N.Y. 1924.

RUSLING, James. *Across America.* New York. 1874.

RYBOLT, Robert, Jr. *Sidney and Fort Sidney.* Sidney, Nebr. 1960.

SAFGREN, Shirley. *The Coteau des Prairies: Land of Lakes and Legend.* Pierre. n.d.

SALISBURY, Albert and Jane. *Here Rolled the Covered Wagons.* Seattle. 1948.

_____. *Two Captains West.* Seattle. 1950.

SAVAGE, Thomas C. *Fort Snelling Park: What's Ahead?* Minneapolis. 1961.

SCHELL, Herbert S. *History of South Dakota.* Lincoln. 1961.

SCHMITT, Martin F. and BROWN, Dee. *Fighting Indians of the West.* New York. 1948.

SCHMITT, Martin F. (ed). *General George Crook, His Autobiography.* Norman. 1960.

SCHUMACHER, Paul J. F. *Study of Proposed Museum for the Wasco County–Dalles City Museum of Natural History.* National Park Service, San Francisco. 1957.

SEYER, Mrs. Earl and BARTLING, Frank A. *Nebraska City, Nebraska.* Nebraska City. 1953.

SHERIDAN, Gen. Philip H. *Personal Memoirs.* New York. 1888. 2 volumes.

SMITH, J. Greg. *Post With a Past, Fort Robinson.* Outdoor Nebraska, Lincoln. February, 1962.

STANKE, Jerry E. *Camp Lyon, Idaho Territory.* Paper at the Idaho Historical Society, Boise. n.d.

STEWART, Edgar I. (ed). *Life and Adventures of Frank Grouard.* Norman. 1958.

SULLIVAN, Charles J. *Army Posts and Towns.* Burlington, Vt. 1935.

SUTTON, Jack. *One Day of Southern Oregon History.* Jacksonville, Ore. 1960.

_____. *The Pictorial History of Southern Oregon and Northern California.* Grant's Pass, Oregon. 1959.

TAFT, Robert. *Artists and Illustrators of the Old West.* New York. 1953.

TEBEL, John and JENNISON, Keith. *The American Indian Wars.* New York. 1960.

UTLEY, Robert (ed). *Military and Indian Frontier.* Manuscript at the National Park Service, Santa Fe. For publication, New York, 1963.

WALLACE, Edward S. *The Great Reconnaissance.* Boston. 1955.

WARE, Captain Eugene F. *The Indian War of 1864.* New York. 1960.

WELLMAN, Paul I. *The Indian Wars of the West.* Garden City. 1954.

WESTERNERS, The (Potomac Corral). *Great Western Indian Fights.* Garden City. 1960.

WHITING, Joseph S. *Forts of the State of Washington.* Seattle. 1951.

_____ and WHITING, R. J. *Forts of the State of California.* Seattle. 1960.

WHITMAN, S. E. *The Troopers.* New York. 1962.

WRIGHT, Dana. *The Fort Totten-Fort Stevenson Trail.* North Dakota History, Bismarck. April, 1953.

NEWSPAPERS AND MAGAZINES

American Heritage Magazine
Billings, Mont., *Gazette*
Buford, N. D. *Tribune*
Burns, Ore., *Hi-Desert News*
Civil War Times Illustrated
Dillon, Mont., *Examiner*
Frontier Times Magazine
Great Falls, Mont., *Tribune*
Hardin, Mont., *Tribune-Herald*

Kremlin, Mont., *Chancellor*
Lewistown, Mont., *Democrat-News*
Omaha, Nebr., *World Herald*
Oregon Historical Society Newsletter
Plevna, Mont., *Herald*
Sidney, Nebr., *Telegraph*
True West Magazine
Walla Walla, Wash., *Union-Bulletin*
Wi-Iyohi, S. D. Historical Society Newsletter

Acknowledgements

It is unfortunate that many letters, many hours of tramping over deserted fort sites, and many periods of waiting must be relegated to this short mention. But here are the kind folks whose help contributed to any worth this project may have. It should be emphasized that they have no responsibility for any errors the author may have included inadvertently.

The historians of the National Park Service were of special help. These included Jack McDermott and Robert Murray, Fort Laramie; Robert M. Utley, Santa Fe; Ray Mattison, Omaha; Charles Snell, San Francisco; Earl Harris, Scotts Bluff; Paul McCrary, Grand Coulee Dam; William R. Sampson, Fort Vancouver; Aubrey L. Haines, Yellowstone, and, at the Service's headquarters in Washington, D.C., Roy E. Appleman, Charles W. Porter III, and John Porter Bloom.

Thanks also are due to the following members of the staffs of the institutions or libraries noted:

National Archives, Milton K. Chamberlain and Mrs. Sara D. Jackson (Old Army Branch), Josephine Motelywski (Still Pictures Branch), and Charlotte Ashby (Cartographic); Smithsonian Institution, Frank H. H. Roberts, Jr., and George Howell, Bureau of American Ethnology and Military History branch, respectively.

Research Library, Marine Corps Educational Center, Quantico, Va.: Mrs. Evelyn Daniels and George Mahoney; Northwestern University Deering Library, Florence Stewart, university archivist; City Art Museum of St. Louis, Vivian C. Fullerton; West Point Museum, U.S. Military Academy, Frederick P. Todd, director.

The staffs of the Library of Congress, Army War College, Denver Public Library, Yale University Library, Newberry Library, Bancroft Library, Museum of the American Indian of the Heye Foundation, Chicago Historical Society, Huntington Library, and the public libraries of Chicago, Ill., and Fitchburg, Mass.

Advice, counsel, and the loan of material came from various authors who have researched this subject: Aurora Hunt, Joseph S. Whiting, Nell Murbarger, James D. Horan, Albert P. Salisbury, Barry Scobee, Frank A. Schilling, and retired Army Colonels Fred Rogers and George Ruhlen. This held true for two book dealers who took special pains to help though little or no financial gain was possible: Don Sharp, Round-Up Book Co., Milton-Freewater, Ore., and San Francisco, Calif., and Kenneth Nebenzahl, Chicago. Advice and technical aid also came from John J. Connolly.

Two other special bows must be taken to acknowledge help that was indispensable to the book. To J. W. (Red) Richardson and his wife, Rosemarie, of Imperial Beach, Calif., who entered the project in its latter stages to rescue through darkroom magic negatives that had been poorly processed elsewhere. And to the author's wife who shared all-night typing sessions, not to mention 43 days of fort-to-fort traveling.

By states, here are the other fine people whose help was invaluable: California: Allan R. Ottley (State Library), James de T. Abajian (Historical Society), Jack R. Dyson (State Park Historian); Mrs. Eugene Fountain, Blue Lake; Roy Mealey, Eureka; Judge Samuel Finley, Apple Valley; Walter Lowell, Ft. Bidwell.

Colorado: Mrs. Alice Wallace (Historical Society); E. T. Hogue, Julesburg; Mrs. George Ewing and Smith D. Phillip, Ft. Lupton. Idaho: Merle W. Wells (Historical Society); Loryn E. Kopan and H. J. Swinney, Boise; Senator J. Cecil Sandberg, Blackfoot.

Minnesota: Lois M. Fawcett and Eugene D. Becker (Historical Society); Thomas C. Savage, S. St. Paul. Montana: Mary K. Dempsey (Historical Society); Claude Windecker, Havre; W. M. Scoville, Walter Lehman, Oscar Mueller, Lewistown; Rev. George S. Ritchey, Ft. Benton; E. O. Preston, Hardin; Casey Barthelmess and Nate Kiefer, Miles City; Mrs. Nancy Bird and M. E. Baechler, White Sulphur Springs; Captain Howard Hupe, U.S.A., Missoula; John Simard, Bainville; Malcolm Story, Bozeman.

Nebraska: Donald F. Danker (Historical Society); Dr. Glen Aubry, Ord; Meroe J. Owens, Loup City; Frank A. Bartling, Nebraska City; Comdr. Emory B. Myers, U.S.N., Omaha; Dr. R. H. Rybolt and Robert Rybolt, Jr., Sidney; George Kelley, MacPherson; Edith L. Neale, Ft. Calhoun; Fred Rusch, Valentine.

ACKNOWLEDGEMENTS (Continued)

Nevada: Mrs. Clara S. Beatty (Historical Society); Earl H. Conrad, Halleck; Roy Harris, Ft. Ruby Ranch; William Rutherford, Winnemucca; Fritz Buckingham and Mr. and Mrs. Fred Buckingham, Paradise Valley.

North Dakota: James B. Connolly (Auto Association), Donald G. Gackle (State Chamber of Commerce), Margaret Rose (Historical Society); G. V. Holmquist, Abercrombie; Ike Smith and Del Skjod, Mandan; David Garcia and Kenneth Larsen, Devils Lake; Mr. and Mrs. John Melland, Otto Seel, and H. Zimmerman, Buford; Arthur Leno, Bismarck; Lowell M. Johnson, Ft. Ransom; B. G. and Mervin Gwyther, Ft. Rice; Phil Hoghaug, Pembina.

Oregon: Priscilla Knuth and Mrs. Barbara Elkins (Historical Society); Martin Schmitt (University of Oregon); Col. Lewis E. Nichols, U.S.A.F. (Retired) and W. S. Nelson, The Dalles; Jack Catterson, Burns; Mary L. Hanley and Jack Sutton, Jacksonville; Senator Carl H. Francis, Dayton City.

South Dakota: Colonel Will G. Robinson (Historical Society); Mrs. Shirley Safgren (Highway Department); Richard B. Williams, Sturgis; Frank Bucker, Edgemont; R. D. Blum, Ft. Randall Dam; R. F. Johnson and Gilbert Elsen, Eden. Utah: John James (Historical Society); Ward Roylance (Tourist & Publicity Council); Staff Sgt. Robert C. Hipes, U.S.A., and Mrs. Helen Foulger, Salt Lake City; Dr. G. R. Aiken, Kanab.

Washington: Margaret E. Felt (Department of Commerce and Economic Development); Mrs. Hazel Mills (State Library); John Parton, Ft. Simcoe; Marie H. Knight, North Bonneville; A. F. Raiter, Jr., Spokane; Dr. F. E. Shovlain, Ft. Steilacoom; Mrs. Margaret Kraemer and Mr. and Mrs. George Kraemer, Seattle; L. K. Jones, Walla Walla; Shirley Payne, Bellingham; E. M. Wetherell, Tacoma.

Wyoming: Lola M. Homsher, Mrs. Kathcrine Halverson, Ruth J. Bradley (State Archives and Historical Department); Laura Dahlquist, Ft. Bridger; Charles F. Guild, Evanston; Clark H. Condit and Fred and Mason Skiles, Kaycee; Mrs. Charles Hord, Casper; Chief of Police Dayton C. Jones, Sinclair; Norman E. Roberts, Laramie; Charles Sharp, Ft. Laramie; Thelma B. Condit and Mr. and Mrs. Lloyd Fordyce, Buffalo; James Harrower, Pinedale.

Index

Adams, Capt. 180
Alexis, Grand Duke of Russia 74
Alvord, Gen. Benjamin 140
American Fur Co. 64, 67, 98
Arapahoe Indians 28, 77, 152
Army headquarters in St. Louis 13
Army posts, see *Fort*
Artifact hunters, advice to 7, 12
Artillery, use of 58, 65, 77, 79, 86, 119, 148
Auble, Dr. G. 124
Auger, Gen. J. 10, 33

Baker, Col. E. M. 137
Banks, James A. 134
Bannock War 11, 100, 126, 130, 132, 167
Bear Paw, Battle of 151
Bear River, Battle of 23
Belle of the West dance hall 113
Bird, Mrs. Nancy 138
Big Foot, Chief 148, 161
Big Hole, Battle of the 26, 98, 137, 139, 151, 169
Big Horn Expedition (1876) 58
Black Hills Expedition (1873) 11, 58, 146, 162, 164
Black Hills Miners 50, 56, 76, 107
Bozeman, John M. 41
Bozeman Trail 11, 28, 41–48, 67, 70, 80
Bridger, Jim 91–93
Brown, Sam 121
Bucher, Frank 76
Buffalo Bill Cody 74
Bull, Charles A. 26
Burnside, Gen. Ambrose 33
Burt, Gen. Andrew 47, 126, 152

Calamity Jane 32, 113
California, Department of 13
California Road 72
Camp, see *Fort*
Cantonment, see *Fort*
Carlton, Col. Caleb 163
Carricks Ford, Battle of 141
Carrington, Col. Henry 41, 42, 45, 70
Carter, Judge W. A. 91–92
Carson, Kit 79
Casey, Lt. 180
Catterson, Jack 130
Cayuse Indians 102
Central Pacific Railroad 96
Challenge Saloon 126
Cheyenne Indians 28, 47, 77, 83, 146–147, 162
Chinese Massacre 126, 130
Civilizing influence of Army 11
Clark, Henry 76
Clark, Capt. William 65
Clearwater, Battle of the 101, 150–151
Coffee, E. 32
Collins, Lt. Casper 83
Columbia, Department of the 13
Comanche (horse) 164
Con Cow Indians 144
Connor, Gen. P. E. 11, 23–25, 42, 49, 94
Cooke, Gen. Phillip 13
Cottonwood, Battle of the 101, 150–151
Crabtree, Nathaniel 65
Crazy Horse, Chief 146–147, 179
Cree Indians 177

Crittenden, Gen. T. 60
Crook, Gen. George 10, 17, 19, 21, 33–34, 80, 102, 126, 141, 146
Crossman, Maj. George 105
Crow Indians 28, 152, 167
Crow King, Chief 61
Cuny, A. 32
Curtis, Maj. James F. 144
Custer, Elizabeth 55, 58, 155, 158–159
Custer, Gen. G. A. 10, 26, 58, 67, 74, 148, 154, 162, 164, 177, 179

Daily Union Vedette 23
Dakota, Department of 13
Daughters of the American Revolution 137, 167–168, 177
Denver Road 72, 77
de Trobriand, Gen. P. 26, 49, 55, 88
Dull Knife, Chief 146–147, 152, 162
Duncan, Matt 66

Egan, Chief 130
Emigration Canyon, Utah 25
Ewing, Mrs. George 79

Far West steamer 67, 159
Fetterman, Capt. William 45
Fetterman Massacre 45–46
Finerty, John S. 80
Fiske, Sgt. 53
Flathead Indians 152
Forsyth, Gen. George 6, 32
Fort Laramie Treaty of 1851 28
Fort Laramie Treaty of 1866 28, 41–42
Fort (including *Camp, Post, Cantonment, Station* and other similar designations; also see Directory 182–185). *Abercrombie* N.D. 86–88, 105. *Abraham Lincoln* N.D. 58, 155–160, 162. *Anderson* Cal. 21. *Assinniboine* Mont. 177–178. *Atkinson* Nebr. 11. *Augur* Wyo. 152. *Baker* Cal. 21. *Baker* Mont. 137–139. *Bartlett* S.D. 55. *Bellingham* Wash. 33. *Bennett* S.D. 49. *Benton* Mont. 49, 55, 65, 67–68, 88, 100. *Berthold* N.D. 49. *Bidwell* Cal. 128–129. *Big Horn Post* Mont. 167. *Boise* Idaho 98–99. *Bragg* Cal. 21. *Bridger* Wyo. 91–93. *Brown* Wyo. 152. *Brule* S.D. 49. *Buford* N.D. 50, 55, 61–64. *Carlin* Wyo. 110. *Casper* Wyo. 7, 83–85. *C. F. Smith* Mont. 47–48. *Chelan* Wash. 173. *Cheyenne Depot Wyo.* (*Quartermaster Depot at Cheyenne*) 110. *Coeur d'Alene* Idaho 171–172. *Coldwater* Minn. 14. *Collier* S.D. 76. *Columbia Barracks* Wash. 17. *Colville* Wash. 141, 173. *Connor* Wyo. 42–45. *Cooke* Mont. 65–66. *Cottonwood* Nebr. 74. *Crittenden* Utah 23. *Crook* Cal. 21. *Crook* Ore. 130. *Crow Creek* Wyo. 110. *Custer* Mont. 167–168. *D. A. Russell* Wyo. 110–112, 162. *Dalles* Ore. 49, 102–103, 141. *Douglas* Utah 23–25. *Drum* Ore. 102. *Dun Glen* Nev. 134. *Ellis* Mont. 67, 118, 137. *"False Alarm"* S.D. 121. *Fetterman* Wyo. 80–82, 154. *Floyd* Utah, 21, 91. *Francis E. Warren* Wyo. 111. *Fred Steele* Wyo. 116–117. *Gaston* Cal. 21, 39–40. *Greely* N.D.

Fort—Continued
157. *Gilette* Nebr. 72. *Hale* S.D. 49. *Hall* Idaho 100. *Halleck* Nev. 95–97. *Halleck* Wyo. 113. *Hancock* N.D. 157. *Harney* Ore. 130–131. *Hartsuff* Nebr. 124–125. *Humboldt* Cal. 21–22, 33. *Iaqua* Cal. 21. *John Buford* Wyo. 113. *John on the Laramie* Wyo. 28. *Jones* Cal. 34. *Kearny* Nebr. 70–71. *Keogh* Mont. 7, 179–181. *Keya Paha* S.D. 50. *Lancaster* Colo. 79. *Lane* Ore. 34–35. *Lapwai* Idaho 7, 132, 150–151. *Laramie* Wyo. 28–32, 41–42, 45, 70, 146, 162. *Lee* Ore. 102. *Lewis* Mont. 67. *Lincoln* Cal. 21, 144–145. *Logan* Mont. 137–139. *Lookout* S.D. 50, 53–54. *Lupton* Colo. 79. *Lyon* Cal. 21. *Lyon* Idaho 7, 126–128. *Macleod* Canada 68. *Maginnis* Mont. 175–176. *McDermit* Nev. 7, 132–133. *McKean* Nebr. 74. *McKeen* N.D. 155–156, 160. *McKenzie* Mont. 67. *Mc-Kinney* Wyo. 42, 165–166. *McPherson* Nebr. 74–75, 109. *Meade* S.D. 162–164. *Missoula* Mont. *Mitchell* (*Kearny, Nebr.*) 72. *Mitchell* Nebr. 70–71. *Mortimer* N.D. 64. *New Hope* Minn. 14. *Omaha* Nebr. 13, 19–20. *Old Platte Bridge* Wyo. 83. *Peck* Mont. 118, 177. *Phil Kearney* Wyo. 45–46. *Piegan* Mont. 67. *Pierre* S.D. 50. *Presidio of San Francisco* Cal. 13, 39. *Randall* S.D. 50–53. *Rankin* Colo. 77. *Ransom* N.D. 105–106. *Rattlesnake Creek* Ore. 130. *Reeve* Mont. 65. *Reno* Wyo. 42–43, 165. *Reynolds* Mont. 26. *Rice* N.D. 58–60. *Robinson* S.D. 146–147, 162. *Ruhlen* S.D. 162. *Ruby* Nev. 94–95. *Robinson* S.D. 146–147, 162. *Ruhlen* S.D. 162. *Sanborn* Minn. 86. *Sanders* Wyo. 113–115. *Scott* Wyo. 91. *Sedgwick* Colo. 70, 77–78, 102. *Shaw* Mont. 26–27, 67. *Sheridan* Nebr. 146. *Sherman* Idaho 171–172. *Shuman* Nebr. 70. *Sidney* Nebr. 107–109. *Simcoe* Wash. 103, 130, 141–143. *Sisseton* S.D. 121–123. *Snelling* Minn. 6, 13–16, 86, 105. *Spokane* Wash. 173–174. *St. Anthony* Minn. 14. *Steele* Ore. 130. *Steilacoom* Wash. 37–38. *Sturgis* S.D. 162–164. *Sully* S.D. 55–57, 162. *Terwaw* Cal. 144. *Three Forks* Idaho 126. *Thompson* S.D. 49. *Tongue River* Mont. 179–181. *Totten* N.D. 88–90, 105. *Union* N.D. 50, 61, 64. *Vancouver* Wash. 17–18, 102. *Wadsworth* S.D. 121. *Walla Walla* Wash. 98, 100–101, 150. *Washakie* Wyo. 6, 152–153. *William* N.D. 64. *William* Wyo. 28. *Winfield Scott* Nev. 134–136. *Yamhill* Ore. 36. *Yates* N.D. 50, 58, 148–149. *Yellowstone, New Post on* Mont. 179.
"Four Pens and a Passage" 17
Fredericks, Jim 162
Fremont, Capt. John 69, 79.
Frontier Index 113

Gall, Chief 61
"Galvanized Yankees" 50, 91
Garnett, Maj. Robert 140
Gibbon, Gen. John 26–27, 154
Goshen Indians 94

Grant, Gen. and Pres. U.S. 10, 11, 21, 33, 39, 113
Grasshoppers 124, 137
Grattan, Lt. John 10, 28
Great Salt Lake Steamboats 49
Guano Valley Nev., Battle of 126
Gwyther, B. G. 59

Halleck, Gen. H. 94, 118
Halleck Station Nev. 96
Hancock, Julia 65
Harney, Gen. W. S. 10, 28, 53
Hastings Nebr., Mob at 19
Hat Creek Indians 145
Hay Box fight 47
Hazen, Gen. W. B. 36
Heath, Joseph T. 37
Hog Ranch 32, 72, 80, 149, 158, 162, 171
Home Defense Corps 165
Hoopa Indians 39–40
Howard, Gen. O. O. 11, 37, 150–151, 171, 173
Hubbard, Maj. V. B. 173
Hudson Bay Company 17, 37, 100, 102
Humboldt, District of the 13, 21
Humboldt Stage Route 126
Hunkpapa Indians 148
Hunton, John 29

Indians, see tribal names
Indian Scouts 180–181
Infantry Bicycle Corps 169
Infernal Caverns, Battle of 126

Johnson County "War" 165
Jones, James 116
Jones, Sgt. 119
Joseph, Chief 61, 67, 150–151, 179, 181

Kappa Kappa Gamma sorority 114
Karge, Lt. Joseph 134
Keogh, Capt. Myles 164
Kicking Bear, Chief 148

LaGuardia, Fiorella 56
Lame Deer, Chief 179
Lane, Gov. Joseph 34
Laramie Country Club 114
Lee, Capt. H. A. G. 102
Leschi, Chief 37
Lewis & Clark 65
Lippitt, Col. Francis J. 21
Liquor troubles 14, 26, 64, 77, 107, 121, 132, 134–135, 171, 175
Little Big Horn, Battle of 11, 26, 58, 67, 107, 148, 154, 158–159, 167, 179
Little Poplar, Chief 177
Loans to pay officers 11
Logan, Capt. William 137
Lower Brule Indians 54
Lower Sioux Agency 119
Luella steamer 49
Lugenbeel, Col. Pinkney 98
Lupton, Lt. Lancaster 79
Lyon, Capt. Nathaniel 53

Mackenzie, Gen. Ranald 11, 63, 80
"Massacre" at Ft. Buford 61
Mathews, John 107
McClellan, Gen. George 10, 17, 37, 69
McKean's saloon 96
McKenzie, Kenneth 64
McLoughlin, John 17
Meeker Massacre 116

Meeker, Nathan 116
Messiah Craze 56, 148, 177
Miles, Gen. Nelson 11, 148, 154, 166, 179–181
Mint at The Dalles 102
Missouri, Division of the 13
Missouri River traffic 49, 67
Mitchell, Gen. Robert 70
Modoc War 11, 100, 126
Montana, District of 26
"Mool Mool" 141
Mormons 23–25, 28, 91–92
Mormon Trail 28, 74
Mormon War 50, 91
Moss, Lt. John 169
Mullan, Lt. John (and Road) 67, 100, 169

National Park Service 5, 29, 31, 174, 186
Nelson, Marianna 141
New Ulm Massacre 119
Nez Perce Indians 140, 150–151
Nez Perce War 11, 26, 67, 96, 100–102, 126, 150–151, 167, 169–170
Northern Montana College 178
Northern Pacific railroad 55–56, 157–158

Oahe Dam 55
Odd Fellows Lodge 50, 52
Ord, Gen. E. 10, 33
Oregon Trail 28–29, 69–72, 74, 83
Ouray, Chief 116
Owyhee Mine Stage 126

Pacific, Division of the 13, 98, 126
Palmer, Frank 88
Pay of the Army 10–11
Pershing, Gen. John 111–112, 178
Pickett, Gen. George 10, 33, 37
Pine Ridge Agency 177
Pit River Indian War 33
Piute Indians 94, 130, 132
Platte, Department of the 13, 19
Pony Express 28, 72, 74, 77, 91
Pope, Gen. John 33
Powder River campaign (1876) 11
Powder River expedition (1865) 23, 42
Power-Norris trading post 65–66
Portugee Phillips 45
Pre-fabricated buildings 53, 155
Princess 147

Railroad strike (1877) 19, 50
Rain-in-the-Face, Chief 61
Rains, Lt. 150
Red Canyon, S.D. 76
Red Cloud, Chief 28, 41, 45, 67
Red Cloud Agency 146
Reil Rebellion 177
Reynolds, Gen. J. P. 36
Rogue River Indian War 32, 34
Rosebud, Battle of the 11, 146, 152
Royal Canadian Mounted Police 68
Ruffee, Charles A. 88
Russell, Gen. D. A. 36
Ryan's tavern 21

Salmon Valley massacre 150
Santa Fe Trail 69
Schultz, Pvt. C. M. 142
Scott, Hiram 71
Scott's Bluff 70–71
Sheridan, Gen. Phillip 10, 17, 33, 36, 74, 102, 113, 162, 165

Sherman, Gen. William 10, 13, 17, 19, 28, 33, 73, 104, 113
Sheepeater War 100
Shiloh, Battle of 60
Shoshone Indians 152–153
Sioux Indians 10–11, 26, 28, 41–48, 50, 83, 86, 119–120, 146, 148, 152–154, 161, 177, 180
Sioux Treaty of 1868 58
Sitting Bull, Chief 50, 58, 61, 63, 148–149, 177, 179
Smith, Capt. A. J. 34
Smallpox 96
Snake Indians 28
Snake River Shoshone Indians 98, 152
Snelling, Col. Josiah 14
Soldiers and Sailors Home, Wyoming 166
Spirit Lake, Iowa, Massacre 50
Spotted Tail Agency 146
Standing Rock agency 148–149
Standing Rock legend 149
Stanley, Gen. 55
"Star Spangled Banner" 163
Steele, Gen. Fred 33
Steptoe Butte, Battle of 141
Stockaded fort philosophy 12, 55–56, 70, 88, 155
Stuart, Lt. J. E. B. 10
Sully Expeditions 50, 55, 58, 61, 64
Sully, Gen. Alfred 10, 33, 50, 55, 58, 64

Table Rock, Ore. 34–35
Telegraph line 28
Telephone 179–180
Terry, Gen. Alfred 58, 154
Thornburg, Maj. Thomas 116
Thornburgh (mascot) 92
"Trail West" pageant 159

Union Pacific railroad 107, 110, 113, 116
Utah, District of 23
Utah Expedition (1857–58) 72
Ute Indians 116

Vander Horck, Capt. John 86

Wagon Box fight 45
Wallace, Gov. William 37
Warren Air Force Base 110–111
Warren, Sen. Francis 111
Washakie, Chief 152–153
Washington, University of 142
Washita, Confederate Council at 10
Wells Fargo 9
West Point 141
White Bird Canyon, Battle of 101, 150–151
Whitestone Hill, Battle of 55
Whitman, Rev. Marcus 100
Wilbur, Rev. James 141, 143
Winchester, Battle of 36
Wind River Indian reservation 152–153
WPA 46, 59–60, 87
Wright, Gen. George 102, 144
Wounded Knee operation 11, 107, 147–148, 161–162, 166
Wyoming, University of 114

Yakima Indian reservation 130, 141–142
Yellowstone expeditions 50, 58, 80
Yellowstone steamer 49
Young, Brigham 23–25, 91
Young, Pvt. George 145

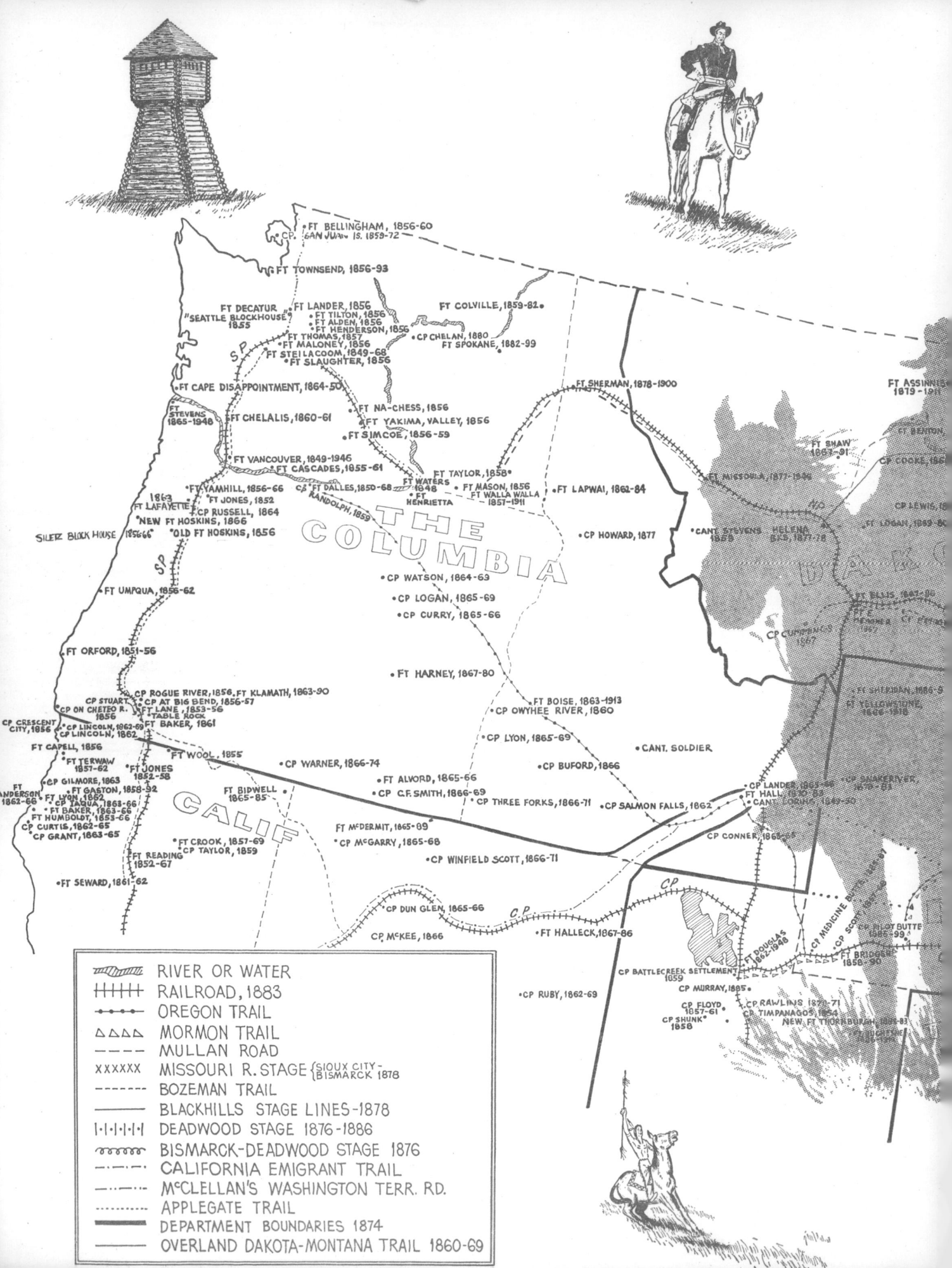

FT BELLINGHAM, 1856-60
CP. SAN JUAN IS. 1859-72

FT TOWNSEND, 1856-93

FT DECATUR   FT LANDER, 1856   FT COLVILLE, 1859-82
"SEATTLE BLOCKHOUSE"   FT TILTON, 1856
1855   FT ALDEN, 1856
                     FT HENDERSON, 1856
                 FT THOMAS, 1857   CP CHELAN, 1880
                 FT MALONEY, 1856   FT SPOKANE, 1882-99
                 FT STEILACOOM, 1849-68
              FT SLAUGHTER, 1856

FT CAPE DISAPPOINTMENT, 1864-50   FT SHERMAN, 1878-1900   FT ASSINNIS
FT   FT NA-CHESS, 1856   1879-1911
STEVENS   FT CHELALIS, 1860-61   FT YAKIMA, VALLEY, 1856   FT BENTON
1865-1948   FT SIMCOE, 1856-59   FT SHAW
                                                                                  1867-91
           FT VANCOUVER, 1849-1946   FT TAYLOR, 1858   CP COOKE, 1861
               FT CASCADES, 1855-61   FT WATERS FT MASON, 1856   FT LAPWAI, 1862-84   FT MISSOULA, 1877-19.46
FT YAMHILL, 1856-66   CP FT DALLES,1850-68 1848   FT WALLA WALLA   CP LEWIS, 18
1863   FT JONES, 1852   RANDOLPH,   FT   -1857-1911   FT LOGAN, 1869-80
FT LAFAYETTE   CP RUSSELL, 1864   1859   HENRIETTA   CANT STEVENS HELENA
    NEW FT HOSKINS, 1866   THE   1879   B.K.S, 1877-78
SILETZ BLOCK HOUSE 1856-66 OLD FT HOSKINS, 1856   COLUMBIA   CP HOWARD, 1877

FT UMPQUA, 1856-62   CP WATSON, 1864-63   FT ELLIS, 1867-86
                                 CP LOGAN, 1865-69   CP CUMMINGS,   FT E
                                 CP CURRY, 1865-66   1867   PHEONIX CP PETE
                                                                                              1867
FT ORFORD, 1851-56   FT HARNEY, 1867-80   FT SHERIDAN, 1866-9
                                                                                     FT YELLOWSTONE,
CP STUART CP ROGUE RIVER, 1856, FT KLAMATH, 1863-90   1866-1878
CP ON CHETCO R. CP AT BIG BEND, 1856-57   FT BOISE, 1863-1913
CP CRESCENT 1856   FT LANE, 1853-56   CP OWYHEE RIVER, 1860
CITY, 1856   CP LINCOLN, 1862-69 TABLE ROCK
CP LINCOLN, 1862   FT BAKER, 1861   CP LYON, 1865-69
FT CAPELL, 1856   CANT. SOLDIER
    FT TERWAW   FT WOOL, 1855   CP WARNER, 1866-74   CP LANDER 1865-66 CP SNAKERIVER
    1857-62   FT JONES   FT ALVORD, 1865-66   FT HALL 1870-83   1876-71
CP GILMORE, 1863 1852-58   CP C.F. SMITH, 1866-69   CANT. LORING, 1849-50
FT   FT GASTON, 1858-92 FT BIDWELL   CP CONNER, 186
ANDERSON   FT LYON 1862   1865-85   CP THREE FORKS, 1866-71   CP SALMON FALLS, 1862
1862-66   CP JAQUA 1861-66
    FT BAKER, 1863-66   FT MCDERMIT, 1865-89
FT HUMBOLDT, 1853-66   CP MCGARRY, 1865-68
CP CURTIS, 1862-65
CP GRANT, 1863-65   FT CROOK, 1857-69   CP WINFIELD SCOTT, 1866-71
              CP TAYLOR, 1859
       FT READING   CP
       1852-67   CP MEDICINE BUTTE, 1886-91
FT SEWARD, 1861-62   CP SCOT
                                                                              CP PILOT BUTTE
                           CP DUN GLEN, 1865-66   CP   FT DOUGLAS 1886-99
                                            C.P   1862-1966   CP BRIDGER
                   CP MCKEE, 1866   FT HALLECK, 1867-86   1858-90

CP BATTLECREEK SETTLEMENT
1859   CP MURRAY, 1865
     CP RUBY, 1862-69
                        CP FLOYD,   CP RAWLINS 1870-71
                        1857-61   CP TIMPANAGOS, 1854
                     CP SHUNK   NEW FT THORNBURGH, 1881-83
                     1858

LEGEND

〰〰〰	RIVER OR WATER
++++++	RAILROAD, 1883
•+•+•+	OREGON TRAIL
△△△△	MORMON TRAIL
– – –	MULLAN ROAD
×××××	MISSOURI R. STAGE (SIOUX CITY–BISMARCK 1878
– – – –	BOZEMAN TRAIL
——	BLACKHILLS STAGE LINES–1878
⊦⊦⊦⊦⊦	DEADWOOD STAGE 1876-1886
ꙮꙮꙮ	BISMARCK-DEADWOOD STAGE 1876
– – –	CALIFORNIA EMIGRANT TRAIL
– • –	MCCLELLAN'S WASHINGTON TERR. RD.
⋯⋯⋯	APPLEGATE TRAIL
▬▬▬	DEPARTMENT BOUNDARIES 1874
——	OVERLAND DAKOTA-MONTANA TRAIL 1860-69